Teaching Notes
and Solutions

DIMENSIONS MATH 7B
Common Core

a Singapore Math® Program

 STAR PUBLISHING PTE LTD

 Singapore Math Inc®

STAR PUBLISHING PTE LTD

Star Publishing Pte Ltd
115A Commonwealth Drive #05-12
Singapore 149596
Tel: (65) 64796800
Website: www.starpub.com.sg
Email: contactus@starpub.com.sg

in association with

 Singapore Math Inc®

Singapore Math Inc
19535, SW 129th Avenue
Tualatin, OR 97062
Website: www.SingaporeMath.com
Email: customerservice@singaporemath.com

Based on the original series entitled
Discovering Mathematics, approved by
Ministry of Education, Singapore.

© 2013 **Star Publishing Pte Ltd**

ISBN 978-981-4431-79-8

Printed by KHL Printing Co Pte Ltd , Singapore

Contents

Notes on Teaching   **1**

Fully Worked Solutions

Chapter 9   Number Patterns   13

Chapter 10   Coordinates and Linear Graphs   28

Chapter 11   Inequalities   45

Chapter 12   Perimeters and Areas of Plane Figures   63

Chapter 13   Volumes and Surface Areas of Solids   88

Chapter 14   Proportions   109

Chapter 15   Data Handling   136

Chapter 16   Probability of Simple Events   160

Chapter 17   Probability of Combined Events   183

Acknowledgements

The publisher wishes to thank the following:

The Geometer's Sketchpad, *Key Curriculum Press, 1150 65th Street, Emeryville, CA 94608, www.keypress.com* for permission to use the screenshots of activities created using The Geometer's Sketchpad.

NOTES ON TEACHING

Chapter 9   Number Patterns

Suggested Approach

This chapter integrates the technique of pattern recognition with algebraic expressions. Students are expected to get the general term of a sequence by observing patterns and guessing. This will develop their idea of a sequence for further mathematics. It is suggested that a variety of patterns, including geometrical patterns and number patterns, be used to stimulate students' interest and creativity. Spreadsheets and calculators can be used as aids for pattern recognition, validation, and continuation of a sequence.

9.1   *Number Patterns and Sequences*

Students should be encouraged to make conjectures about number patterns. However, they should learn to express the reasons for their conjectures. Arithmetic and geometric sequences may be demonstrated in examples to consolidate the idea of a sequence.

9.2   *General Term of a Sequence*

Students should understand that the general term of a sequence is its nth term. Applying the skills of writing algebraic expressions, students should be able to form the formula for the general term with some practice. When the first few terms of a sequence are given, there may be more than one general term formula corresponding to it. When applying a sequence to solve a problem, it is important for students to observe the relationship between the pattern, particular terms, and the general term of the problem.

Chapter 10 Coordinates and Linear Graphs

Suggested Approach

In this chapter, students are expected to use an ordered pair to represent a point on a plane. The story of René Descartes can be mentioned so that students know the origin of the coordinate system. Chess games, seating plans, and the longitudes and latitudes in a map can be used to motivate students to learn the concept of ordered pairs. Overhead projectors or graph boards are good teaching aids for this topic.

10.1 Cartesian Coordinate System

Students should understand the one-to-one correspondence between a coordinate pair (x, y) and a point on the plane. Teachers can include a class activity on identifying points and plotting points on a projected coordinate plane to consolidate students' concept about the coordinate system. When they plot points on a coordinate plane for the first time, it is advisable to use the same scale for both the x-axis and the y-axis.

10.2 Linear Graphs

A linear graph is a special relationship between an x-coordinate and a y- coordinate on the plane. Students should understand how an algebraic equation of two variables such as $y = 2x + 3$ can be represented as a line on the coordinate plane. Some students may not recognize that $y = 4$ and $x = 4$ are equations of two different lines.

10.3 Slopes of Linear Graphs

The slope of a linear graph is introduced as the rise over run of the line. Students are not expected to use a formula to find the value of the slope yet. They should have ample practice of evaluating the slopes of lines with different orientations. Hence, by observing a linear graph, they should be able to tell whether the slope of the graph is positive, negative, zero, or undefined.

Chapter 11   Inequalities

Suggested Approach

This chapter is an extension of simple ordering of numbers. The theme of this chapter is to introduce the basic properties of inequalities and apply them to solving inequality problems. Students may find it more interesting if they explore the basic properties by themselves. These properties may also be demonstrated with numerical examples.

The solutions of linear inequalities in one variable can be vividly represented on a number line with the use of an arrow with the arrow head at one end, and a hollow or solid circle at the other.

11.1   Solving Simple Inequalities

Students should understand the idea of solution of an inequality and compare it with the solution of an equation. Through Class Activity 1, students should learn that an inequality relationship is unchanged when both sides are multiplied or divided by a *positive* quantity. Hence, the method of solving the inequality $ax < b$, where $a > 0$, is introduced.

11.2   More Properties of Inequalities

The property that "For any two numbers a and b, one and only one of the following relationships holds: $a < b$, $a = b$, or $a > b$." is called the **law of trichotomy**. The property that "If $a < b$ and $b < c$, then $a < c$." is called the **transitive law**.

Students should realize that transposing terms in an inequality is basically the same as that for an equality. However, when an inequality is multiplied by a negative number, the inequality sign should be reversed. Students should explore this property through Class Activity 2.

11.3   Simple Linear Inequalities

A varied form of linear inequalities involving $>$, $<$, $\geq$, and $\leq$ should be introduced. Students should distinguish whether the solution of an inequality includes an end point or not. Care must be taken when an inequality is multiplied by a negative number.

11.4   Applications of Simple Inequalities

Students should learn how to set up an inequality from an application problem. They should be aware of the physical limitations of a variable in an inequality. For instance, some variables may only take integer values or positive values.

Chapter 12   Perimeters and Areas of Plane Figures

Suggested Approach

The idea of perimeter and area has been studied in elementary schools. This chapter extends the idea to find the perimeters and areas of plane figures such as quadrilaterals, other polygons, and some composite figures. We can develop a specific formula by dissecting and rearranging figures, or using Sketchpad software. Activities may be provided so that students can explore the formulas by themselves.

12.1 Perimeters and Areas of a Square, a Rectangle, and a Triangle

Students have learned perimeters and areas of a square, a rectangle, and a triangle in elementary schools. This section revises and extends what they have learned. Emphasis is placed on solving reverse problems using the formulas in this unit.

12.2 Circumference and Area of a Circle

The parts of a circle should be clearly defined and illustrated. Students should explore the formulas for the circumference and area of a circle through Class Activities 1 and 2. Emphasis should be given to explore and research on the interesting constant π. Teachers can motivate students in the learning of a circle through examples in real life.

12.3 Area of a Parallelogram

Apart from the activities mentioned in the book, dissecting a parallelogram along a diagonal into two triangles can lead to the derivation of the formula of its area. The areas of parallelograms in different orientations should be evaluated. It is important for students to know the height corresponding to a base in a parallelogram.

12.4 Area of a Trapezoid

In applying the formula of the area of a trapezoid, some students may omit the factor $\frac{1}{2}$ unknowingly.

Teachers may like to show students how to derive the formula of the area of a trapezoid by cutting it into two triangles and a rectangle. This may help students to remember the formula better.

12.5 Perimeters and Areas of Composite Plane Figures

Some plane figures are composed of two or more basic geometric shapes, such as triangles and trapezoids. Their perimeters and areas can be found by considering the sum or difference of the perimeters and areas of those basic shapes. Students are expected to be able to visualize and describe the two-dimensional figures that result from slicing three-dimensional solids, as in uniform cross-sections of right solids. They should be able to sketch the two-dimensional figures, and find their perimeters and areas.

Chapter 13   Volumes and Surface Areas of Solids

Suggested Approach

Making models of geometric shapes can build up the 3D visualization ability of students. Students should also be encouraged to draw the nets of solids. This can provide them with a better understanding of the idea of the surface area of a solid.

Prisms are solids of uniform cross-sectional areas. We can stack up solids to explain intuitively how the formulas of their volumes are derived. However, rigorous treatment is not necessary.

13.1   Volumes and Total Surface Areas of a Cube and a Cuboid

A solid may have more than one net. In building a solid from a net, some overlapping flaps are necessary. Students should also be encouraged to draw the corresponding 3D figures based on their nets.

13.2   Volume and Total Surface Area of a Prism

Students should understand the terms cross-section, base, and height of a prism. In some cases, the heights of prisms may not be vertical. Some students may not be able to visualize the heights in such cases.

They should understand the method of finding the surface area of a prism rather than just memorizing its formula.

13.3   Volumes and Surface Areas of Composite Solids

Students should learn how to convert between different units of measurements of length, area, and volume. When given problems on solids with dimensions of lengths involving both centimeters and meters, students should be reminded to convert the dimensions to the same unit before finding the volumes and surface areas.

For composite solids, students are expected to be able to visualize and adopt the method of breaking or dissecting a given composite solid into two or more basic solids.

Chapter 14 Proportions

Suggested Approach

Teachers can show why it is relevant to learn how to calculate distance and area based on a map using some daily life examples. Students can integrate the knowledge learned in this topic with what they learn on map reading.

Teachers can also introduce direct and indirect proportions by using daily life examples. Students are expected to recognize these relations from tables, graphs, equations, and verbal descriptions of proportional relationships. Further real-life problems that can be modeled by these relations could be explored. Students should learn to differentiate cases such as "x and y are in direct (or inverse) proportion" and "x^2 and y are in direct (or inverse) proportion".

14.1 Scale Drawings

Students should understand that the scale factor is the ratio of a side of the image to the corresponding side of the object. They are expected to draw simple scale drawings of models and floor plans, and get actual dimensions from scale drawings.

14.2 Map Scale and Calculation of Area

Students should note that a map scale can be represented as a ratio or a fraction. They should learn to calculate the actual distance from a given distance on a map and vice versa. Teachers, when teaching the concept of ratio of actual area to the area on a map, can use squares and rectangles to illustrate the relationship with the scale of the map.

14.3 Direct Proportion

When learning direct proportion, students are expected to observe patterns of the variation between two quantities and express the generalization in algebraic form. Students should be able to relate linear graphs learned earlier with direct relation of two quantities. Real-life examples will make learning more effective and interesting.

14.4 Inverse Proportion

Teachers need to emphasize to their students that they have to draw a linear graph of y against $\frac{1}{x}$ to show that x and y are in inverse proportion. This is because some students may have a misconception that a straight line with a negative slope in x-y plane indicates an inverse proportion between x and y.

Chapter 15 Data Handling

Suggested Approach

This chapter provides an overview of data-collection methods, and the process of organizing and presenting data. Teachers may design some activities or projects suitable for students to arouse their interest and reinforce their understanding in this topic. Students should understand the role of random sampling to draw inferences about a population in statistics.

Students will learn how to draw and apply dot plots to informally assess the visual overlap of two numerical data distributions. This chapter also introduces mean and median as measures of center, and the mean absolute deviation (MAD) as measure of variability for numerical data. Teachers may present data sets from real-life situations and guide their students to discuss the necessity to obtain a measure of center to represent each set data. Students should be encouraged to propose their ways of measurement. The emphasis is on students' understanding of the significance of measures of center. Teachers should show students how the mean absolute deviation (MAD) of a data set is calculated. They should also demonstrate how the MADs of two data distributions can be compared to draw informal comparative inferences about two populations.

15.1 Collection of Data

Students should learn that the method of data collection depends on the nature of the investigation. They should understand that statistics can be used to gain information about a population by examining a random sample of the population. They should also learn that the data from a random sample, which is a representative sample of a population, can be used to draw valid inferences about the population.

Students may be asked to collect some questionnaires to evaluate their effectiveness and to propose possible areas for improvement.

15.2 Dot Plots

Teachers, when introducing dot plots, may show how these diagrams are constructed first before teaching students how to interpret the diagram. However, if preferred, teachers may also teach their students how to interpret such diagrams first before they learn how to construct them. Students should be able to read individual items from a dot plot. They should be guided to observe the patterns of distribution and clusters revealed by dot plots, discuss the shape of the distribution, and hence analyze the data.

Students are expected to draw informal comparative inferences about two populations by assessing the visual overlap of two numerical data distributions with similar variabilities.

15.3 Measure of Center: Mean

Teachers should emphasize the role of measures of center in comparing and analyzing one or two sets of data. Teachers may choose some data sets, which are likely to arouse interest in students, to facilitate students' exploration and discussion of the meaning of mean.

This section also introduces the mean absolute deviation (MAD) as a measure of variability of the mean value. Some students may be overwhelmed by the computation of MAD. Teachers may have to give more hand-holding in the completion of the computation table for MAD initially. Students will learn to measure the difference between the means of two populations by expressing it as a multiple of their MAD. Given more exposure to different numerical data distributions, students should be able to use the mean and MAD to draw informal comparative inferences about two populations.

15.4 Measure of Center: Median

Students should understand the meaning of median. Teachers should show how the median of a data set is obtained by locating the middle item or the two middle items of the ordered data.

15.5 Mode

Students should realize that mode is used for categorical data, as in finding the most popular size of shoes or most frequently occurred test score. Hence, it is not a measure of center. Students should be able to find the mode of an ungrouped data set easily. Based on numerical data sets in Class Activity 2, the merits of mean, median, and mode are discussed.

Chapter 16 Probability of Simple Events

Suggested Approach

Some students may find the topic on probability difficult to grasp. Teachers may explore the meaning of probability through various simple games, simulation, and real-life activities. It is advisable to lead students to associate their daily life experiences on chance with the idea of probability.

Upon gaining an intuitive idea of probability, through some simple counting examples, students should recognize that the probability p of an event is a measure of its chance of occurring and $0 \leqslant p \leqslant 1$.

16.1 Set Notation

Teachers should discuss different ways of representing sets. These include listing, using description statements and set-builder notation. Students should learn to grasp the meanings of a subset, an universal set, an empty set, and the complement of a set. Teachers can provide some simple and interesting examples to help their students grasp the meanings easily.

16.2 The Meaning of Probability

Teachers can use the random experiments of tossing a coin, rolling a die, and generating random numbers in a spreadsheet, to introduce the idea of randomness. Class Activities 1, 2, and 3 will help students to investigate chance processes. Teachers can use an intuitive idea of chance to discuss the probability of an equally likely outcome in a random experiment before introducing the classical definition of probability to students. Students should be given the opportunity to develop a probability model (Class Activity 4) and use it to find probabilities from the model to observed frequencies. They are also expected to explain possible sources of discrepancy if any. The idea of probability can be consolidated with some examples of counting the number of favorable outcomes of an event.

16.3 Sample Space

The concept of sample space is important for further study in probability. Students should list the outcomes in a sample space. Teachers can encourage abler students to use set notation to describe a sample space. After showing some examples, teachers may want to highlight the properties of probability. Some students may find it difficult to apply the property of the probability of the complement event. They should be encouraged to express the complement of an event in words.

Chapter 17 Probability of Combined Events

Suggested Approach

In this chapter, we shall consider the probabilities of compound events and finding these probabilities using possibility diagrams and tree diagrams. It is important that students can present a sample space in a clear and systematic way. Teachers may use more real-life examples to ensure better understanding at each section.

It is advisable that students should learn mutually exclusive events (Section 17.2), independent events (Section 17.3), and finding probabilites of such events at a steady pace. It is not uncommon that students mix up the addition of probability for multiplication, and vice versa. To avoid this error by students, teachers may need to pay more attention to distinguishing between mutually exclusive events and independent events.

As a consequence of finding the probabilities for cases like drawing balls without replacement (Section 17.4), we introduce the multiplication of probabilities for the case of conditional probability through using tree diagrams. However, it is not necessary to mention the terms "multiplication law" and "conditional probability".

17.1 Probabilities of Simple Combined Events

Students are required to present a sample space by a possibility diagram or a tree diagram. Then they can find the probability of a simple combined (compound) event by counting the number of favorable outcomes in the diagram. Students should differentiate carefully the meanings of statements such as "at least 1 head" and " more than 1 head". They should also know the events which are complement to the events corresponding to the above statements.

In presenting a two-stage experiment where the number of possible outcomes in each stage is less than 10, the possibility diagram has the advantage over the tree diagram. On the other hand, the tree diagram can present the sample space of an experiment which involves two or more stages.

17.2 Mutually Exclusive Events

Discussions using real-life situations can enable students to master the concept of mutually exclusive events and the calculation of probabilities of such events better. It should be noted that if two events are not mutually exclusive, then $P(A \text{ or } B) = P(A) + P(B) - P(A \text{ and } B)$. Students need not deal with this formula at this level.

17.3 Independent Events

We take an intuitive approach to convey the idea of independent events. By considering the probabilities on the branches in a tree diagram, students can better recognize the multiplication law of probability.

17.4 Further Probabilities

Students should distinguish between the case of drawing with replacement and the case of drawing without replacement. As the difference between these two cases is very subtle, teachers may have to use hands-on experiments to help students visualize the difference. They should be aware that in the case of drawing without replacement, the sample space in the second stage is a reduced sample space, which depends on the outcome of the first stage. Students are encouraged to use tree diagrams to solve such probability problems. This is because it is easier for them to visualize the required computation.

FULLY

WORKED

SOLUTIONS

Chapter 9   Number Patterns

Class Activity 1

Objective: To observe number patterns.

Questions

1. In each case, the first four terms of a sequence are given. Find the 5th and 6th terms of each sequence.

    (a)   2, 5, 8, 11, _____14_____, _____17_____, ...

    (b)   30, 25, 20, 15, _____10_____, _____5_____, ...

    (c)   1, 3, 9, 27, _____81_____, _____243_____, ...

    (d)   96, 48, 24, 12, _____6_____, _____3_____, ...

2. Look at the following patterns of dots.

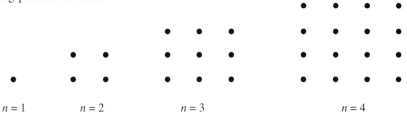

$n = 1$ $n = 2$ $n = 3$ $n = 4$

Let a_n be the number of green dots and T_n be the total number of dots in the nth pattern of the figure.

    (a)   Write down the terms $T_1, T_2, T_3,$ and T_4.

    $T_1 =$ _____1_____, $T_2 =$ _____4_____, $T_3 =$ _____9_____, $T_4 =$ _____16_____

    (b)   What will T_5 and T_6 be?

    $T_5 =$ _____25_____, $T_6 =$ _____36_____

    (c)   How are the numbers T_n related in the sequence?

    $T_n = n^2$, which is a square number. T_n is a sequence of square numbers $1^2, 2^2, 3^2, ..., n^2, ...$

    (d)   Write down the terms $a_1, a_2, a_3,$ and a_4.

    $a_1 =$ _____1_____, $a_2 =$ _____3_____, $a_3 =$ _____5_____, $a_4 =$ _____7_____

    (e)   What will a_5 and a_6 be?

    $a_5 =$ _____9s_____, $a_6 =$ _____11_____

    (f)   How are the numbers a_n related in the sequence?

    a_n is a sequence of odd numbers 1, 3, 5, 7, ..., $(2n - 1), ...$

Class Activity 2

Objective: To observe number patterns and write down the general term of a sequence.

Questions

1. The first three members of a family of hydrogen and carbon compounds have bonding structures as shown below. (CH_4 stands for C_1H_4.)

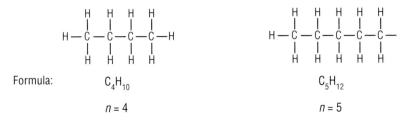

    Formula: CH_4 C_2H_6 C_3H_8

            $n = 1$ $n = 2$ $n = 3$

    (a) Draw the structures for the 4th and 5th members of the family.

    Formula: C_4H_{10} C_5H_{12}

                $n = 4$ $n = 5$

    (b) Copy and complete the following table.

n	Number of carbon atoms	Number of hydrogen atoms
1	1	4
2	2	6
3	3	8
4	4	10
5	5	12

    (c) Write down a general formula for the nth member in the family. C_nH_{2n+2}

    (d) How many hydrogen atoms does a member have when it has 100 carbon atoms?

    Number of hydrogen atoms = $2 \times 100 + 2 = 202$

2. The figures below show a sequence of patterns. Each pattern is formed by using joiners to connect identical short sticks. The joiners used are corner joiner (⌐), edge joiner (⊣), and cross joiner (✚). Let C_n, E_n, and R_n be the numbers of corner, edge, and cross joiners used in the nth figure respectively.

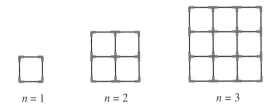

            $n = 1$ $n = 2$ $n = 3$

(a) Draw the 4th figure in the sequence, showing clearly the types of joiners used.

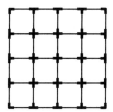

(b) Copy and complete the following table.

n	1	2	3	4	5
C_n	4	4	4	4	4
E_n	0	4	8	12	16
R_n	0	1	4	9	16

(c) Find the general terms for C_n, E_n, and R_n.

$C_n = \underline{ 4 }$

$E_n = \underline{ 4(n-1) }$

$R_n = \underline{ (n-1)^2 }$

(d) Find the total number of joiners needed for the 10th figure.

Number of joiners needed for the 10th figure $= C_{10} + E_{10} + R_{10} = 4 + 4(10-1) + (10-1)^2 = 121$

Discuss

Page 3

What are the sequences in Class Activity 1 that can be generated by the method used in Example 1?

The sequences (a) and (b) can be generated by the method used in Example 1,
i.e., in sequence (a), a term is obtained by adding 3 to the previous term;
in sequence (b), a term is obtained by adding (−5) to the previous term.

Page 4

What are the sequences in Class Activity 1 that can be generated by the method used in Example 2?

The sequences (c) and (d) can be generated by the method used in Example 2,
i.e., in sequence (c), a term is obtained by multiplying the previous term by 3;

in sequence (d), a term is obtained by multiplying the previous term by $\left(-\frac{1}{2}\right)$.

Extend Your Learning Curve

Fibonacci Sequence

The Fibonacci sequence 1, 1, 2, 3, 5, ... is formed by the rules:

$$T_1 = 1, T_2 = 1, \text{ and } T_n = T_{n-2} + T_{n-1} \text{ for } n \geqslant 3.$$

The numbers in this sequence often appear in nature.
Use the Internet to explore the properties of this sequence.

Suggested Answer:

The Fibonacci sequence is:

1, 1, 2, 3, 5, 8, 13, 21, ...

The terms in a Fibonacci sequence are called **Fibonacci numbers**.
Fibonacci numbers often occur in nature. For example, on many plants, the number of petals of a flower is a Fibonacci number.

The Fibonacci sequence has the following properties.

1. $T_{n+1} \times T_{n-1} - T_n^2 = (-1)^n$
2. $T_{n-1}^2 + T_n^2 = T_{2n-1}$
3. $T_1 + T_2 + ... + T_n = T_{n+2} - 1$
4. The ratio of consecutive terms, $\dfrac{T_n}{T_{n+1}}$, approaches the value of the golden ratio $\dfrac{\sqrt{5}-1}{2}$ (≈ 0.618).

Try It!

Section 9.1

1. Find the next two terms of the following sequences.
   (a) 2, 6, 10, 14, ...
   (b) 7, 1, –5, –11, ...

   ### Solution
   (a) 2, 6, 10, 14, ...
   A term is obtained by adding 4 to the previous term.
   The 5th term = 14 + 4
   $\qquad$ = 18
   The 6th term = 18 + 4
   $\qquad$ = 22

   (b) 7, 1, –5, –11, ...
   A term is obtained by adding –6 to the previous term.
   The 5th term = –11 + (–6)
   $\qquad$ = –17
   The 6th term = –17 + (–6)
   $\qquad$ = –23

2. Find the next two terms of the following sequences.
   (a) 2, 6, 18, 54, ...
   (b) 625, –250, 100, – 40, ...

   ### Solution
   (a) 2, 6, 18, 54, ...
   A term is obtained by multiplying the previous term by 3.
   The 5th term = 54 × 3
   $\qquad$ = 162
   The 6th term = 162 × 3
   $\qquad$ = 486

   (b) 625, –250, 100, –40, ...
   A term is obtained by multiplying the previous term by $\left(-\dfrac{2}{5}\right)$.
   The 5th term = $-40 \times \left(-\dfrac{2}{5}\right)$
   $\qquad$ = 16
   The 6th term = $16 \times \left(-\dfrac{2}{5}\right)$
   $\qquad$ = –6.4

3. From the figures below, study and compare the matchstick patterns.

   $n = 1$ $n = 2$ $n = 3$ $n = 4$

Each matchstick is 3 cm long and the matchsticks are arranged as shown. Let the number of matchsticks in the nth pattern be T_n and the perimeter of the nth pattern be P_n cm.

(a) Complete the following table.

n	1	2	3	4
T_n	3			
P_n	9			

(b) Find T_5 and P_5.

Solution
(a)

n	1	2	3	4
T_n	3	5	7	9
P_n	9	12	15	18

(b) $T_5 = T_4 + 2$
$\qquad$ = 9 + 2
$\qquad$ = 11
$P_5 = P_4 + 3$
$\qquad$ = 18 + 3
$\qquad$ = 21

Section 9.2

4. The general term of a sequence is $T_n = n(n + 3)$. Find its 2nd term and 9th term.

   ### Solution
   $T_n = n(n + 3)$
   $T_2 = 2(2 + 3)$
   $\qquad$ = 10
   $T_9 = 9(9 + 3)$
   $\qquad$ = 108

5. Consider the sequence 4, 7, 10, 13, ...
   (a) Find its general term.
   (b) Hence, find its 15th term.

   ### Solution
   (a) $T_1 = 4$
   $T_2 = 7 \quad = 4 + 3 \qquad\qquad = 4 + 3 \times 1$
   $T_3 = 10 = 4 + 3 + 3 \qquad = 4 + 3 \times 2$
   $T_4 = 13 = 4 + 3 + 3 + 3 = 4 + 3 \times 3$
   ∴ the general term $T_n = 4 + 3 \times (n - 1)$
   $\qquad\qquad\qquad\quad = 4 + 3n - 3$
   $\qquad\qquad\qquad\quad = 3n + 1$

   (b) $T_{15} = 3(15) + 1$
   $\qquad$ = 46

6. The figures below shows a sequence of dot patterns.

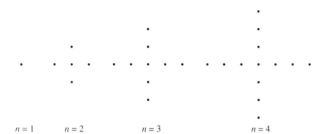

$n = 1$ $n = 2$ $n = 3$ $n = 4$

Let T_n be the number of dots in the nth pattern.
(a) Find the general term T_n of the sequence.
(b) Find the 18th term T_{18}.

Solution

(a) The sequence of T_n is 1, 5, 9, 13, ...
$T_1 = 1$
$T_2 = 5 = 1 + 4 \qquad\qquad = 1 + 4 \times 1$
$T_3 = 9 = 1 + 4 + 4 \qquad\quad = 1 + 4 \times 2$
$T_4 = 13 = 1 + 4 + 4 + 4 = 1 + 4 \times 3$

$\therefore$ the general term $T_n = 1 + 4 \times (n - 1)$
$\qquad\qquad\qquad\qquad = 1 + 4n - 4$
$\qquad\qquad\qquad\qquad = 4n - 3$

(b) The 18th term $T_{18} = 4(18) - 3$
$\qquad\qquad\qquad\quad\ = 69$

Exercise 9.1
Basic Practice

1. Write down the next two terms of each sequence.
   - (a) 11, 13, 15, 17, ...
   - (b) 1, 4, 7, 10, ...
   - (c) 16, 12, 8, 4, ...
   - (d) 49, 38, 27, 16, ...

   Solution
   - (a) 11, 13, 15, 17, ...
     $$T_5 = 17 + 2$$
     $$= 19$$
     $$T_6 = 19 + 2$$
     $$= 21$$
   - (b) 1, 4, 7, 10, ...
     $$T_5 = 10 + 3$$
     $$= 13$$
     $$T_6 = 13 + 3$$
     $$= 16$$
   - (c) 16, 12, 8, 4, ...
     $$T_5 = 4 - 4$$
     $$= 0$$
     $$T_6 = 0 - 4$$
     $$= -4$$
   - (d) 49, 38, 27, 16, ...
     $$T_5 = 16 - 11$$
     $$= 5$$
     $$T_6 = 5 - 11$$
     $$= -6$$

2. Write down the next two terms of each sequence.
   - (a) 1, 2, 4, 8, ...
   - (b) 375, 75, 15, 3, ...
   - (c) 1, −1, 1, −1, ...
   - (d) −4, 12, −36, 108, ...

   Solution
   - (a) 1, 2, 4, 8, ...
     $$T_5 = 8 \times 2$$
     $$= 16$$
     $$T_6 = 16 \times 2$$
     $$= 32$$
   - (b) 375, 75, 15, 3, ...
     $$T_5 = 3 \times \frac{1}{5}$$
     $$= \frac{3}{5}$$
     $$T_6 = \frac{3}{5} \times \frac{1}{5}$$
     $$= \frac{3}{25}$$

   - (c) 1, −1, 1, −1, ...
     $$T_5 = -1 \times (-1)$$
     $$= 1$$
     $$T_6 = 1 \times (-1)$$
     $$= -1$$
   - (d) −4, 12, −36, 108, ...
     $$T_5 = 108 \times (-3)$$
     $$= -324$$
     $$T_6 = -324 \times (-3)$$
     $$= 972$$

3. Write down the next two terms of each sequence.
   - (a) 1, 8, 27, 64, ...
   - (b) 1, 3, 6, 10, ...
   - (c) $1, \frac{1}{2}, \frac{1}{4}, \frac{1}{8}, ...$
   - (d) $\frac{1}{2}, \frac{2}{3}, \frac{3}{4}, \frac{4}{5}, ...$

   Solution
   - (a) 1, 8, 27, 64, ...
     The sequence can be written as
     $$1^3, 2^3, 3^3, 4^3, ...$$
     $$T_5 = 5^3$$
     $$= 125$$
     $$T_6 = 6^3$$
     $$= 216$$
   - (b) 1, 3, 6, 10, ...
     The sequence can be written as
     $$1, 1 + 2, 1 + 2 + 3, 1 + 2 + 3 + 4, ...$$
     $$T_5 = 1 + 2 + 3 + 4 + 5$$
     $$= 15$$
     $$T_6 = T_5 + 6$$
     $$= 15 + 6$$
     $$= 21$$
   - (c) $1, \frac{1}{2}, \frac{1}{4}, \frac{1}{8}, ...$
     $$T_5 = \frac{1}{8} \times \frac{1}{2}$$
     $$= \frac{1}{16}$$
     $$T_6 = \frac{1}{16} \times \frac{1}{2}$$
     $$= \frac{1}{32}$$

   - (d) $\frac{1}{2}, \frac{2}{3}, \frac{3}{4}, \frac{4}{5} ...$
     $$T_5 = \frac{5}{6}$$
     $$T_6 = \frac{6}{7}$$

Further Practice

4. Find the 7th term of each sequence.
   (a) 2, 4, 6, 8, ...
   (b) 23, 20, 17, 14, ...
   (c) 5, 10, 20, 40, ...
   (d) 216, −144, 96, −64, ...

Solution
(a) 2, 4, 6, 8, ...
   $T_5 = 8 + 2 = 10$
   $T_6 = 10 + 2 = 12$
   $T_7 = 12 + 2 = 14$

(b) 23, 20, 17, 14, ...
   $T_5 = 14 − 3 = 11$
   $T_6 = 11 − 3 = 8$
   $T_7 = 8 − 3 = 5$

(c) 5, 10, 20, 40, ...
   $T_5 = 40 × 2 = 80$
   $T_6 = 80 × 2 = 160$
   $T_7 = 160 × 2 = 320$

(d) 216, −144, 96, −64, ...
   $$T_5 = −64 × \left(−\frac{2}{3}\right) = \frac{128}{3}$$
   $$T_6 = \frac{128}{3} × \left(−\frac{2}{3}\right) = −\frac{256}{9}$$
   $$T_7 = −\frac{128}{3} × \left(−\frac{2}{3}\right)$$
   $$= \frac{512}{27}$$

5. A sequence is formed by
   $$2 × 1^2, 2 × 2^2, 2 × 3^2, 2 × 4^2, ...$$
   (a) Write down the first four terms of the sequence.
   (b) Find the 8th term of the sequence.

Solution
(a) $2 × 1^2, 2 × 2^2, 2 × 3^2, 2 × 4^2, ...$
   $T_1 = 2 × 1^2$
   $= 2$
   $T_2 = 2 × 2^2$
   $= 8$
   $T_3 = 2 × 3^2$
   $= 18$
   $T_4 = 2 × 4^2$
   $= 32$

(b) The 8th term $= 2 × 8^2$
   $= 128$

6. A sequence is formed by
   $$1 × 2, 2 × 3, 3 × 4, 4 × 5, ...$$
   (a) Write down the first four terms of the sequence.
   (b) Find the 10th term of the sequence.

Solution
(a) $1 × 2, 2 × 3, 3 × 4, 4 × 5, ...$
   $T_1 = 1 × 2$
   $= 2$
   $T_2 = 2 × 3$
   $= 6$
   $T_3 = 3 × 4$
   $= 12$
   $T_4 = 4 × 5$
   $= 20$

(b) The 10th term $= 10 × 11$
   $= 110$

Math@Work

7. The figures below show a sequence of patterns formed by small square tiles.

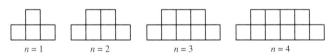

   (a) Draw the 5th figure according to the pattern.
   (b) If T_n is the number of small tiles in the nth figure, find T_1, T_2, T_3, T_4, and T_5.
   (c) Let P_n cm be the perimeter of the nth figure. Find P_n for $n = 1$ to 5, taking the length of each side of the square tile to be 2 cm.

Solution
(a) The 5th figure is as shown below.

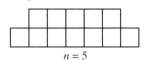

   $n = 5$

(b) By counting the tiles,
   $T_1 = 4$
   $T_2 = 6$
   $T_3 = 8$
   $T_4 = 10$
   $T_5 = 12$

(c) $P_1 = 10 × 2$
   $= 20$
   $P_2 = 20 + 4$
   $= 24$
   $P_3 = 24 + 4$
   $= 28$
   $P_4 = 28 + 4$
   $= 32$
   $P_5 = 32 + 4$
   $= 36$

8. The figures below show a sequence of patterns formed by matchsticks.

$n = 1$ $n = 2$ $n = 3$ $n = 4$

The matchsticks, 3 cm each, are arranged end to end. If T_n is the number of matchsticks in the nth figure and P_n is its respective perimeter, find

(a) T_n for $n = 1$ to 5,   **(b)** T_8,

(c) P_n for $n = 1$ to 5,   **(d)** P_8.

Solution

(a)   By counting,

$T_1 = 5$

$T_2 = 9$ $T_2 = 5 + 4 = 5 + (2 - 1) \times 4$

$T_3 = 13$ $T_3 = 5 + 4 + 4 = 5 + (3 - 1) \times 4$

$T_4 = 17$ $T_4 = 5 + 4 + 4 + 4 = 5 + (4 - 1) \times 4$

$T_5 = 21$ $T_5 = 5 + 4 + 4 + 4 + 4 = 5 + (5 - 1) \times 4$

(b) $T_8 = 5 + (8 - 1) \times 4$
$$= 33$$

(c) $P_1 = 5 \times 3$
$$= 15$$

$P_2 = 8 \times 3$ $T_2 = (5 + 3) \times 3$
$$= 24 \qquad\qquad = [5 + (2 - 1) \times 3] \times 3$$

$P_3 = 11 \times 3$ $T_3 = (5 + 3 + 3) \times 3$
$$= 33 \qquad\qquad = [5 + (3 - 1) \times 3] \times 3$$

$P_4 = 14 \times 3$ $T_4 = (5 + 3 + 3 + 3) \times 3$
$$= 42 \qquad\qquad = [5 + (4 - 1) \times 3] \times 3$$

$P_5 = 17 \times 3$ $T_5 = (5 + 3 + 3 + 3 + 3) \times 3$
$$= 51 \qquad\qquad = [5 + (5 - 1) \times 3] \times 3$$

(d) $P_8 = [5 + (8 - 1) \times 3)] \times 3$
$$= 78$$

Brainworks

9. Find the 7th term of the sequence
$$3, 4, 10, 24, 49, 88, \dots .$$

Solution

n	Term	First difference	Second difference	Third difference
1	3	$4 - 3 = 1$	$6 - 1 = 5$	$8 - 5 = 3$
2	4	$10 - 4 = 6$	$14 - 6 = 8$	$11 - 8 = 3$
3	10	$24 - 10 = 14$	$25 - 14 = 11$	$14 - 11 = 3$
4	24	$49 - 24 = 25$	$39 - 25 = 14$	a
5	49	$88 - 49 = 39$	b	
6	88	c		
7	T_7			

From the above difference table,

$a = 3$

$b = 14 + a$
$$= 14 + 3$$
$$= 17$$

$c = 39 + b$
$$= 39 + 17$$
$$= 56$$

$T_7 = 88 + c$
$$= 88 + 56$$
$$= 144$$

10. The sequence 1, 1, 2, 3, 5, 8, 13, ... is known as the **Fibonacci sequence**.

(a)   What is the rule used to obtain the terms in the sequence?

(b)   Write down the next three terms of the sequence.

(c)   Complete the following where each value in the lower row is the difference of the two terms just above it.

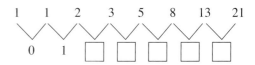

Write a paragraph to explain what you have discovered.

Solution

(a)   1, 1, 2, 3, 5, 8, 13, ...

In the Fibonacci sequence, starting from the 3rd term, each term is equal to the sum of the two preceding terms, whereas the first two terms are each equal to 1.

(b)   The next three terms are:

$T_8 = 8 + 13 = 21$

$T_9 = 13 + 21 = 34$

$T_{10} = 21 + 34 = 55$

(c)

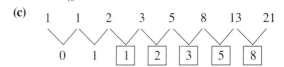

Ignoring the first term, the difference between successive terms of the Fibonacci sequence is the Fibonacci sequence itself.

Exercise 9.2

Basic Practice

1. Find the first three terms of each sequence from the given general term T_n.

   (a) $T_n = 2n + 1$ (b) $T_n = 7 - 3n$

   (c) $T_n = 2(n - 1)^2$ (d) $T_n = \dfrac{n}{n + 2}$

   Solution

   (a) $T_n = 2n + 1$ (b) $T_n = 7 - 3n$

   $T_1 = 2(1) + 1$ $T_1 = 7 - 3(1)$

       $= 3$ $= 4$

   $T_2 = 2(2) + 1$ $T_2 = 7 - 3(2)$

       $= 5$ $= 1$

   $T_3 = 2(3) + 1$ $T_3 = 7 - 3(3)$

       $= 7$ $= -2$

   (c) $T_n = 2(n - 1)^2$ (d) $T_n = \dfrac{n}{n + 2}$

   $T_1 = 2(1 - 1)^2$

       $= 0$ $T_1 = \dfrac{1}{1 + 2}$

   $T_2 = 2(2 - 1)^2$

       $= 2$ $= \dfrac{1}{3}$

   $T_3 = 2(3 - 1)^2$

       $= 8$ $T_2 = \dfrac{2}{2 + 2}$

                            $= \dfrac{1}{2}$

                            $T_3 = \dfrac{3}{3 + 2}$

                            $= \dfrac{3}{5}$

2. The general term of a sequence is $T_n = n(n + 3)$. Find its 11th term.

   Solution

   $T_n = n(n + 3)$

   $T_{11} = 11(11 + 3) = 154$

3. The general term of a sequence is $T_n = n^3 - 1$. Find its 7th term.

   Solution

   $T_n = n^3 - 1$

   $T_7 = 7^3 - 1 = 342$

4. The general term of a sequence is $T_n = 108 \times \left(\dfrac{2}{3}\right)^3$. Find its 3rd term.

   Solution

   $T_n = 108 \times \left(\dfrac{2}{3}\right)^3$

   $T_3 = 108 \times \left(\dfrac{2}{3}\right)^3 = 32$

Further Practice

5. If the general term of a sequence is $T_n = 7n + 4$, find the sum of its 5th term and 6th term.

   Solution

   $T_n = 7n + 4$

   $T_5 = 7(5) + 4 = 39$

   $T_6 = 7(6) + 4 = 46$

   The required sum $= T_5 + T_6$

                     $= 39 + 46$

                     $= 85$

6. Consider the sequence 39, 37, 35, 33, ...

   (a) Find its general term.

   (b) Hence, find its 18th term.

   Solution

   (a) 39, 37, 35, 33, ...

       $T_1 = 39$

       $T_2 = 37 = 39 + (-2) = 39 + (2 - 1) \times (-2)$

       $T_3 = 35 = 39 + (-2) + (-2) = 39 + (3 - 1) \times (-2)$

       $T_4 = 33 = 39 + (-2) + (-2) + (-2) = 39 + (4 - 1) \times (-2)$

       $\therefore$ general term $T_n = 39 + (n - 1) \times (-2)$

                             $= 41 - 2n$

   (b) The 18th term $T_{18} = 41 - 2(18)$

                             $= 5$

7. Consider the sequence 4, 10, 18, 28, ... Adam and Elisa observe different number patterns as shown in the table.

n	Term	Adam's pattern	Elisa's pattern
1	4	1×4	$1^2 + 3 \times 1$
2	10	2×5	$2^2 + 3 \times 2$
3	18	3×6	$3^2 + 3 \times 3$
4	28	4×7	$4^2 + 3 \times 4$

   (a) Find the general term a_n based on Adam's number patterns.

   (b) Find the general term T_n based on Elisa's number patterns.

   (c) Is $a_n = T_n$? Explain your answer.

   Solution

   (a) $a_n = n \times (n + 3) = n(n + 3)$

   (b) $T_n = n^2 + 3 \times n = n^2 + 3n$

   (c) Since $n(n + 3) = n^2 + 3n$, $a_n = T_n$.

8. The figures below show a sequence of patterns.

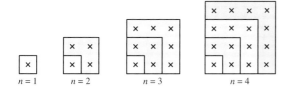

(a) Observe the patterns. What are the missing numbers in the parentheses.

$$1 = 1^2$$
$$1 + 3 = (\quad)^2$$
$$1 + 3 + 5 = (\quad)^2$$
$$1 + 3 + 5 + 7 = (\quad)^2$$

(b) Express the sum $1 + 3 + 5 + 7 + 9$ as a square number.

(c) Express the sum $1 + 3 + 5 + ... + (2n - 1)$ as a square number, where n is a positive integer.

Solution

(a)
$$1 = 1^2$$
$$1 + 3 = (2)^2$$
$$1 + 3 + 5 = (3)^2$$
$$1 + 3 + 5 + 7 = (4)^2$$

(b) $\quad 1 + 3 + 5 + 7 + 9 = 5^2$

(c) $\quad 1 + 3 + 5 + ... + (2n - 1) = n^2$

9. The figures below show a sequence of rectangular array of dots.

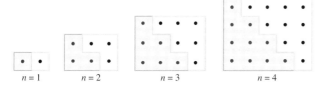

(a) Observe the patterns and complete the following table.

n	Number of red dots	Total number of dots
1	1	1×2
2	$1 + 2$	2×3
3		
4		
5		

(b) What is the ratio of the number of red dots to the total number of dots in each pattern?

(c) Hence, find a formula for the sum
$$1 + 2 + 3 + ... + n.$$

(d) Evaluate the sum $51 + 52 + 53 + ... + 200$ using the result in **(c)**.

Solution

(a)

n	Number of red dots	Total number of dots
1	1	1×2
2	$1 + 2$	2×3
3	$1 + 2 + 3$	3×4
4	$1 + 2 + 3 + 4$	4×5
5	$1 + 2 + 3 + 4 + 5$	5×6

(b) $\quad \dfrac{\text{Number of red dots}}{\text{Total number of dots}} = \dfrac{1}{2} = 1 : 2$

(c) For the nth pattern,
number of red dots $= 1 + 2 + 3 + ... + n$,
total number of dots $= n(n + 1)$.
From the result in **(b)**, we have
$$1 + 2 + 3 + ... + n = \frac{1}{2}n(n + 1).$$

(d) $1 + 2 + 3 + ... + 200 = \frac{1}{2} \times 200 \times (200 + 1)$
$$= 20{,}100$$
$1 + 2 + 3 + ... + 50 = \frac{1}{2} \times 50 \times (50 + 1)$
$$= 1{,}275$$
$\therefore \; 51 + 52 + 53 + ... + 200 = 20{,}100 - 1{,}275$
$$= 18{,}825$$

Math@Work

10. Study the rectangles formed by small square tiles in the figures below.

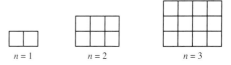

Each side of the small tile is 2 cm and P_n cm is the perimeter of the nth rectangle.
(a) Find P_1, P_2, and P_3.
(b) State the general term P_n.
(c) Hence, find the perimeter of the 15th rectangle.

Solution

(a) $P_1 = 6 \times 2$
$\quad\quad = 12$
$\quad P_2 = 10 \times 2 \quad\quad P_2 = 12 + 8 = 12 + (2 - 1) \times 8$
$\quad\quad = 20$
$\quad P_3 = 14 \times 2 \quad\quad P_3 = 12 + 8 + 8 = 12 + (3 - 1) \times 8$
$\quad\quad = 28$

(b) $P_n = 12 + (n - 1) \times 8$
$\quad\quad = 8n + 4$

(c) Perimeter of the 15th rectangle $= P_{15}$ cm
$\quad P_{15} = 8 \times 15 + 4$
$\quad\quad = 124$

The perimeter of the 15th rectangle is 124 cm.

11. The figures below show a sequence of tiling patterns formed by small white and red tiles.

$n = 1$

$n = 2$

$n = 3$

(a) R_n is the number of red tiles in the nth square. Find
   (i) R_4,   **(ii)** R_n.
(b) W_n is the number of white tiles in the nth square. Find
   (i) W_4,   **(ii)** W_n.

Solution

(a) **(i)** $R_4 = 4 \times 4$
$\quad\quad\quad = 16$
    (ii) $R_n = n \times n$
$\quad\quad\quad = n^2$

(b) **(i)** $W_4 = 6^2 - 4^2$
$\quad\quad\quad = 20$
    (ii) $W_n = (n + 2)^2 - n^2$
$\quad\quad\quad = n^2 + 4n + 4 - n^2$
$\quad\quad\quad = 4n + 4$

12. The first three members of a family of hydrogen (H) and carbon (C) compounds have bonding structures as shown below.

$n = 1$ $n = 2$ $n = 3$
Ethene   Propene   Butene

(a) Draw the structure for the 4th member of the family.

(b) Copy and complete the following table.

n	Number of carbon atoms	Number of hydrogen atoms
1		
2		
3		
4		

(c) The formulas for the first three members are written as C_2H_4, C_3H_6, and C_4H_8 respectively. Write down a general formula for the nth member of the family.

Solution

(a) The structure for the 4th member of the family is given below.

(b)

n	Number of carbon atoms	Number of hydrogen atoms
1	2	4
2	3	6
3	4	8
4	5	10

(c) The formula for the nth member is $C_{n+1}H_{2(n+1)}$.

13. The figures below show a sequence of patterns formed by lines joining the markings on the horizontal and vertical axes.

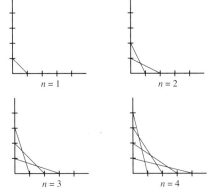

$n = 1$ $n = 2$
$n = 3$ $n = 4$

(a) Draw the pattern for $n = 5$.
(b) Let T_n be the number of points of intersection of the line segments other than the two axes. Copy and complete the following table.

n	1	2	3	4	5
T_n					

(c) Find T_6 and T_7.

Solution

(a) The figure below shows the pattern for $n = 5$.

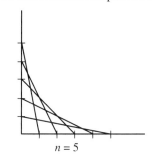

$n = 5$

(b)

n	1	2	3	4	5
T_n	0	1	3	6	10

(c)
$$T_6 = T_5 + 5 \qquad T_7 = T_6 + 6$$
$$= 10 + 5 \qquad \quad = 15 + 6$$
$$= 15 \qquad \qquad = 21$$

Brainworks

14. (a) Design a sequence of tiling patterns using small square tiles as your building blocks.

(b) Describe your pattern in words.

(c) T_n is the number of tiles in the nth pattern. Find a formula for T_n.

Solution

(a) A simple sequence of tiling patterns is as shown below.

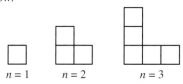

$n = 1$ $\qquad$ $n = 2$ $\qquad$ $n = 3$

(b) The first pattern has 1 tile.
For $n \geq 2$, the nth pattern is formed by adding a tile to the right-end and a tile to the top of the $(n-1)$th pattern.

(c) $T_n = 1 + (n-1) \times 2$
$$= 2n - 1$$

15. Study the figures below. They show the maximum number of parts obtained when one line, two lines, and three lines divide a plane respectively.

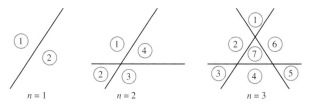

$n = 1$ $\qquad$ $n = 2$ $\qquad$ $n = 3$

Find the maximum number of parts that can be obtained when five lines divide a plane.

Solution

When a 4th line, which is not parallel to the existing three lines and does not pass through any existing intersecting points of the lines, is added to the 3rd pattern, it will divide the plane into the maximum number of parts.
Actually, the 4th line adds 4 parts to the plane.
Maximum number of parts that can be obtained with 4 lines = 7 + 4
$$= 11$$
Along the same line of argument, the maximum number of parts that can be obtained with 5 lines = 11 + 5
$$= 16$$

Review Exercise 9

1. Find the next two terms in each sequence.
   (a) 25, 27, 29, 31, ...
   (b) 41, 35, 29, 23, ...
   (c) 1, 4, 16, 64, ...
   (d) 5, –10, 20, –40, ...

Solution

(a) $T_5 = 31 + 2$
$$= 33$$
$T_6 = 33 + 2$
$$= 35$$

(b) $T_5 = 23 - 6$
$$= 17$$
$T_6 = 17 - 6$
$$= 11$$

(c) $T_5 = 64 \times 4$
$$= 256$$
$T_6 = 256 \times 4$
$$= 1,024$$

(d) $T_5 = -40 \times (-2)$
$$= 80$$
$T_6 = 80 \times (-2)$
$$= -160$$

2. If the general term T_n of a sequence is $T_n = n(n + 2)$, find T_3 and T_{20}.

Solution

$T_n = n(n + 2)$

$T_3 = 3(3 + 2)$
$$= 15$$

$T_{20} = 20(20 + 2)$
$$= 440$$

3. If the general term T_n of a sequence is $T_n = \dfrac{1}{2n+1}$, find the sum of the first three terms.

Solution

$T_n = \dfrac{1}{2n+1}$

Sum of the first three terms

$= \dfrac{1}{2(1)+1} + \dfrac{1}{2(2)+1} + \dfrac{1}{2(3)+1}$

$= \dfrac{1}{3} + \dfrac{1}{5} + \dfrac{1}{7}$

$= \dfrac{35+21+15}{105}$ LCM of 3, 5, and 7 = 105

$= \dfrac{71}{105}$

4. Find the general term of each sequence in terms of n.
  (a) 2, 3, 4, 5, ...
  (b) 2, 6, 18, 54, ...
  (c) $\dfrac{1}{4}, \dfrac{2}{5}, \dfrac{3}{6}, \dfrac{4}{7}, ...$
  (d) $1 \times 2, 2 \times 3, 3 \times 4, 4 \times 5, ...$

Solution
  (a) 2, 3, 4, 5, ...
     General term $T_n = n + 1$
  (b) 2, 6, 18, 54, ...
     General term $T_n = 2(3^{n-1})$
  (c) $\dfrac{1}{4}, \dfrac{2}{5}, \dfrac{3}{6}, \dfrac{4}{7}, ...$
     General term $T_n = \dfrac{n}{n+3}$
  (d) $1 \times 2, 2 \times 3, 3 \times 4, 4 \times 5, ...$
     General term $= n(n+1)$

5. Study the patterns formed by green and white tiles in the figures below.

$n = 1$ $n = 2$ $n = 3$

  (a) Draw the pattern for $n = 4$.
  (b) Let G_n be the number of green tiles and W_n be the number of white tiles in the nth pattern. Copy and complete the following table.

n	1	2	3	4
G_n				
W_n				

  (c) Find the general term of G_n.
  (d) Find the general term of W_n.

Solution
(a) The figure below shows the pattern for $n = 4$.

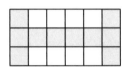

(b)

n	1	2	3	4
G_n	7	8	9	10
W_n	2	4	6	8

(c) General term of $G_n = n + 6$

(d) General term of $W_n = 2n$

6. Study the square patterns formed by matchsticks in the figures below. T_n is the number of matchsticks in the nth pattern.

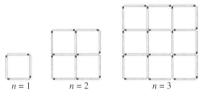

$n = 1$ $n = 2$ $n = 3$

(a) Copy and complete the following table.

n	1	2	3	4
T_n				

(b) Express T_n in terms of n.
(c) How many matchsticks are required for a 10×10 square pattern?

Solution
(a)

n	1	2	3	4
T_n	4	12	24	40

(b) In the nth pattern, there are $(n + 1)$ rows and $(n + 1)$ columns of n matchsticks each.
  $\therefore T_n = n(n + 1) + n(n + 1)$
     $= 2n(n + 1)$

(c) The required number of matchsticks for a 10×10 square pattern $= T_{10}$
     $= 2 \times 10 \times (10 + 1)$
     $= 220$

7. The figures below show a sequence of triangle patterns. Each small triangle in a pattern is the same size as the small triangle for $n = 1$.

$n = 1$ $n = 2$ $n = 3$

T_n is the number of small triangles in the nth pattern.
P_n cm is the perimeter of the nth pattern.
Suppose $P_1 = 7$.

(a) Draw the 4th pattern.

(b) Copy and complete the following table.

n	1	2	3	4
T_n				
P_n				

(c) Find the general term of T_n.

(d) Find the general term of P_n.

Solution

(a) The figure below shows the 4th pattern.

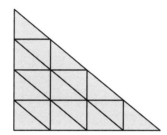

(b)

n	1	2	3	4
T_n	1	4	9	16
P_n	7	14	21	28

(c) $T_n = n^2$ **(d)** $P_n = 7n$

Chapter 10 Coordinates And Linear Graphs

Class Activity 1

Objective: To explore the graphs of linear functions.

Questions

1. **(a)** Copy and complete the following table of values for x and y.

x	-4	-2	0	2	4
$y = x$	-4	-2	0	2	4
$y = -x + 2$	6	4	2	0	-2
$y = \frac{1}{2}x + 1$	-1	0	1	2	3

(b) Using a scale of 1 cm to 1 unit on both axes, draw and label the graphs of the following equations on a sheet of graph paper.

$$y = x, \ y = -x + 2, \text{ and } y = \frac{1}{2}x + 1$$

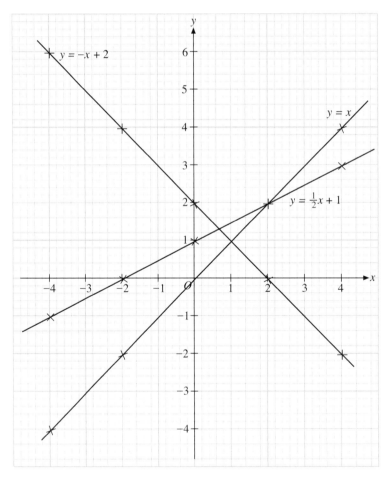

(c) What do you observe about the graphs of these equations?

Each graph is a straight line.

2. (a) Using a scale of 1 cm to 1 unit on both axes and the following tables of values for x and y, draw and label the graphs of $y = 3$ and $y = -1$ on a sheet of graph paper.

x	–3	–1	1	3
$y = 3$	3	3	3	3

x	–3	–1	1	3
$y = -1$	–1	–1	–1	–1

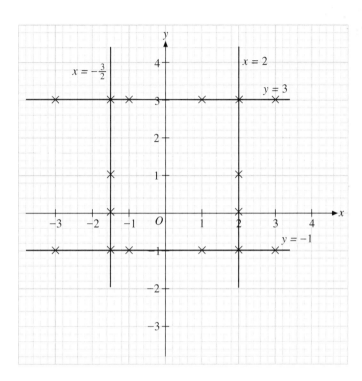

(b) What do you observe about the graphs of $y = 3$ and $y = -1$?

They are horizontal lines parallel to the x-axis.

(c) Using the following tables of values for x and y, draw and label the graphs of $x = 2$ and $x = -\frac{3}{2}$ on the same axes in **(a)**.

$x = 2$	2	2	2	2
y	3	1	0	–1

$x = \frac{3}{2}$	$-\frac{3}{2}$	$-\frac{3}{2}$	$-\frac{3}{2}$	$-\frac{3}{2}$
y	3	1	0	–1

(d) What do you observe about the graphs of $x = 2$ and $x = -\frac{3}{2}$?

They are vertical lines parallel to the y-axis.

(e) What are the equations of the x-axis and the y-axis?

x-axis: $y = 0$; y-axis: $x = 0$.

Discuss

Page 26

What values of x should you substitute into the equation $y = -\frac{1}{3}x + 2$ so as to get integral values of y?

x should be the multiples of 3 so as to get integral values of y.

Extend Your Learning Curve

Global Positioning System

Global Positioning System (GPS) is a satellite navigation system used to locate the position of an object that bears a GPS receiver. It has wide applications in defence, navigation, and tracking. Find out more about GPS on the Internet and briefly describe how it relates to the coordinate system.

Suggested Answer:

The Global Positioning System (GPS) is funded and controlled by the U.S. Department of Defence. It allows a GPS receiver to receive satellite signals from 4 out of at least 24 GPS satellites. This enables the receiver to compute position, velocity, and time with a high degree of accuracy. The position is determined by three coordinates (X, Y, Z), where X is the longitude, Y is the latitude, and Z is the altitude.

For more information, visit *http://www.colorado.edu/geography/gcraft/notes/gps/gps.html*.

Try It!

Section 10.1

1.

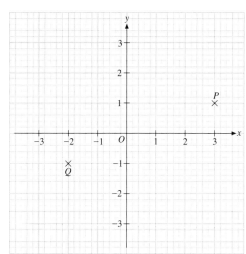

(a) State the coordinates of the points P and Q in the above diagram.

(b) State the quadrants in which P and Q lie.

(c) Using a scale of 1 cm to 1 unit on both axes, draw a coordinate plane on a sheet of graph paper and plot the points $R(1, 3)$, $S(-2, 3)$, $T(0, -1)$, and $U(2, -2)$.

Solution

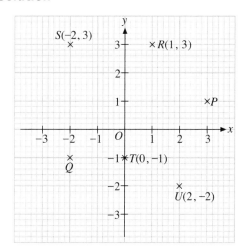

(a) Coordinates of $P = (3, 1)$
Coordinates of $Q = (-2, -1)$

(b) P is in the first quadrant.
Q is in the third quadrant.

(c) Points R, S, T, U are plotted on the above diagram.

Section 10.2

2. (a) Draw the graph of $y = -\frac{1}{2}x - 1$ for values of x from -4 to 4.

(b) Does the point $B(1, -1)$ lie on the graph?

(c) Using the graph, find the value of y when $x = -3$.

Solution

(a)

x	-4	-2	0	2	4
$y = -\frac{1}{2}x - 1$	1	0	-1	-2	-3

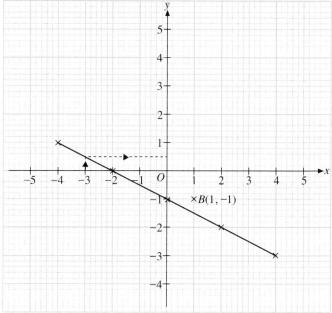

(b) When $x = 1$, $y = -\frac{1}{2}(1) - 1$
$= -\frac{3}{2}$
$\neq -1$

The point $B(1, -1)$ does not lie on the graph of $y = -\frac{1}{2}x - 1$.

(c) From the graph in (a), when $x = -3$, $y = \frac{1}{2}$.

3. Water is being drained from a tank. The water level h cm at time t minutes is given by $h = 40 - 5t$.

(a) Draw the graph of $h = 40 - 5t$ from $t = 0$ to $t = 8$.

(b) From your graph, find the time when the water level is 15 cm.

Solution

(a)

t	0	2	4	6	8
$h = 40 - 5t$	40	30	20	10	0

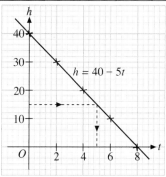

(b) When $t = 5$, the water level will be 15 cm.

Section 10.3

4. The vertices of $\triangle PQR$ are $P(-2, -1)$, $Q(3, -1)$, and $R(1, 2)$. Find the slopes of the sides of $\triangle PQR$.

Solution

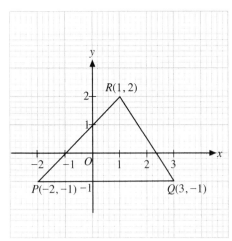

Since PQ is horizontal,
slope of $PQ = 0$,
slope of $QR = \dfrac{-1-2}{3-1} = -\dfrac{3}{2}$,
slope of $PR = \dfrac{2-(-1)}{1-(-2)} = \dfrac{3}{3} = 1$.

5. (a) Draw a straight line which passes through the points $E(-2, 5)$, $F(0, 1)$, $G(1, -1)$, and $H(3, -5)$ on a coordinate plane.
(b) Find the slope of the line using the points
   (i) E and G,   **(ii)** F and H,
   (iii) G and H,   **(iv)** E and H.

Solution
(a)

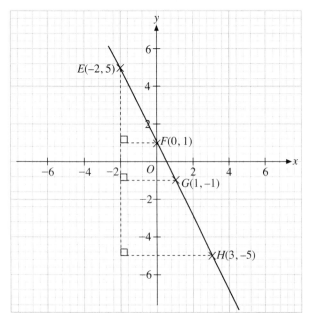

(b) (i) Slope of $EG = \dfrac{\text{Rise of } EG}{\text{Run of } EG}$

$\qquad = \dfrac{-1-5}{1-(-2)}$

$\qquad = \dfrac{-6}{3}$

$\qquad = -2$

(ii) Slope of $FH = \dfrac{\text{Rise of } FH}{\text{Run of } FH}$

$\qquad = \dfrac{-5-1}{3-0}$

$\qquad = \dfrac{-6}{3}$

$\qquad = -2$

(iii) Slope of $GH = \dfrac{\text{Rise of } GH}{\text{Run of } GH}$

$\qquad = \dfrac{-5-(-1)}{3-1}$

$\qquad = \dfrac{-4}{2}$

$\qquad = -2$

(iv) Slope of $EH = \dfrac{\text{Rise of } EH}{\text{Run of } EH}$

$\qquad = \dfrac{-5-5}{3-(-2)}$

$\qquad = \dfrac{-10}{5}$

$\qquad = -2$

Exercise 10.1

Basic Practice

1. (a) Write down the coordinates of the points A to J in the diagram below.
    (b) Which points are in the first quadrant?
    (c) Which points are in the fourth quadrant?
    (d) Which points are on the y-axis?

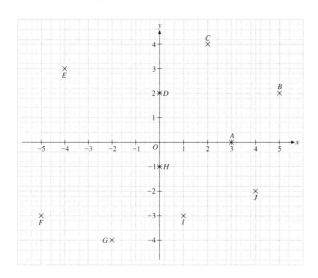

Solution

(a) The coordinates of the points are:

   $A(3, 0)$, $B(5, 2)$, $C(2, 4)$, $D(0, 2)$,
   $E(-4, 3)$, $F(-5, -3)$, $G(-2, -4)$, $H(0, -1)$,
   $I(1, -3)$, $J(4, -2)$.

(b) The points B and C are in the 1st quadrant.
(c) The points I and J are in the 4th quadrant.
(d) The points D and H are on the y-axis.

2. Write down the x-coordinate of each point.
    (a) $A(3, -2)$ (b) $B(-2, 7)$
    (c) $C(-1, 4)$ (d) $D(0, 0)$

Solution

(a) x-coordinate of $A = 3$
(b) x-coordinate of $B = -2$
(c) x-coordinate of $C = -1$
(d) x-coordinate of $D = 0$

3. Write down the y-coordinate of each point.
    (a) $P(4, -5)$ (b) $Q(3, 2)$
    (c) $R(-6, 7)$ (d) $S(9, 0)$

Solution

(a) y-coordinate of $P = -5$
(b) y-coordinate of $Q = 2$
(c) y-coordinate of $R = 7$
(d) y-coordinate of $S = 0$

4. Using a scale of 1 cm to 1 unit on both axes, draw a coordinate plane on a sheet of graph paper. Then plot and label the following points.

   $A(0, 4)$, $B(5, 3)$, $C(1, 3)$, $D(0, 6)$
   $E(-3, 2)$, $F(-2, 0)$, $G(-5, -2)$, $H(3, -4)$

Solution

The points are plotted and labeled in the following diagram.

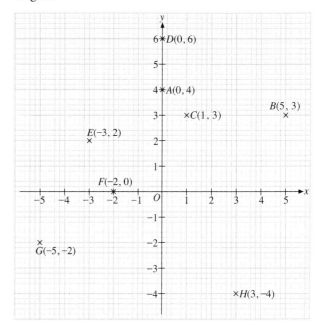

Further Practice

5. (a) Plot the points $A(3, 3)$, $B(0, 3)$, and $C(-3, 3)$ on a coordinate plane.
    (b) Which point(s) is/are in the second quadrant?
    (c) Join OA and OC. Then measure $\angle AOB$ and $\angle BOC$.
    (d) Give at least two relationships between the line segments OA and OC.

Solution

(a)

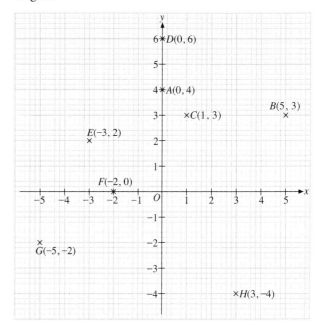

(b) The point $C(-3, 3)$ is in the second quadrant.
(c) $m\angle AOB = 45°$; $m\angle BOC = 45°$
(d) 1. $OA = OC$ 2. $OA \perp OC$
     3. OA and OC are symmetrical about the y-axis.

6. (a) Plot the points $P(1, -2)$ and $Q(-4, -2)$ on a coordinate plane.

(b) State the quadrant in which P lies.

(c) State the quadrant in which Q lies.

(d) Join OP and OQ. Then measure $\angle POQ$.

(e) Find the coordinates of a point R such that the x-axis is the perpendicular bisector of the line segment QR.

Solution

(a)

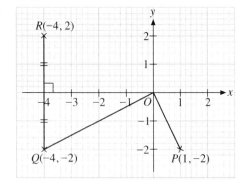

(b) $P(1, -2)$ lies in the fourth quadrant.

(c) $Q(-4, -2)$ lies in the third quadrant.

(d) $m\angle POQ = 90°$

(e) Coordinates of $R = (-4, 2)$

7. (a) Plot the points $S(-5, 0)$ and $T(0, 2)$ on a coordinate plane.

(b) Join ST. Find the area of nSOT.

(c) Mark the midpoint of S and T with the letter M, and state its coordinates.

(d) State the relationship between the lengths of MO, MS, and MT.

Solution

(a)

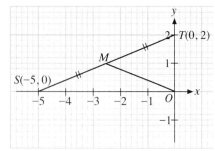

(b) Area of $\triangle SOT = \dfrac{1}{2} \times OS \times OT$

$$= \dfrac{1}{2} \times 5 \times 2$$

$$= 5 \text{ units}^2$$

(c) Coordinates of $M = \left(-2\dfrac{1}{2}, 1\right)$

(d) $MO = MS = MT$

8. (a) Plot the points $A(-3, 1)$, $B(0, -1)$, $C(1, -1)$, and $D(4, -1)$ on a coordinate plane.

(b) Which of the above points are in the fourth quadrant?

(c) If a point is in the fourth quadrant, what is the sign of its

(i) x-coordinate,

(ii) y-coordinate?

Solution

(a)

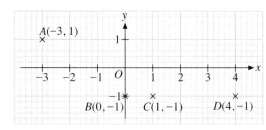

(b) $C(1, -1)$ and $D(4, -1)$ are in the fourth quadrant.

(c) **(i)** The sign of its x-coordinate is positive.

(ii) The sign of its y-coordinate is negative.

Math@Work

9. (a) On a sheet of graph paper, draw a coordinate plane using a scale of 1 cm to represent 2 units on both axes and plot the following points.

$A(6, 0)$, $B(3, 1)$, $C(2, 6)$, $D(0, 2)$,
$E(-4, 2)$, $F(-2, 0)$, $G(-6, -6)$, $H(-1, -3)$,
$I(4, -6)$, $J(2, -2)$

(b) Draw the design formed by joining the points successively by line segments, and the points A and J.

Solution

(a) and (b)

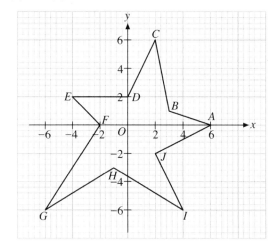

Brainworks

10. Study the pattern of squares in the diagram below. Each square is drawn with its vertices on the axes. The lengths of the diagonals of Square 1, Square 2, and Square 3 are 2 units, 4 units, and 6 units respectively.

(a) Find the area of each square.

(b) What is the area of Square 10?

(c) Express, in terms of n, the area of Square n.

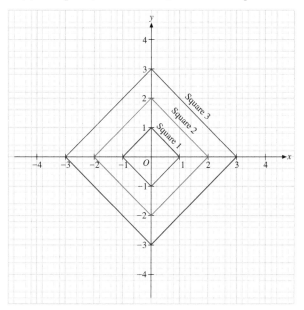

Solution

(a) Area of each square is 4 times the area of the triangle formed by its side in the first quadrant and the two axes.

Area of Square 1
$$= 4 \times \left(\frac{1}{2} \times 1 \times 1 \right)$$
$$= 2 \text{ units}^2$$

Area of a triangle
$$= \frac{1}{2} \times \text{Base} \times \text{Height}$$

Area of Square 2
$$= 4 \times \left(\frac{1}{2} \times 2 \times 2 \right)$$
$$= 8 \text{ units}^2$$

Area of Square 3
$$= 4 \times \left(\frac{1}{2} \times 3 \times 3 \right)$$
$$= 18 \text{ units}^2$$

(b) Area of Square 10
$$= 4 \times \left(\frac{1}{2} \times 10 \times 10 \right)$$
$$= 200 \text{ units}^2$$

(c) Area of Square n
$$= 4 \times \left(\frac{1}{2} \times n \times n \right)$$
$$= 2n^2 \text{ units}^2$$

Exercise 10.2

Basic Practice

1. (a) Copy and complete the following table.

x	–3	0	2	4
$y = x - 2$				

(b) Draw the graph of $y = x - 2$ for values of x from –3 to 4.

Solution

(a)

x	–3	0	2	4
$y = x - 2$	–5	–2	0	2

(b)

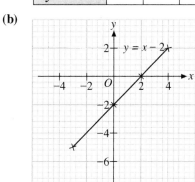

2. (a) Copy and complete the following table.

x	–2	0	1	3
$y = -2x + 1$				

(b) Draw the graph of $y = -2x + 1$ from $x = -2$ to $x = 3$.

Solution

(a)

x	–2	0	1	3
$y = -2x + 1$	5	1	–1	–5

(b)

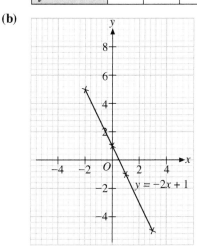

3. (a) Draw the graph of $y = \frac{1}{2}x + 3$ from $x = -4$ to $x = 4$.

(b) Does the point $A(1, 3)$ lie on the graph?

Solution

(a)

x	-4	-2	0	2	4
$y = \frac{1}{2}x + 3$	1	2	3	4	5

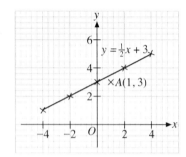

(b) When $x = 1$,

$$y = \frac{1}{2}(1) + 3$$

$$= 3\frac{1}{2}$$

$$\neq 3$$

The point $A(1, 3)$ does not lie on the graph.

4. (a) Draw the graph of $y = 3 - x$ from $x = -1$ to $x = 4$.

(b) Does the point $B(2, 1)$ lie on the graph?

(c) From your graph, find the value of x when $y = 0$.

Solution

(a)

x	-1	0	2	4
$y = 3 - x$	4	3	1	-1

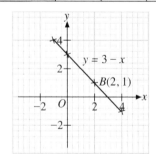

(b) As shown in the table and graph, the point $B(2, 1)$ lies on the graph.

(c) From the graph, $x = 3$ when $y = 0$.

5. (a) Draw the graph of $y = 3(x - 1)$ for values of x from -3 to 3.

(b) Find the coordinates of the point at which the graph cuts the x-axis.

Solution

(a)

x	-3	-1	1	3
$y = 3(x - 1)$	-12	-6	0	6

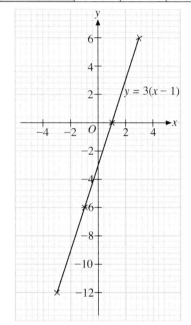

(b) The graph cuts the x-axis at $(1, 0)$.

6. (a) Draw the graph of $y = \frac{x + 2}{4}$ from $x = -8$ to $x = 4$.

(b) Find the coordinates of the point at which the graph cuts the axes.

Solution

(a)

x	-8	-4	0	4
$y = \dfrac{x + 2}{4}$	-1.5	-0.5	0.5	1.5

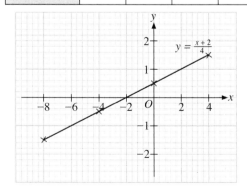

(b) The graph cuts the x-axis at $(-2, 0)$ and the y-axis at $\left(0, \frac{1}{2}\right)$.

7. **(a)** Draw the following lines on the same coordinate plane.
  (i) $x = 1$
  (ii) $x = 3$
  (iii) $y = 2$
  (iv) $y = -3$
  (b) Label the coordinates of the points of intersection of the lines.
  (c) Find the area of the rectangle formed by the lines in **(a)**.

Solution
(a) and **(b)**

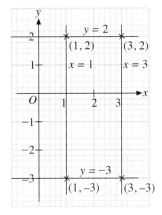

(b) Area of the rectangle
    $= 2 \times 5$
    $= 10$ units^2

Further Practice

8. **(a)** Draw the following lines on the same coordinate plane for values of x from -3 to 3.

  (i) $y = x + 1$ **(ii)** $y = \frac{1}{3}x + 1$
  (iii) $y = -\frac{1}{2}x + 1$ **(iv)** $y = 1$

  (b) What is the common property of the above lines?
  (c) What is the common property of the equations of the above lines?

Solution
(a)

x	-3	0	3
$y = x + 1$	-2	1	4
$y = \frac{1}{3}x + 1$	0	1	2
$y = -\frac{1}{2}x + 1$	2.5	1	-0.5
$y = 1$	1	1	1

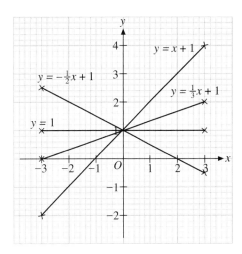

(b) All the lines in **(a)** pass through the point $(0, 1)$.
(c) The constant term of each equation is 1.

9. **(a)** Draw the following lines on the same diagram for values of x from -3 to 3.
  (i) $y = -x$
  (ii) $y = -x + 1$
  (iii) $y = -x - 2$
  (iv) $y = -x + 3$
  (b) What is the common property of the above lines?
  (c) What is the common property of the equations of the above lines?

Solution
(a)

x	-3	0	3
$y = -x$	3	0	-3
$y = -x + 1$	4	1	-2
$y = -x - 2$	1	-2	-5
$y = -x + 3$	6	3	0

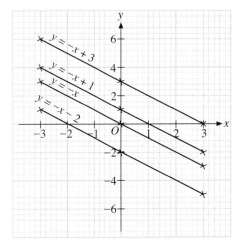

(b) All the lines in **(a)** are parallel to each other.
(c) The coefficient of x of each equation is -1.

10. (a) Draw the graph of $y = 12 - 3x$ from $x = -2$ to $x = 5$.

(b) The points $(a, 0)$, $(1, b)$, and $(c, 5)$ are some points on the graph. Find the values of a, b, and c from the graph.

Solution

(a)

x	-2	0	2	5
$y = 12 - 3x$	18	12	6	-3

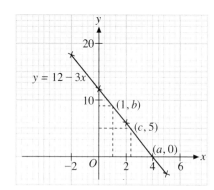

(b) When $y = 0$, the graph cuts the x-axis at $(4, 0)$.
$\therefore\ a = 4$
The line $x = 1$ meets the graph at $(1, 9)$.
$\therefore\ b = 9$
The line $y = 5$ meets the graph at $\left(2\frac{1}{3}, 5\right)$.
$\therefore\ c = 2\frac{1}{3}$

Math@Work

11. The volume $V\,\text{cm}^3$ of a gas formed in a chemical reaction at time t minutes is given by $V = 5t$.

(a) Draw the graph of $V = 5t$ from $t = 0$ to $t = 6$.

(b) Use your graph to find the time taken to produce $20\ \text{cm}^3$ of the gas.

Solution

(a)

t	0	2	4	6
$V = 5t$	0	10	20	30

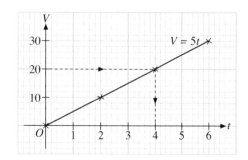

(b) From the graph, we can see that when $V = 20$, $t = 4$.
The required time is 4 min.

12. Steven is driving to a city. His distance d miles from the city at time t hours after starting is given by
$$d = 180 - 60t \text{ for } 0 < t < 3.$$

(a) Draw the graph of $d = 180 - 60t$ for $0 < t < 3$.

(b) Use your graph to find the time when Steven is 30 miles from the city.

Solution

(a)

t	0	1	2	3
$d = 180 - 60t$	180	120	60	0

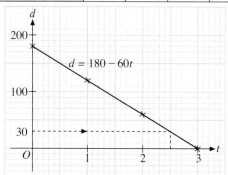

(b) From the graph, when $d = 30$, $t = 2.5$.
Steven is 30 miles from the city after 2.5 hours.

Brainworks

13. On a coordinate plane where values of x and of y are from -5 to 5, plot five different locations of a point (x, y)

(a) if the y-coordinate is one unit greater than the x-coordinate,

(b) if the y-coordinate is the additive inverse of the x-coordinate.

Solution

(a)

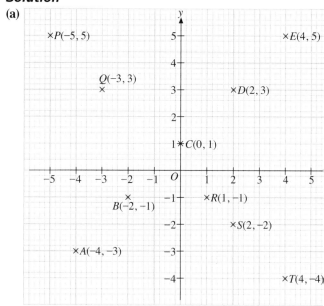

$A(-4, -3)$, $B(-2, -1)$, $C(0, 1)$, $D(2, 3)$, and $E(4, 5)$ are some of the possible points.

(b) $P(-5, 5)$, $Q(-3, 3)$, $R(1, -1)$, $S(2, -2)$, and $T(4, -4)$ are some of the possible points.

Exercise 10.3

Basic Practice

1. Find the slopes of the lines L_1, L_2, and L_3 in the following diagram.

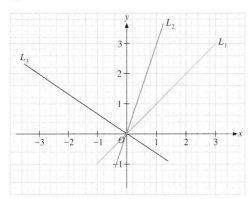

Solution

Slope of $L_1 = \dfrac{3}{3} = 1$

Slope of $L_2 = \dfrac{3}{1} = 3$

Slope of $L_3 = \dfrac{-2}{3} = -\dfrac{2}{3}$

2. Find the slopes of the lines L_4, L_5, and L_6 in the following diagram.

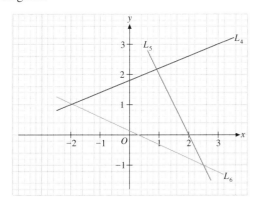

Solution

$(-2, 1)$ and $(3, 3)$ are on the line L_4.

$\therefore$ slope of $L_4 = \dfrac{3-1}{3-(-2)} = \dfrac{2}{5}$

$(1, 2)$ and $(2, 0)$ are on the line L_5.

$\therefore$ slope of $L_5 = \dfrac{0-2}{2-1} = \dfrac{-2}{1} = -2$

$(-2, 1)$ and $(2.5, -1)$ are on the line L_6.

$\therefore$ slope of $L_6 = \dfrac{-1-1}{2.5-(-2)} = \dfrac{-2}{4.5} = -\dfrac{4}{9}$

3. Find the slopes of the sides of $\triangle ABC$ in the following diagram.

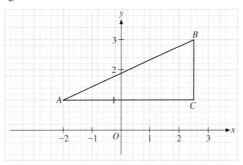

Solution

The vertices of $\triangle ABC$ are $A(-2, 1)$, $B(2.5, 3)$, and $C(2.5, 1)$.

Slope of $AB = \dfrac{2}{4.5}$

$\qquad\qquad = \dfrac{4}{9}$

Since BC is vertical, slope of BC is undefined.
Since AC is horizontal, slope of $AC = 0$.

Further Practice

4. In each case, draw the line through the given pair of points and find its slope.
   (a) $O(0, 0), A(2, 2)$ (b) $B(1, 2), C(3, 3)$
   (c) $D(-2, 3), E(2, 1)$ (d) $F(-5, 2), G(1, -3)$
   (e) $H(-2, 1), I(3, 1)$ (f) $J(-3, 2), K(-3, -2)$

Solution

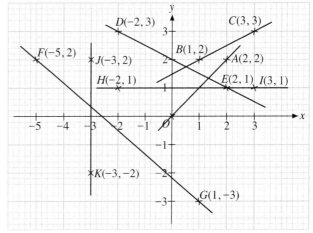

(a) Slope of $OA = \dfrac{2-0}{2-0} = \dfrac{2}{2} = 1$

(b) Slope of $BC = \dfrac{3-2}{3-1} = \dfrac{1}{2}$

(c) Slope of $DE = \dfrac{1-3}{2-(-2)} = \dfrac{-2}{4} = -\dfrac{1}{2}$

(d) Slope of $FG = \dfrac{-3-2}{1-(-5)} = \dfrac{-5}{6} = -\dfrac{5}{6}$

(e) Slope of $HI = 0$

(f) Since the line JK is vertical, slope of JK is undefined.

5. The vertices of nABC are $A(-2, 0)$, $B(3, -2)$, and $C(0, 2)$. Find the slopes of the sides of nABC.

Solution

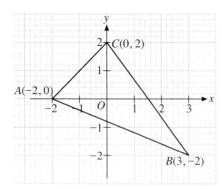

Slope of $AB = \dfrac{-2-0}{3-(-2)} = \dfrac{-2}{5} = -\dfrac{2}{5}$

Slope of $BC = \dfrac{-2-2}{3-0} = \dfrac{-4}{3} = -\dfrac{4}{3}$

Slope of $CA = \dfrac{2-0}{0-(-2)} = \dfrac{2}{2} = 1$

6. The vertices of a trapezoid $ABCD$ are $A(-1, -1)$, $B(7, 3)$, $C(4, 6)$, and $D(0, 4)$.
   (a) Find the slopes of the sides of $ABCD$.
   (b) What can you say about the slopes of the opposite sides of a trapezoid?

Solution

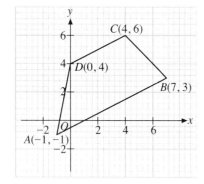

(a) Slope of $AB = \dfrac{3-(-1)}{7-(-1)} = \dfrac{4}{8} = \dfrac{1}{2}$

Slope of $BC = \dfrac{3-6}{7-4} = \dfrac{-3}{3} = -1$

Slope of $CD = \dfrac{6-4}{4-0} = \dfrac{2}{4} = \dfrac{1}{2}$

Slope of $DA = \dfrac{4-(-1)}{0-(-1)} = \dfrac{5}{1} = 5$

(b) The slopes of one pair of opposite sides are equal.

7. The vertices of a parallelogram $PQRS$ are $P(-4, -2)$, $Q(5, 1)$, $R(6, 4)$, and $S(-3, 1)$.
   (a) Find the slopes of the sides of $PQRS$.
   (b) What can you say about the slopes of the opposite sides of a parallelogram?

Solution

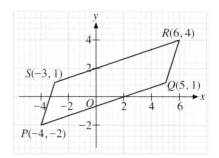

(a) Slope of $PQ = \dfrac{1-(-2)}{5-(-4)} = \dfrac{3}{9} = \dfrac{1}{3}$

Slope of $QR = \dfrac{4-1}{6-5} = \dfrac{3}{1} = 3$

Slope of $RS = \dfrac{4-1}{6-(-3)} = \dfrac{3}{9} = \dfrac{1}{3}$

Slope of $SP = \dfrac{1-(-2)}{-3-(-4)} = \dfrac{3}{1} = 3$

(b) The slopes of the opposite sides of a parallelogram are equal.

8. The following diagram shows a straight line passing through the points $P(-4, 8)$, $Q(a, 5)$, $R(3, b)$, and $S(4, -4)$.

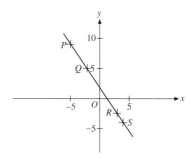

(a) Find the slope of the line.
(b) Find the values of a and b.

Solution

(a) Slope of the line = Slope of PS

$= \dfrac{-4-8}{4-(-4)}$

$= \dfrac{-12}{8}$

$= -\dfrac{3}{2}$

(b) Slope of PQ = Slope of the line found in **(a)**

$$\frac{5-8}{a-(-4)} = -\frac{3}{2}$$

$$\frac{-3}{a+4} = -\frac{3}{2}$$

$$\therefore\ a+4 = 2$$

$$a = -2$$

Slope of RS = Slope of the line found in **(a)**

$$\frac{-4-b}{4-3} = -\frac{3}{2}$$

$$-4-b = -\frac{3}{2}$$

$$\therefore\ 2(-4-b) = -3$$

$$-8-2b = -3$$

$$-2b = 5$$

$$b = -\frac{5}{2}$$

Math@Work

9. The distance y meters, of a boy at time t seconds from a fixed point F is given by

$$y = 3 + 0.5t\ \text{ for }\ 0 \leqslant t \leqslant 10.$$

(a) Draw the graph of $y = 3 + 0.5t$ for $0 \leqslant t \leqslant 10$.

(b) Find the slope of the graph.

(c) What is the physical meaning of the slope in this case?

Solution

(a)

t	0	2	4	6	8	10
$y = 3 + 0.5t$	3	4	5	6	7	8

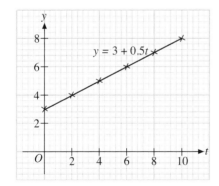

(b) Slope of the graph $= \dfrac{8-3}{10-0} = \dfrac{5}{10} = 0.5$

(c) The slope is the speed of the boy in m/s. That is, the boy's speed away from the fixed point F is 0.5 m/s.

10. The volume V cm^3 of a piece of melting ice at time t minutes is given by

$$V = 24 - 3t\ \text{ for }\ 0 \leqslant t \leqslant 8.$$

(a) Draw the graph of $V = 24 - 3t$ for $0 \leqslant t \leqslant 8$.

(b) Find the slope of the graph.

(c) What is the physical meaning of the slope in this case?

(d) What is the physical meaning of 24 in the equation $V = 24 - 3t$?

Solution

(a)

t	0	2	4	6	8
$V = 24 - 3t$	24	18	12	6	0

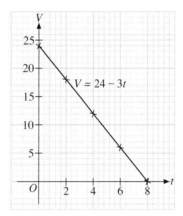

(b) Slope of the graph $= \dfrac{0-24}{8-0} = \dfrac{-24}{8} = -3$

(c) The slope is the rate of change of the volume of the piece of ice in cm^3/min. That is, the piece of ice melts at 3 cm^3/min.

Note: The negative sign of the slope indicates that the volume is decreasing.

(d) In the equation $V = 24 - 3t$, 24 represents the initial volume of the ice.

Brainworks

11. (a) Name three public buildings that have access ramps at the entrance for people in wheelchairs.

(b) Search the maximum slope for an access ramp for wheelchairs.

(c) Based on your result in **(b)**, find the horizontal run required for a vertical rise of 0.5 m.

Solution

(a) Three public buildings that have access ramps are: United States Capitol, The White House, The Pentagon.

(b) The maximum slope of an access ramp $= \dfrac{1}{12}$ in the United States.

(c) When rise = 0.5 m,

$$\frac{0.5}{\text{run}} = \frac{1}{12}$$

run = 6 m

Note: For more information, you can ask students to visit the website *http://www.access-board. gov/adaag/html/adaag.htm#4.8.*

Review Exercise 10

1. Refer to the given diagram.

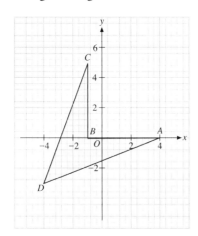

(a) State the coordinates of *A*, *B*, *C*, and *D*.
(b) Which point is in the second quadrant?
(c) Find the slopes of
   (i) *AB*,
   (ii) *BC*,
   (iii) *CD*.
(d) State the equations of the lines
   (i) *AB*,
   (ii) *BC*.

Solution
(a) The coordinates are
   A(4, 0), *B*(−1, 0), *C*(−1, 5), *D*(−4, −3).
(b) Point *C* is in the second quadrant.
(c) **(i)** Slope of *AB* = 0
   (ii) Since *BC* is vertical, slope of *BC* is undefined.
   (iii) Slope of *CD* = $\frac{8}{3}$
(d) **(i)** The equation of *AB* is *y* = 0.
   (ii) The equation of *BC* is *x* = −1.

2. **(a)** On a coordinate plane, draw the line connecting *A*(−3, 5) and *B*(4, −2).
   (b) What is the slope of the line?
   (c) Write down the coordinates of the point at which the line cuts
      (i) the *x*-axis,
      (ii) the *y*-axis.

Solution
(a)

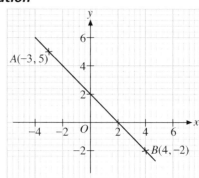

(b) Slope of the line *AB* = $\frac{-2-5}{4-(-3)}$

$$= \frac{-7}{7}$$
$$= -1$$

(c) **(i)** The line cuts the *x*-axis at (2, 0).
   (ii) The line cuts the *y*-axis at (0, 2).

3. The vertices of △*ABC* are *A*(1, 6), *B*(−4, 3), and *C*(5, −2).
   (a) Draw △*ABC* on a coordinate plane.
   (b) Find the slopes of the sides of △*ABC*.

Solution
(a)

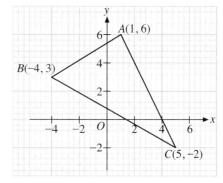

(b) Slope of *AB* = $\frac{6-3}{1-(-4)}$

$$= \frac{3}{5}$$

Slope of *BC* = $\frac{-2-3}{5-(-4)}$

$$= \frac{-5}{9}$$
$$= -\frac{5}{9}$$

Slope of *CA* = $\frac{-2-6}{5-1}$

$$= \frac{-8}{4}$$
$$= -2$$

4. (a) Plot the points $P(-4, 2)$, $Q(0, 4)$, and $R(2, 5)$ on a coordinate plane.
(b) Find the slopes of PQ, QR, and PR.
(c) Are the points P, Q, and R on the same straight line?
(d) Find the slopes of the lines OP and OQ, where O is the origin.

Solution
(a)

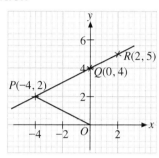

(b) Slope of $PQ = \dfrac{4-2}{0-(-4)}$

$= \dfrac{2}{4}$

$= \dfrac{1}{2}$

Slope of $QR = \dfrac{5-4}{2-0}$

$= \dfrac{1}{2}$

Slope of $PR = \dfrac{5-2}{2-(-4)}$

$= \dfrac{3}{6}$

$= \dfrac{1}{2}$

(c) Yes, the points P, Q, and R are on the same straight line.

(d) Slope of $OP = \dfrac{0-2}{0-(-4)}$

$= \dfrac{-2}{4}$

$= -\dfrac{1}{2}$

Slope of OQ is undefined.

5. The vertices of a quadrilateral $ABCD$ are $A(-3, -2)$, $B(-5, 1)$, $C(2, 3)$, and $D(4, 0)$.
(a) Draw the quadrilateral $ABCD$ on a coordinate plane.
(b) Find the slopes of the sides of $ABCD$.

Solution
(a)

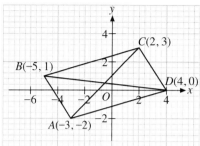

(b) Slope of $AB = \dfrac{-2-1}{-3-(-5)}$

$= \dfrac{-3}{2}$

$= -\dfrac{3}{2}$

Slope of $BC = \dfrac{3-1}{2-(-5)}$

$= \dfrac{2}{7}$

Slope of $CD = \dfrac{0-3}{4-2}$

$= \dfrac{-3}{2}$

$= -\dfrac{3}{2}$

Slope of $DA = \dfrac{0-(-2)}{4-(-3)}$

$= \dfrac{2}{7}$

6. The equation of a line L is

$$y = \frac{1}{3}x + 2.$$

(a) Draw the graph of L from $x = -6$ to $x = 6$.
(b) Does the point $(2, 3)$ lie on the line L?
(c) Find the slope of the line L.
(d) State the coordinates of the point at which the line L cuts the y-axis.

Solution
(a)

x	-6	0	6
$y = \dfrac{1}{3}x + 2$	0	2	4

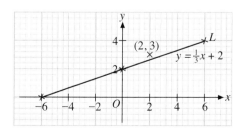

(b) When $x = 2$,
$$y = \frac{1}{3}x + 2$$
$$= \frac{1}{3}(2) + 2$$
$$= 2\frac{2}{3}$$
$$\neq 3$$
The point $(2, 3)$ does not lie on the line L.

(c) Slope of the line $L = \dfrac{4 - 0}{6 - (-6)}$
$$= \frac{4}{12}$$
$$= \frac{1}{3}$$

(d) The line L cuts the y-axis at $(0, 2)$.

7. The cost, $\$C$, for traveling a distance of x miles on a taxi in Garden City, is given by $C = 3 + 0.4x$.
   (a) Draw the graph of $C = 3 + 0.4x$ for values of x between 0 and 10.
   (b) Find the slope of the graph.
   (c) What is the physical meaning of the slope in this case?
   (d) What is the physical meaning of 3 in the equation $C = 3 + 0.4x$?
   (e) Philip makes a taxi journey of 7 miles. How much would it cost him?

Solution

(a)

x	0	5	10
$C = 3 + 0.4x$	3	5	7

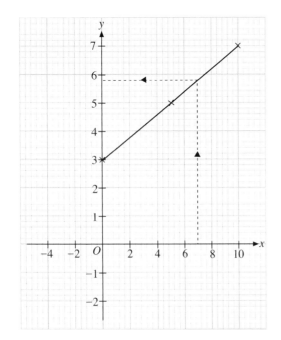

(b) Slope of the graph $= \dfrac{7 - 3}{10 - 0}$
$$= \frac{4}{10}$$
$$= \frac{2}{5}$$

(c) The slope is the rate of change of the traveling cost in \$/miles. That is, the traveling cost charges at the rate \$0.40/miles after the passenger has boarded.

(d) In the equation $C = 3 + 0.4x$, 3 represents the flag-down fare.

(e) When $x = 7$, $C = 5.8$.
Hence, the required traveling cost is \$5.80.

Chapter 11   Inequalities

Class Activity 1

Objective: To explore the properties of simple inequalities.

Questions

1. Copy and complete the following table. Fill the "solutions" column in your table from the following selection of numbers.

$$-3, 0, 2, 7.9, 8, 8\frac{1}{4}, 10, 13$$

Inequality	Read as	Solution
$x \leqslant 8$	x is less than or equal to 8	$-3, 0, 2, 7.9, 8$
$x < 8$	x is less than 8	$-3, 0, 2, 7.9$
$x \geqslant 8$	x is greater than or equal to 8	$8, 8\frac{1}{4}, 10, 13$
$x > 8$	x is greater than 8	$8\frac{1}{4}, 10, 13$

2. Fill in each ▢ with either ">" or "<" to make it a true statement.

   (a) $8 > 6$, $5 \times 8 \boxed{>} 5 \times 6$

   (b) $8 > 6$, $\frac{1}{2} \times 8 \boxed{>} \frac{1}{2} \times 6$

   (c) $9 \boxed{>} -18$, $2 \times 9 \boxed{>} 2 \times (-18)$

   (d) $9 \boxed{>} -18$, $\frac{2}{3} \times 9 \boxed{>} \frac{2}{3} \times (-18)$

   (e) $-21 \boxed{<} 14$, $3 \times (-21) \boxed{<} 3 \times 14$

   (f) $-21 \boxed{<} 14$, $\frac{4}{7} \times (-21) \boxed{<} \frac{4}{7} \times 14$

   (g) $-20 \boxed{<} -15$, $4 \times (-20) \boxed{<} 4 \times (-15)$

   (h) $-20 \boxed{<} -15$, $\frac{1}{5} \times (-20) \boxed{<} \frac{1}{5} \times (-15)$

   (i)   If $a > b$ and $k > 0$, then $ka \boxed{>} kb$.

   (j)   If $a < b$ and $k > 0$, then $ka \boxed{<} kb$.

Class Activity 2

Objective: To explore other properties of inequalities.

Questions

1. Fill in each ☐ with either "<" or ">" to make it a true statement.

   (a)   3 < 5,   3 + 6 < 5 + 6

   (b)   –9 < 2,   –9 + 3 < 2 + 3

   (c)   7 < 10,   7 – 8 < 10 – 8

   (d)   If $a < b$, then $a + k$ < $b + k$.

2. **(a)**   2 < 8, 5×2 < 5×8

   (b)   –3 < –1, $7 \times (-3)$ < $7 \times (-1)$

   (c)   –12 < 6, $\frac{1}{2} \times (-12)$ < $\frac{1}{2} \times 6$

   (d)   If $a < b$ and $k > 0$, then ka < kb.

3. **(a)**   4 < 7, $(-3) \times 4$ > $(-3) \times 7$

   (b)   –15 < 10, $\left(-\frac{2}{5}\right) \times (-15)$ > $\left(-\frac{2}{5}\right) \times 10$

   (c)   –28 < –14, $\left(-\frac{3}{7}\right) \times (-28)$ > $\left(-\frac{3}{7}\right) \times (-14)$

   (d)   If $a < b$ and $k < 0$, then ka > kb.

Extend Your Learning Curve

Purchasing Power

Ann plans to spend not more than $39 on fish and chickens from a supermarket. The price of a fish is $7 and the price of a chicken is $5. What are the combinations of different numbers of fish and chickens can she buy? Assume that the fish and chickens are bought whole. You may wish to present your answers in a list or table.

Suggested Answer:

Let x be the number of fish and y be the number of chickens bought.

Then $\qquad\qquad\qquad 7x + 5y \leqslant 39$ .... (1)

When $y = 0$, $\qquad 7x + 5(0) \leqslant 39$

$$x \leqslant \frac{39}{7}$$

$$x \leqslant 5\frac{4}{7}$$

Hence, the possible number of fish bought is $x = 0, 1, 2, ..., 5$. For each value of x, we can put the value into (1) and find the possible corresponding values of y.

For example, when $x = 2$,

$$7(2) + 5y \leqslant 39$$
$$5y \leqslant 25$$
$$y \leqslant 5$$

$\therefore$ $(2, 0), (2, 1), ..., (2, 5)$ are possible combinations of the purchase.

We can present the overall solution as shown in the following table. The cells with check marks indicate the possible combinations of the purchase.

Number of chickens bought	Number of fish bought					
	0	1	2	3	4	5
0	✓	✓	✓	✓	✓	✓
1	✓	✓	✓	✓	✓	
2	✓	✓	✓	✓	✓	
3	✓	✓	✓	✓		
4	✓	✓	✓			
5	✓	✓	✓			
6	✓	✓				
7	✓					

Discuss

Page 43
Why are the solutions of $x \leqslant b$ different from the solutions of $x < b$?

It is because $x = b$ is a solution of $x \leqslant b$ but not a solution of $x < b$.

Page 50
What is the difference between the following inequalities?
- x is greater than 2.
- x is not smaller than 2.

The number 2 is one of the solutions for "x is not smaller than 2" but not for "x is greater than 2".

Try It!

Section 11.1

1. Solve the inequality $3x < 36$.

Solution

$$3x < 36$$
$$\frac{1}{3}(3x) < \frac{1}{3} \times 36$$
$$x < 12$$

2. Solve the inequality $\frac{2}{7}x \geqslant -6$.

Solution

$$\frac{2}{7}x \geqslant -6$$
$$\frac{7}{2}\left(\frac{2}{7}x\right) \geqslant \frac{7}{2} \times (-6)$$
$$x \geqslant -21$$

Section 11.2

3. It is given that $p < 0$. Is $p < 2$?

Solution

Since $\quad p < 0$
and $\quad 0 < 2$,
$\therefore \quad p < 2$.

4. It is given that $p < q$. Compare the values of the following pairs of numbers and write an inequality statement for each pair.
(a) $p - 1$ and $q - 1$
(b) $-4p$ and $-4q$
(c) $\frac{1}{5}p$ and $\frac{1}{5}q$

Solution

(a) Since $\quad p < q$,
$\therefore \quad p - 1 < q - 1$

(b) Since $p < q$ and $-4 < 0$,
$\therefore \quad -4p > -4q$

(c) Since $p < q$ and $\frac{1}{5} > 0$,
$\therefore \quad \frac{1}{5}p < \frac{1}{5}q$

Section 11.3

5. Solve the inequality $2x + 3 < 15$.

Solution

$$2x + 3 < 15$$
$$2x + 3 - 3 < 15 - 3$$
$$2x < 12$$
$$x < \frac{12}{2}$$
$$\therefore \quad x < 6$$

6. Solve the inequality $3x - 8 \leqslant 7x + 16$ and represent the solution on a number line.

Solution

$$3x - 8 \leqslant 7x + 16$$
$$3x - 8 + 8 \leqslant 7x + 16 + 8$$
$$3x \leqslant 7x + 24$$
$$3x - 7x \leqslant 7x + 24 - 7x$$
$$-4x \leqslant 24$$
$$x \geqslant \frac{24}{-4}$$
$$\therefore \quad x \geqslant -6$$

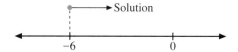

7. Solve the inequality $\frac{x-4}{5} \geqslant \frac{2x+1}{7}$ and represent the solution on a number line.

Solution

$$\frac{x-4}{5} \geqslant \frac{2x+1}{7}$$
$$35 \times \frac{x-4}{5} \geqslant 35 \times \frac{2x+1}{7} \qquad \text{LCM of 5 and 7 = 35}$$
$$7(x-4) \geqslant 5(2x+1)$$
$$7x - 28 \geqslant 10x + 5$$
$$7x \geqslant 10x + 33$$
$$-3x \geqslant 33$$
$$x \leqslant \frac{33}{-3}$$
$$\therefore \quad x \leqslant -11$$

Section 11.4

8. The maximum load that a small cart can carry is 40 kg. If the mass of each box of goods is 5 kg, find the possible numbers of boxes the cart can carry at any one time.

Solution

Let x be the possible number of boxes.

$$5x \leqslant 40$$
$$\frac{1}{5}(5x) \leqslant \frac{1}{5} \times 40$$
$$x \leqslant 8$$

The possible number of boxes is 1, 2, 3, …, 8.

9. An 8-inch submarine roll contains 70 g of carbohydrate. Suppose the recommended daily carbohydrate intake of a woman is 130 g, find the minimum whole number of submarine rolls that the woman should eat per day to meet her recommended daily carbohydrate intake.

    Solution

    Let x be the number of submarine rolls that the woman should eat per day.

    $$70x \geqslant 130$$
    $$\frac{1}{70}(70x) \geqslant \frac{1}{70} \times 130$$
    $$x \geqslant 1\frac{6}{7}$$

    The woman should eat at least 2 submarine rolls per day.

10. Sally has $70 in her money box. She saves $40 every month in her money box. What is the minimum number of complete months required in order for Sally to have more than $500 in her money box?

    Solution

    Let t be the number of months required.
    $$70 + 40t > 500$$
    $$40t > 430$$
    $$t > 10.75$$
    $\therefore$ there will be more than $500 after 11 months.

Exercise 11.1

Basic Practice

1. Determine whether the value of x in each case is a solution of the given inequality.
   (a) $x < 6$; $x = 3$
   (b) $x \geqslant 4$; $x = 2$
   (c) $x > -5$; $x = -1$
   (d) $x \leqslant -3$; $x = -3$
   (e) $x \geqslant 0$; $x = -8$
   (f) $x < 7$; $x = 7$
   (g) $2x < -1$; $x = -\dfrac{3}{2}$
   (h) $\dfrac{1}{4}x > -5$; $x = \dfrac{1}{3}$

Solution

(a) $3 < 6$
   $\therefore x = 3$ is a solution of $x < 6$.

(b) $2 < 4$
   $\therefore x = 2$ is NOT a solution of $x \geqslant 4$.

(c) $-1 > -5$
   $\therefore x = -1$ is a solution of $x > -5$.

(d) $-3 = -3$
   $\therefore x = -3$ is a solution of $x \leqslant -3$.

(e) $-8 < 0$
   $\therefore x = -8$ is NOT a solution of $x \geqslant 0$.

(f) $7 = 7$
   $\therefore x = 7$ is NOT a solution of $x < 7$.

(g) When $x = -\dfrac{3}{2}$, $2x = -3 < -1$
   $\therefore x = -\dfrac{3}{2}$ is a solution of $2x < -1$.

(h) When $x = \dfrac{1}{3}$, $\dfrac{1}{4}x = \dfrac{1}{12} > -5$
   $\therefore x = \dfrac{1}{3}$ is a solution of $\dfrac{1}{4}x > -5$.

2. Solve the following inequalities.
   (a) $2x < 10$ (b) $3x > 18$
   (c) $4x \leqslant 6$ (d) $5x \geqslant 11$
   (e) $6x > -9$ (f) $8x \leqslant -30$
   (g) $14x \geqslant -35$ (h) $15x < -40$

Solution

(a) $2x < 10$
   $\dfrac{1}{2}(2x) < \dfrac{1}{2} \times 10$
   $x < 5$

(b) $3x > 18$
   $\dfrac{1}{3}(3x) > \dfrac{1}{3} \times 18$
   $x > 6$

(c) $4x \leqslant 6$
   $\dfrac{1}{4}(4x) \leqslant \dfrac{1}{4} \times 6$
   $x \leqslant 1\dfrac{3}{2}$

(d) $5x \geqslant 11$
   $\dfrac{1}{5}(5x) \geqslant \dfrac{1}{5} \times 11$
   $x \geqslant 2\dfrac{1}{5}$

(e) $6x > -9$
   $\dfrac{1}{6}(6x) > \dfrac{1}{6} \times (-9)$
   $x > -1\dfrac{1}{2}$

(f) $8x \leqslant -30$
   $\dfrac{1}{8}(8x) \leqslant \dfrac{1}{8} \times (-30)$
   $x \leqslant -3\dfrac{3}{4}$

(g) $14x \geqslant -35$
   $\dfrac{1}{14}(14x) \geqslant \dfrac{1}{14} \times (-35)$
   $x \geqslant -2\dfrac{1}{2}$

(h) $15x < -40$
   $\dfrac{1}{15}(15x) < \dfrac{1}{15} \times (-40)$
   $x < -2\dfrac{2}{3}$

Further Practice

3. Solve the following inequalities.
   (a) $\dfrac{1}{2}x > 5$ (b) $\dfrac{1}{3}x < -4$
   (c) $\dfrac{5}{8}x < -\dfrac{15}{4}$ (d) $\dfrac{11}{9}x \leqslant \dfrac{22}{27}$
   (e) $\dfrac{12}{7}x \geqslant -3$ (f) $\dfrac{4}{15}x > 2\dfrac{2}{3}$

Solution

(a) $\dfrac{1}{2}x > 5$
   $2\left(\dfrac{1}{2}x\right) > 2 \times 5$
   $x > 10$

(b) $\dfrac{1}{3}x < -4$
   $3\left(\dfrac{1}{3}x\right) < 3 \times (-4)$
   $x < -12$

(c)
$$\frac{5}{8}x < -\frac{15}{4}$$
$$\frac{5}{8} < \frac{8}{5} \times \left(-\frac{15}{4}\right)$$
$$x < -6$$

(d)
$$\frac{11}{9}x \leqslant \frac{22}{27}$$
$$\frac{9}{11}\left(\frac{11}{9}x\right) \leqslant \frac{9}{11} \times \frac{22}{27}$$
$$x \leqslant \frac{2}{3}$$

(e)
$$\frac{12}{7}x \geqslant -3$$
$$\frac{7}{12}\left(\frac{12}{7}x\right) \geqslant \frac{7}{12} \times (-3)$$
$$x \geqslant -1\frac{3}{4}$$

(f)
$$\frac{4}{15}x > 2\frac{2}{3}$$
$$\frac{15}{4}\left(\frac{4}{15}x\right) > \frac{15}{4} \times \frac{8}{3}$$
$$x > 10$$

4. Solve the following inequalities.
(a) $x + x \geqslant 3$ (b) $5x - 2x < -24$
(c) $\frac{x}{2} + \frac{x}{3} > -10$ (d) $\frac{4}{5}x - \frac{2}{7}x \leqslant 1 + \frac{1}{2}$

Solution

(a) $x + x \geqslant 3$
$$2x \geqslant 3$$
$$x \geqslant 1\frac{1}{2}$$

(b) $5x - 2x < -24$
$$3x < -24$$
$$x < \frac{1}{3} \times (-24)$$
$$x < -8$$

(c) $\frac{x}{2} + \frac{x}{3} > -10$
$$\frac{3x + 2x}{6} > -10$$
$$\frac{5x}{6} > -10$$
$$x > \frac{6}{5} \times (-10)$$
$$x > -12$$

(d)
$$\frac{4}{5}x - \frac{2}{7}x \leqslant 1 + \frac{1}{2}$$
$$\frac{28x - 10x}{35} \leqslant \frac{3}{2}$$
$$\frac{18x}{35} \leqslant \frac{3}{2}$$
$$x \leqslant \frac{35}{18} \times \frac{3}{2}$$
$$x \leqslant \frac{35}{12}$$
$$x \leqslant 2\frac{11}{12}$$

Math@Work

5. Find the greatest integer x that satisfies each inequality.
(a) $11x < 36$ (b) $8x \leqslant 72$
(c) $3x \leqslant -8$ (d) $5x < -30$

Solution

(a) $11x < 36$
$$x < \frac{36}{11}$$
$$x < 3\frac{3}{11}$$
The greatest integer x is 3.

(b) $8x \leqslant 72$
$$x \leqslant \frac{1}{8} \times 72$$
$$x \leqslant 9$$
The greatest integer x is 9.

(c) $3x \leqslant -8$
$$x \leqslant \frac{1}{3} \times (-8)$$
$$x \leqslant -2\frac{2}{3}$$
The greatest integer is -3.

(d) $5x < -30$
$$x < \frac{1}{5} \times (-30)$$
$$x < -6$$
The greatest integer is -7.

6. Find the smallest integer x that satisfies each inequality.
(a) $4x \geqslant 12$ (b) $\frac{2}{3}x > \frac{4}{7}$
(c) $\frac{5}{6}x > -\frac{7}{3}$ (d) $\frac{9}{4}x \geqslant -\frac{15}{2}$

Solution

(a) $4x \geqslant 12$

$x \geqslant \dfrac{1}{4} \times 12$

$x \geqslant 3$

The smallest integer x is 3.

(b) $\dfrac{2}{3}x > \dfrac{4}{7}$

$x > \dfrac{3}{2} \times \dfrac{4}{7}$

$x > \dfrac{6}{7}$

The smallest integer x is 1.

(c) $\dfrac{5}{6}x > -\dfrac{7}{3}$

$x > \dfrac{6}{5} \times \left(-\dfrac{7}{3}\right)$

$x > -\dfrac{14}{5}$

$x > -2\dfrac{4}{5}$

The smallest integer x is -2.

(d) $\dfrac{9}{4}x \geqslant -\dfrac{15}{2}$

$x \geqslant \dfrac{4}{9} \times \left(-\dfrac{15}{2}\right)$

$x \geqslant -\dfrac{10}{3}$

$x \geqslant -3\dfrac{1}{3}$

The smallest integer x is -3.

Brainworks

7. Write down an inequality of the form $ax > b$, where $a \neq 1$, such that its solution is $x > 7$.

Solution

One possible inequality is
$5x > 35$.

The solution is given by

$x > \dfrac{1}{5} \times 35$.

i.e., $x > 7$.

8. Write down an inequality of the form $ax \leqslant b$, where $a \neq 1$, such that its solution is $x \leqslant -\dfrac{3}{4}$.

Solution

One possible inequality is
$8x \leqslant -6$.

The solution is given by

$x \leqslant \dfrac{1}{3} \times (-6)$.

i.e., $x \leqslant -\dfrac{3}{4}$.

Exercise 11.2
Basic Practice

1. If $a < 7$, determine whether the following inequalities are true.
    (a) $a < 10$
    (b) $a < 2$
    (c) $a + 2 < 9$
    (d) $-a < -7$

    Solution
    (a)   Since $a < 7$
          and $7 < 10$,
          $\therefore$ $a < 10$ is true.

    (b)   When $a = 5$,
          then $a < 7$
          but $a > 2$.
          $\therefore$ $a < 2$ is false.

    (c)   Since $a < 7$,
          $a + 2 < 7 + 2$.
          $\therefore$ $a + 2 < 9$ is true.

    (d)   Since $a < 7$,
          $(-1)a > (-1)7$
          $-a > -7$
          $\therefore$ $-a < -7$ is false.

2. If $p > -5$, determine whether the following inequalities are true.
    (a) $p > -3$
    (b) $p > -9$
    (c) $p + 5 > 0$
    (d) $-p < -5$

    Solution
    (a)   When $p = -4$,
          then $p > -5$
          but $p < -3$.
          $\therefore$ $p > -3$ is false.

    (b)   Since $p > -5$
          and $-5 > -9$,
          $\therefore$ $p > -9$ is true.

    (c)   Since $p > -5$,
          $p + 5 > -5 + 5$.
          $\therefore$ $p + 5 > 0$ is true.

(d) When $p = 3$,
  then $p > -5$
  but $-3 > -5$.
  $\therefore -p < -5$ is false.

3. Copy and fill in each box with an inequality sign.

 (a) If $a < b$, then $a - 6$ ☐ $b - 6$.

 (b) If $p > q$, then $p + 7$ ☐ $q + 7$.

 (c) If $r \leqslant s$, then $2r$ ☐ $2s$.

 (d) If $x \geqslant y$, then $-\dfrac{1}{3}x$ ☐ $-\dfrac{1}{3}y$.

Solution

 (a) If $a < b$, then $a - 6$ $<$ $b - 6$.

 (b) If $p > q$, then $p + 7$ $>$ $q + 7$.

 (c) If $r \leqslant s$, then $2r$ $\leqslant$ $2s$.

 (d) If $x \geqslant y$, then $-\dfrac{1}{3}x$ $\leqslant$ $-\dfrac{1}{3}y$.

Further Practice

4. Copy and fill in each box with an inequality sign.
 (a) If $a < b$, then

  (i) $4a$ ☐ $4b$,

  (ii) $4a + 3$ ☐ $4b + 3$.

 (b) If $m \geqslant n$, then

  (i) $-m$ ☐ $-n$,

  (ii) $-m + 1$ ☐ $-n + 1$.

Solution
 (a) If $a < b$, then
  (i) $4a$ $<$ $4b$,

  (ii) $4a + 3$ $<$ $4b + 3$.

 (b) If $m \geqslant n$, then
  (i) $-m$ $\leqslant$ $-n$,

  (ii) $-m + 1$ $\leqslant$ $-n + 1$.

5. If $p \leqslant q$, compare the values of the following pairs of numbers.
 (a) $2p - 7$ and $2q - 7$
 (b) $-4 - \dfrac{1}{5}$ and $-4 - \dfrac{1}{5}q$

Solution
 (a) If $p \leqslant q$, then
   $$2p \leqslant 2q$$
   $\therefore 2p - 7 \leqslant 2q - 7$
 (b) If $p \leqslant q$, then
   $$-\dfrac{1}{5}p \geqslant -\dfrac{1}{5}q$$
   $\therefore -4 - \dfrac{1}{5}p \geqslant -4 - \dfrac{1}{5}q$

Math@Work

6. **(a)** If $a < b$ and $c < d$, what is the inequality relationship between
  (i) $a + c$ and $b + c$,
  (ii) $b + c$ and $b + d$,
  (iii) $a + c$ and $b + d$?
 (b) If Mr. and Mrs. Smith's monthly salaries are more than \$4,000 and \$3,500 respectively, what can you say about their combined monthly salary?

Solution
 (a) **(i)** $\qquad a < b$
   $\therefore a + c < b + c$ .... (1)
  (ii) $\qquad c < d$
   $\therefore b + c < b + d$ .... (2)
  (iii) From (1) and (2), we have $a + c < b + d$.
 (b) $\qquad$ Mr. Smith's monthly salary $> \$4,000$
  and Mrs. Smith's monthly salary $> \$3,500$
  $\therefore$ their total salary $> \$4,000 + \$3,500$
  i.e., their total salary $> \$7,500$

Brainworks

7. If $a < b$ and $c < d$, is it necessary that $a - c < b - d$? If it is not true, give a counterexample.

Solution
If $a < b$ and $c < d$, it is NOT necessary that $a - c < b - d$.
For example, when $a = 8$, $b = 11$, $c = 3$, and $d = 9$,
then $\qquad a < b$ and $c < d$,
but $\qquad a - c = 8 - 3 = 5$,
and $\qquad b - d = 11 - 9 = 2$.
Hence, $a - c > b - d$.

8. If $a < b$, must a^2 be less than b^2?

Solution
If $a < b$, then a^2 may not be less than b^2.
For example, $\qquad -4 < 3$
but $\qquad (-4)^2 > 3^2$.

Exercise 11.3
Basic Practice

1. Solve each of the following inequalities and represent its solution on a number line.

   (a) $x - 2 < 7$

   (b) $x + 3 \geqslant 4$

   (c) $\frac{1}{5}x \leqslant 2$

   (d) $-4x > 12$

   (e) $3x + 5 \geqslant 2$

   (f) $7x - 13 < 1$

   (g) $9x - 2 < 4x + 8$

   (h) $6x + 7 \geqslant 8x - 5$

Solution

(a)
$$x - 2 < 7$$
$$x - 2 + 2 < 7 + 2$$
$$\therefore \quad x < 9$$

(b)
$$x + 3 \geqslant 4$$
$$x + 3 - 3 \geqslant 4 - 3$$
$$\therefore \quad x \geqslant 1$$

(c)
$$\frac{1}{5}x \leqslant 2$$
$$5\left(\frac{1}{5}x\right) \leqslant 5 \times 2$$
$$\therefore \quad x \leqslant 10$$

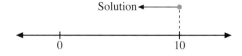

(d)
$$-4x > 12$$
$$-\frac{1}{4}(-4x) < -\frac{1}{4} \times 12$$
$$\therefore \quad x < -3$$

(e)
$$3x + 5 \geqslant 2$$
$$3x \geqslant -3$$
$$x \geqslant -1$$

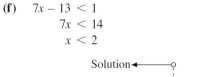

(f)
$$7x - 13 < 1$$
$$7x < 14$$
$$x < 2$$

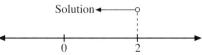

(g)
$$9x - 2 < 4x + 8$$
$$5x < 10$$
$$x < 2$$

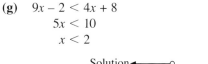

(h)
$$6x + 7 \geqslant 8x - 5$$
$$-2x \geqslant -12$$
$$x \leqslant 6$$

Further Practice

2. Solve each of the following inequalities and represent its solution on a number line.

   (a) $5(2x + 3) > 4(x - 2) - 13$

   (b) $11 - 2(3x - 7) \leqslant 6(9 - 2x)$

   (c) $2(x + 3) \geqslant 19 - 3(5 - 2x)$

   (d) $\frac{1}{3}x + 1 > \frac{5}{6}$

   (e) $\frac{2x - 1}{5} < \frac{x}{2}$

   (f) $\frac{2}{7} + \frac{1}{4}x \leqslant \frac{3}{4}x - \frac{5}{7}$

   (g) $\frac{2(3x + 1)}{5} \geqslant \frac{3(x - 1)}{8}$

   (h) $\frac{4x - 5}{3} - \frac{1}{4} > \frac{1 - x}{9}$

   (i) $\frac{x - 3}{2} > \frac{4}{13}(2x + 5) - 1$

   (j) $\frac{x + 1}{2} - \frac{x - 1}{3} \leqslant \frac{2x - 7}{4}$

Solution

(a) $5(2x + 3) > 4(x - 2) - 13$

$\qquad 10x + 15 > 4x - 8 - 13$

$\qquad\qquad 6x > -36$

$\qquad\qquad\quad x > -6$

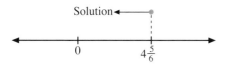

(b) $11 - 2(3x - 7) \leqslant 6(9 - 2x)$

$\qquad 11 - 6x + 14 \leqslant 54 - 12x$

$\qquad\qquad\quad 6x \leqslant 29$

$\qquad\qquad\quad\; x \leqslant 4\dfrac{5}{6}$

(c) $2(x + 3) \geqslant 19 - 3(5 - 2x)$

$\qquad 2x + 6 \geqslant 19 - 15 + 6x$

$\qquad\quad -4x \geqslant -2$

$\qquad\qquad\; x \leqslant \dfrac{1}{2}$

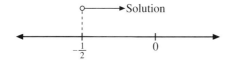

(d) $\dfrac{1}{3}x + 1 > \dfrac{5}{6}$

$\qquad 2x + 6 > 5$

$\qquad\quad 2x > -1$

$\qquad\quad\; x > -\dfrac{1}{2}$

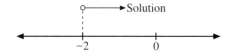

(e) $\dfrac{2x - 1}{5} < \dfrac{x}{2}$

$\qquad 2(2x - 1) < 5x$

$\qquad\; 4x - 2 < 5x$

$\qquad\qquad -x < 2$

$\qquad\qquad\; x > -2$

(f) $\dfrac{2}{7} + \dfrac{1}{4}x \leqslant \dfrac{3}{4}x - \dfrac{5}{7}$

$\qquad 8 + 7x \leqslant 21x - 20$

$\qquad\quad -14x \leqslant -28$

$\qquad\qquad\; x \geqslant 2$

(g) $\dfrac{2(3x + 1)}{5} \geqslant \dfrac{3(x - 1)}{8}$

$\qquad 16(3x + 1) \geqslant 15(x - 1)$

$\qquad\; 48x + 16 \geqslant 15x - 15$

$\qquad\qquad 33x \geqslant -31$

$\qquad\qquad\quad x \geqslant -\dfrac{31}{33}$

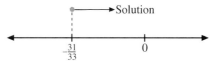

(h) $\dfrac{4x - 5}{3} - \dfrac{1}{4} > \dfrac{1 - x}{9}$

$\qquad 12(4x - 5) - 9 > 4(1 - x)$

$\qquad 48x - 60 - 9 > 4 - 4x$

$\qquad\qquad\quad 52x > 73$

$\qquad\qquad\qquad x > 1\dfrac{21}{52}$

(i) $\dfrac{x - 3}{2} > \dfrac{4}{13}(2x + 5) - 1$

$\qquad 13(x - 3) > 8(2x + 5) - 26$

$\qquad 13x - 39 > 16x + 40 - 26$

$\qquad\qquad -3x > 53$

$\qquad\qquad\quad x < -17\dfrac{2}{3}$

(j) $\dfrac{x + 1}{2} - \dfrac{x - 1}{3} \leqslant \dfrac{2x - 7}{4}$

$\qquad 6(x + 1) - 4(x - 1) \leqslant 3(2x - 7)$

$\qquad\; 6x + 6 - 4x + 4 \leqslant 6x - 21$

$\qquad\qquad\quad -4x \leqslant -31$

$\qquad\qquad\qquad\; x \geqslant 7\dfrac{3}{4}$

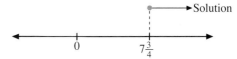

Math@Work

3. The maximum loading of electric current on a power strip is 13 amperes (A). A lamp of $\frac{1}{2}$ A is already plugged into it. How many hairdryers of 3A can be plugged into the power strip and turned on without overloading it?

Solution
Let x be the number of hairdryers required.

$$\frac{1}{2} + 3x \le 13$$
$$1 + 6x \le 26$$
$$6x \le 25$$
$$x \le \frac{25}{6}$$
i.e., $x \le 4\frac{1}{6}$

∴ the required number of hairdryers is 1, 2, 3, or 4.

Brainworks

4. Write a linear inequality in the form $ax + b < cx + d$ such that the solution is $x > 8$, where a, b, c, and d are constants.

Solution
One example is $\quad x + 16 < 2x + 8$.
Then $\quad\quad\quad\quad\quad -x < -8$.
∴ $x > 8$ is the solution.

Exercise 11.4
Basic Practice

1. Jane works in a store and is paid by the hour. Her hourly rate of pay is $15.
   (a) If she works for x hours, how much does she get?
   (b) What are the possible numbers of hours she has worked if she earns less than $75?

Solution
(a) The amount Jane gets = $15 \times x$
$$= \$15x$$
(b) $15x < 75$
$$x < \frac{1}{15} \times 75$$
$$x < 5$$
She works for less than 5 hours.

2. The price of a concert ticket is $50.
   (a) Find the total price for x tickets.
   (b) Henry has $200 to spend on tickets. Find the possible numbers of concert tickets he can buy.

Solution
(a) The total price for x tickets = $50 \times x$
$$= \$50x$$
(b) $50x \le 200$
$$x \le \frac{1}{50} \times 200$$
$$x \le 4$$
The possible numbers of concert tickets that he can buy are 1, 2, 3, and 4.

3. The weight of a book is $1\frac{1}{5}$ lb.
   (a) Find the total weight of x books.
   (b) If the weight of a pile of books is more than 18 lb, find the minimum number of books in the pile.

Solution
(a) Total weight of x books = $1\frac{1}{5} \times x$ lb
$$= 1\frac{1}{5}x \text{ lb}$$
(b) $1\frac{1}{5}x > 18$
$$\frac{6}{5}x > 18$$
$$x > \frac{5}{6} \times 18$$
$$x > 15$$
The minimum number of books in the pile is 16.

4. Josh took two math tests. He scored 57 out of 100 on the first test. If his total score has to be at least 120 to pass both tests, what is the minimum points he should score on the next test?

Solution
Let x be the points he scored on the second test.
$$57 + x \ge 120$$
$$x \ge 63$$
The minimum points he should score is 63.

Further Practice

5. Mr. Lee wants to travel more than 130 miles in $2\frac{1}{2}$ hours. What should his average speed of driving be?

Solution
Let x mph be the required speed.
$$2\frac{1}{2} \times x > 130$$
$$\frac{5}{2} \times x > 130$$
$$x > \frac{2}{5} \times 130$$
$$x > 52$$
His average speed should be greater than 52 mph.

6. How many chairs can a carpenter make in 7 hours assuming that each chair takes $\frac{3}{4}$ of an hour to make?

Solution

Let x be the number of chairs made.

$$\frac{3}{4}x \leq 7$$
$$x \leq \frac{4}{3} \times 7$$
$$x \leq \frac{28}{3}$$
$$x \leq 9\frac{1}{3}$$

The possible numbers of chairs he can make are 1, 2, 3, ..., 9.

7. The selling price of a bouquet of flowers is $25. Find the minimum number of bouquets of flowers a florist must sell if she wants her total sales to be more than $360.

Solution

Let x be the number of bouquets of flowers sold.

$$25x > 360$$
$$x > \frac{1}{25} \times 360$$
$$x > \frac{72}{5}$$
$$x > 14\frac{2}{5}$$

The minimum number of bouquets of flowers she must sell is 15.

8. Mr. Haris has six $10 bills and some $20 bills in his wallet. If the total value of the bills is less than $150, how many $20 bills are there?

Solution

Let x be the number of $20 bills.

$$10 \times 6 + 20x < 150$$
$$60 + 20x < 150$$
$$20x < 90$$
$$x < \frac{9}{2}$$
$$\text{i.e., } x < 4.5$$

$\therefore$ the possible numbers of $20 bills are 1, 2, 3, and 4.

9. In a chemical reaction, the mass of a product grows 11 g in every hour. The current mass of the product is 46 g. When will the mass of the product first exceed 101 g?

Solution

Let t be the number of hours required.

$$46 + 11t > 101$$
$$11t > 55$$
$$t > 5$$

$\therefore$ after 5 hours, the mass of the product will be more than 101 g.

10. Rachael weighed 164 lb. After joining a weight-loss program, she lost 6 lb a month. Find the number of months Racheal has to be in this program if she continues to lose 6 lb a month and wants her weight to become less than 128 lb.

Solution

Let m be the number of months required.
$$164 - 6m < 126$$
$$-6m < -36$$
$$m > 6$$
$\therefore$ her weight would be under 128 lb after 6 months.

Math@Work

11. A school needs to raise $45,000 to equip a multimedia room. The school has 800 students.
   (a) If every student donates the same amount, how much must each student donate to meet the target?
   (b) If each computer costs $1,700, find the possible numbers of computers that can be bought with $45,000.

Solution

(a) Let $x be the amount that each student needs to donate.
$$800x = 45,000$$
$$x = \frac{45,000}{800}$$
$$x = 56.25$$
Each student needs to donate $56.25.

(b) Let y be the possible numbers of computers that can be bought.
$$1,700y \leq 45,000$$
$$y \leq \frac{1}{1,700} \times 45,000$$
$$y \leq \frac{450}{17}$$
$$y \leq 26$$
The possible numbers of computers that can be bought are 1, 2, 3, ..., 26.

12. The length of a rectangle is twice its width. Suppose the width is x cm.
   (a) Express the perimeter of the rectangle in terms of x.
   (b) If the perimeter of the rectangle is 102 cm, find its width.
   (c) If the perimeter of the rectangle is less than 120 cm, what are the possible values of its widths?

Solution

(a) Length of the rectangle = $2x$ cm
Perimeter of the rectangle = $2(2x + x)$
$$= 6x \text{ cm}$$

(b) $6x = 102$

$$x = \frac{102}{6}$$

$$x = 17$$

The width of the rectangle is 17 cm.

(c) $6x < 120$

$$x < \frac{1}{6} \times 120$$

$$x < 20$$

Its possible widths are greater than 0 cm but less than 20 cm.

Brainworks

13. Company A quotes a rental rate for a car at \$45 per day. Company B quotes a rate of \$38 per day, but with an initial charge of \$75. Find the minimum number of complete days of rental required such that the charges by Company B will become lower than those by Company A.

Solution

Let x be the number of days required.

$$75 + 38x < 45x$$

$$-7x < -75$$

$$7x > 75$$

$$x > \frac{75}{7}$$

$$x > 10\frac{5}{7}$$

∴ the charges by company B will become lower after 11 days of rental.

14. The sum of three consecutive odd numbers is between 90 and 100. Find two possible sets of the three consecutive odd numbers.

Solution

Let x be the middle odd number required.

Sum of the three consecutive odd numbers

$$= (x - 2) + x + (x + 2)$$

$$= 3x$$

We require

$$90 < 3x < 100$$

$$\frac{1}{3} \times 90 < x < \frac{1}{3} \times 100$$

$$30 < x < 33\frac{1}{3}$$

∴ $x = 31, 33$ or 32 (rejected)

i.e., $x = 31$ or 33

Two possible sets of the three consecutive odd numbers are $\{29, 31, \text{and } 33\}$ and $\{31, 33, \text{and } 35\}$.

Review Exercise 11

1. State whether each of the following statements is **true** or **false**. If it is false, give a numerical example to support your claim.

(a) If $x > 0$, then $x^2 > x$.

(b) If $x < 0$, then $\frac{1}{x} > 0$.

(c) If $x > 0$, then $-\frac{1}{x} < 0$.

(d) If $a < 0$ and $b < 0$, then $a + b < 0$.

(e) If $a < b$, then $\frac{1}{a} > \frac{1}{b}$.

Solution

(a) When $x = 0.1 > 0$,

$$x^2 = 0.01 < x.$$

∴ $x^2 > x$ is false.

(b) When $x = -2 < 0$,

then $\frac{1}{x} = -\frac{1}{2} < 0.$

∴ $\frac{1}{x} > 0$ is false.

(c) When $x > 0,$

$$-x < 0$$

and $(-x)\left(\frac{1}{x^2}\right) < 0\left(\frac{1}{x^2}\right).$

∴ $-\frac{1}{x} < 0$ is true.

(d) When $a < 0$

and $b < 0,$

then $a + b < 0 + 0.$

∴ $a + b < 0$ is true.

(e) When $a = -2$ and $b = 5,$

$$a < b$$

but $-\frac{1}{2} < \frac{1}{5}$

i.e., $\frac{1}{a} < \frac{1}{b}.$

∴ $\frac{1}{a} > \frac{1}{b}$ is false.

2. If $a < 7$, state which of the following statements are **true**?

(a) $a < 17$ **(b)** $-a < -7$

(c) $3a + 4 < 25$ **(d)** $a^2 < 49$

Solution

(a) $a < 7$

and $7 < 17,$

∴ $a < 17$ is true.

(b) $a > 7$

∴ $(-1)a > (-1)7$

$$-a > -7$$

∴ $-a < -7$ is false.

(c)
$$a < 7$$
$$3a < 3(7)$$
$$3a + 4 < 21 + 4$$
i.e., $3a + 4 < 25$ is true.

(d) Let $a = -8$.
Then $a < 7$
but $a^2 = (-8)^2 = 64 > 49$.
$\therefore a^2 < 49$ is false.

3. Solve each of the following inequalities and represent the solution on a number line.

(a) $3x < 24$ **(b)** $-5x \geqslant 75$

(c) $\dfrac{4}{9}x > -\dfrac{8}{3}$ **(d)** $-\dfrac{1}{7}x \leqslant -\dfrac{10}{21}$

Solution

(a) $3x < 24$
$$x < \frac{1}{3} \times 24$$
$$x < 8$$

(b) $-5x \geqslant 75$
$$x \leqslant -\frac{1}{5} \times 75$$
$$x \leqslant -15$$

(c) $\dfrac{4}{9}x > -\dfrac{8}{3}$
$$x > \frac{9}{4} \times \left(-\frac{8}{3}\right)$$
$$x > -6$$

(d) $-\dfrac{1}{7}x \leqslant -\dfrac{10}{21}$
$$x \geqslant -7 \times \left(-\frac{10}{21}\right)$$
$$x \geqslant \frac{10}{3}$$
$$x \geqslant 3\frac{1}{3}$$

4. Find the greatest integer x that satisfies each inequality.
(a) $8x \leqslant 32$
(b) $2x + x < -31$

Solution

(a) $8x \leqslant 32$
$$x \leqslant \frac{1}{3} \times 32$$
$$x \leqslant 4$$
The greatest integer x is 4.

(b) $2x + x < -31$
$$3x < -31$$
$$x < -\frac{31}{3}$$
$$x < -10\frac{1}{3}$$
The greatest integer x is -11.

5. Find the smallest integer x that satisfies each inequality.
(a) $2x > -9$ **(b)** $\dfrac{2}{3}x + \dfrac{1}{4}x > 15$

Solution

(a) $2x > -9$
$$x > -\frac{9}{2}$$
$$x > -4\frac{1}{2}$$
The smallest integer x is -4.

(b) $\dfrac{2}{3}x + \dfrac{1}{4}x > 15$
$$\frac{8x + 3x}{12} > 15$$
$$\frac{11x}{12} > 15$$
$$x > \frac{12}{11} \times 15$$
$$x > 16\frac{4}{11}$$
The smallest integer x is 17.

6. **(a)** Simplify $3(5x - 4) + 2(x + 6)$.
(b) Hence, solve the inequality
$$3(5x - 4) + 2(x + 6) \geqslant -51.$$

Solution

(a) $3(5 - 4) + 2(+ 6) = 15 - 12 + 2 + 12$
$$= 17$$

(b) $3(5 - 4) + 2(+ 6) \geqslant -51$
$$17x \geqslant -51$$
$$x \geqslant \frac{-51}{17}$$
$$x \geqslant -3$$

7. Solve each of the following linear inequalities and represent the solution on a number line.
(a) $4x + 9 < -11$
(b) $15 - 2x \geqslant 23$
(c) $7(3x - 5) > 6(2x + 1)$
(d) $\dfrac{5x - 8}{11} \leqslant 2$

Solution

(a) $4x + 9 < -11$
$4x < -20$
$x < -5$

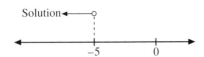

(b) $15 - 2x \geqslant 23$
$-2x \geqslant 8$
$x \leqslant -4$

(c) $7(3x - 5) > 6(2x + 1)$
$21x - 35 > 12x + 6$
$9x > 41$
$x > 4\dfrac{5}{9}$

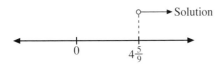

(d) $\dfrac{5x - 8}{11} \leqslant 2$
$5x - 8 \leqslant 22$
$5x \leqslant 30$
$x \leqslant 6$

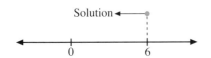

8. Solve the following linear inequalities.

(a) $\dfrac{1}{5}x - 2(x - 3) < 4$

(b) $\dfrac{1}{2}x - \dfrac{1}{3}x \geqslant -13$

(c) $\dfrac{7 - x}{4} \leqslant \dfrac{1 - 3x}{6}$

(d) $(x - 1)^2 < (x + 9)^2$

Solution

(a) $\dfrac{1}{5}x - 2(x - 3) < 4$
$x - 10(x - 3) < 20$
$x - 10x + 30 < 20$
$-9x < -10$
$x > \dfrac{10}{9}$
$x > 1\dfrac{1}{9}$

(b) $\dfrac{1}{2}x - \dfrac{1}{3}x \geqslant -13$
$3x - 2x \geqslant -78$
$x \geqslant -78$

(c) $\dfrac{7 - x}{4} \leqslant \dfrac{1 - 3x}{6}$
$3(7 - x) \leqslant 2(1 - 3x)$
$21 - 3x \leqslant 2 - 6x$
$3x \leqslant -19$
$x \leqslant -\dfrac{19}{3}$
$x \leqslant -6\dfrac{1}{3}$

(d) $(x - 1)^2 < (x + 9)^2$
$x^2 - 2x + 1 < x^2 + 18x + 81$
$-20x < 80$
$x > -4$

9. The Chan family consumes $\dfrac{3}{10}$ kg of rice a day. If the family has 15 kg of rice, what is the maximum number of days the family can consume the rice such that at least 4 kg of it is left?

Solution
Let x be the number of days required.
$15 - \dfrac{3}{10}x > 4$
$150 - 3x > 40$
$-3x > -110$
$x < \dfrac{110}{3}$
i.e., $x < 36\dfrac{2}{3}$
$\therefore$ the required number of days is 36.

10. A swimming club charges a monthly membership fee of \$20 and an admission fee of \$3 per entry. Cathy paid more than \$50 to the club last month. Find the minimum number of times she had swum in the club last month.

Solution
Let x be the minimum number of times that Cathy swims in a month.
$20 + 3x > 50$
$3x > 30$
$x > 10$
$\therefore$ the minimum number of times is 11.

11. (a) Solve the inequalities
(i) $8x > 40$,   **(ii)** $6y \leqslant -42$.
(b) $P(x, y)$ is a point on the coordinate plane such that $8x > 40$ and $6y \leqslant -42$. In which quadrant does the point P lie?

Solution

(a) **(i)** $8x > 40$

$$x > \frac{40}{8}$$

$$x > 5$$

(ii) $6y \leqslant -42$

$$y \leqslant \frac{1}{6} \times (-42)$$

$$y \leqslant -7$$

(b) Since x is positive and y is negative, $P(x, y)$ lies in the fourth quadrant.

---

12. The diagram shows a square $OABC$ of side n units. It has a perimeter that is not more than 20 units.

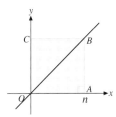

(a) Express the perimeter of the square in terms of n.
(b) Find the possible values of n.
(c) Suppose the square has a maximum possible area, find
  (i) the coordinates of A, B, and C,
  (ii) the slopes of the side AB and the diagonal OB.

Solution

(a) Perimeter of the square = $4n$ units

(b) $4n \leqslant 20$

$$n \leqslant \frac{20}{4}$$

$$n \leqslant 5$$

The possible values of n are greater than 0 and equal to or less than 5.
i.e., $0 < n \leqslant 5$.

(c) When the square has a maximum possible area, $n = 5$.
  (i) Coordinates of $n = (5, 0)$
  Coordinates of $n = (5, 5)$
  Coordinates of $n = (0, 5)$
  (ii) Since the side AB is vertical, the slope of AB is undefined.

$$\text{Slope of } OB = \frac{AB}{OA}$$

$$= \frac{5}{5}$$

$$= 1$$

---

13. Consider the sequence 3, 6, 9, 12, ...
(a) Find the general term of the sequence.
(b) Find the 11th term of the sequence.
(c) What is the largest term of the sequence that is less than 101?

Solution

(a) The general term = nth term
$$= 3n$$

(b) The 11th term = 3×11
$$= 33$$

(c) $3n < 101$

$$n < \frac{101}{3}$$

$$n < 33\frac{2}{3}$$

The largest possible n is 33.

Since $3 \times 33 = 99$,
∴ the largest term of the sequence that is less than 101 is 99.

---

14. A store offers $x\%$ discount on goods such that $4x < 60$.
(a) Find the maximum percentage discount.
(b) A desk lamp and a magazine rack are sold at the maximum percentage discount.
  (i) If the marked price of the desk lamp is $200, find its selling price.
  (ii) If the selling price of the magazine rack is $51, find its marked price.

Solution

(a) $4x \leqslant 60$

$$x \leqslant \frac{60}{4}$$

$$x \leqslant 15$$

The maximum percentage discount is 15%.

(b) **(i)** Selling price of the lamp
$$= \$200 \times (100\% - 15\%)$$
$$= \$170$$

  (ii) Marked price of the rack
$$= \$51 \div (100\% - 15\%)$$
$$= \$60$$

---

15. A game center offers two charge schemes, A and B, for using its stations.

Scheme A: $6 per game
Scheme B: $0.75 per minute (time of play is counted in seconds)

Let $y be the charge for a game that lasts t minutes.
(a) **(i)** Find y under scheme A.
  (ii) Express y in terms of t under scheme B.

(b) On the same diagram, draw the graphs of the equations involving y obtained in **(a)** for $0 < t < 12$.

(c) What is the minimum duration of a game if the charge on scheme A is not more than that on scheme B?

Solution

(a) **(i)** Charge under scheme A = \$6
$$\therefore \ y = 6$$

(ii) Charge under scheme B
$$= \$0.75 \times t$$
$$= \$0.75t$$
$$\therefore \ y = 0.75t$$

(b)

t	0	4	8	12
$y = 6$	6	6	6	6
$y = 0.75t$	0	3	6	9

The diagram below shows the graphs of $y = 6$ and $y = 0.75t$.

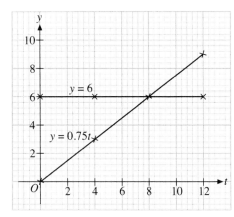

(c) From the graph, we can see that the charge on scheme A is not more than that on scheme B when $t \geqslant 8$.

The minimum duration of a game is 8 minutes if the charge on scheme A is not more than that on scheme B.

Chapter 12   Perimeters And Areas Of Plane Figures

Class Activity 1

Objective: To explore the formulas for the circumference and area of a circle using Sketchpad.

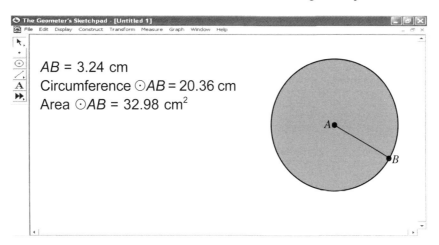

Tasks

(a)   Use the **Compass** tool to create a circle with center A.

(b)   Use the **Segment** tool to construct a radius from center A to a point B on the circle.

(c)   Select the points A and B. Then select **Measure I Distance**.

(d)   Select the circle. Then select **Measure I Circumference**.

(e)   Select center A. Then select **Construct I Circle Interior** to shade the circle.

(f)   Select the shaded circle. Then select **Measure I Area** to calculate the area of the circle.

(g)   Repeat the steps with additional circles. Record the radius, circumference, and area of each circle.

Questions

1.   Determine the diameter of each circle.

Answers may vary. In the diagram above, the diameter of the circle is $2 \times 3.24 = 6.48$ cm.

2.   Find the ratio of the circumference to the diameter for each circle. What do you observe?

$$\frac{\text{Circumference of the circle}}{\text{Diameter of the circle}} = \frac{20.36 \text{ cm}}{6.48 \text{ cm}} = 3.14 \text{ (correct to 2 d.p.)}$$

For each circle, the ratio of the circumference to the diameter is approximately equal to 3.14.

3.   Determine the square of the radius of each circle.

Answers may vary. In the diagram above, the square of the radius of the circle is $3.24^2 = 10.4976$ cm^2.

4.   Find the ratio of the area to the square of the radius for each circle. What do you observe?

$$\frac{\text{Area of the circle}}{\text{Square of the radius of the circle}} = \frac{32.98 \text{ cm}^2}{10.4976 \text{ cm}^2} = 3.14 \text{ (correct to 2 d.p.)}$$

For each circle, the ratio of the area to the square of the radius is approximately equal to 3.14.

Class Activity 2

Objective: To derive the formula for the area of a circle.

Tasks

(a) Draw a circle on a piece of card or paper. The exact size does not matter; for instance you may draw a circle with a radius of 5 cm.

(b) Use your protractor to divide the circle into 12 equal sectors or wedges. Divide just one of the sectors into two equal parts. You now have 13 sectors. Number each sector from 1 to 13.

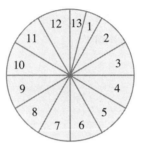

(c) Cut out the 13 sectors using the scissors.

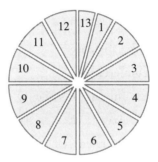

(d) Rearrange the 13 sectors as follows (you can glue them onto a piece of paper).

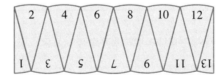

Now the shape resembles a rectangle as shown below.

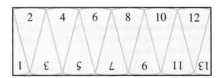

(e) What are the approximate width and length of the rectangle formed? Notice that its width is the radius of the circle and its length is half of the curved parts along the edge of the circle. In other words, the length is half the circumference of the original circle. We have learned that "circumference = $2 \times \pi \times$ radius", so the length of the rectangle is $\pi \times$ radius.

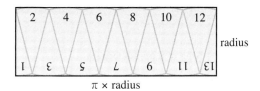

$\pi \times$ radius

Hence, the area of the rectangle above is

$$(\pi \times \text{radius}) \times \text{radius} \text{ or } \pi r^2.$$

Do you remember where this rectangle comes from?

Thus, the area of the circle = πr^2.

(f) Measure the length of this rectangle as accurately as you can using a ruler. Divide by the radius (5 cm) to get an approximation for π.

Record your answer here:

Length of the rectangle	Divide by 5 cm (approximation for π)
The answer should be approximately equal to 15.71 cm.	The answer should be approximately equal to 3.142 cm.

Recall that π is about 3.14159. How close was your answer?

Note: You could probably get a more accurate answer if you used a bigger circle or divided your circle into more sectors.

Class Activity 3

Objective: To explore the formula for the area of a paralleogram using Sketchpad.

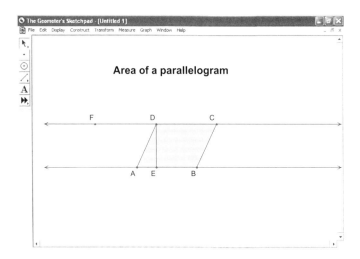

Tasks

(a) Construct two parallel lines *AB* and *FD* as shown.

(b) Construct a parallelogram *ABCD*.

(c) Construct the line segment *DE* perpendicular to *AB* with *E* on *AB*.

(d) Select the points *A*, *B*, *C*, and *D* in order. Then select **Construct | Quadrilateral Interior** to shade the parallelogram *ABCD*.

(e) Measure the lengths *AB*, *AD*, and *DE*.

(f) Calculate *AB* × *AD* and *AB* × *DE*.

(g) Select the shaded parallelogram and then select **Measure | Area** to calculate the area of *ABCD*.

(h) Drag the point *D* along the line *FD* and observe the variation of the figure and the numerical values obtained in **(e)** to **(g)**.

Questions

1. Which numerical values remain the same as the position of *D* changes?

AB, DE, and AB × DE

2. Suggest a formula for the area of a parallelogram.

Area of a parallelogram = Base × Height

Extend Your Learning Curve

Maximum Area with Given Perimeter

1. You are given a piece of wire of a certain length. Your task is to bend the wire into a rectangle with the greatest possible area. What type of rectangle do you think it should be? Explain your answer.

2. Which shape gives the greatest possible area for a given perimeter?

Suggested Answer:

1. Suppose the piece of wire is 100 cm long.
   Let x cm be a side of the rectangle formed.

   Then, the other side of the rectangle $= \dfrac{100}{2} - x$

   $$= (50 - x) \text{ cm}$$

   Area of the rectangle $= x(50 - x) \text{ cm}^2$

   By making a table of values of $A = x(50 - x)$ for $x = 1$ to 49, we find that A is maximum when $x = 25$. Hence, the rectangle is a square of side 25 cm.

   In general, when the piece of wire is L cm long, it should be bent into a square of side $\dfrac{L}{4}$ cm to get the greatest possible area.

2. For a given perimeter, a circle gives the greatest possible area.

Try It!

Section 12.1

1. The length and width of a rectangle are 40 cm and 10 cm respectively. A square of side y cm has the same area as the rectangle. Find
   (a) the area of the rectangle,
   (b) the value of y,
   (c) the perimeter of the square.

Solution

(a) Area of the rectangle = 40×10
$$= 400 \text{ cm}^2$$

(b) Area of the square = Area of the rectangle
$$y^2 = 400$$
$$y = \sqrt{400}$$
$$= 20$$

(c) Perimeter of the square = $4y$
$$= 4 \times 20$$
$$= 80 \text{ cm}$$

2. In the figure, $AB = 5$ cm, $BC = 4$ cm, and $AC = 3$ cm. Find
   (a) the area of $\triangle ABC$,
   (b) the length of CD.

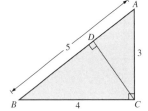

Solution

(a) Area of $\triangle ABC = \dfrac{1}{2} \times BC \times CA$
$$= \dfrac{1}{2} \times 4 \times 3$$
$$= 6 \text{ cm}^2$$

(b) $\dfrac{1}{2} \times AB \times CD = 6$
$$\dfrac{1}{2} \times 5 \times CD = 6$$
$$CD = \dfrac{12}{5}$$
$$= 2.4 \text{ cm}$$

Section 12.2

3. The radius of a circle is 15 cm. By using the value of π on your calculator, find the area and the circumference of the circle, giving your answers correct to 2 decimal places.

Solution

Area of the circle = $\pi \times 15^2$
$$= 706.86 \text{ cm}^2 \text{ (correct to 2 d.p.)}$$

Circumference of the circle = $2 \times \pi \times 15$
$$= 94.25 \text{ cm (correct to 2 d.p.)}$$

4. The circumference of a circle is 12π cm. Find
   (a) the radius of the circle,
   (b) the area of the circle (leaving your answer in terms of π),
   (c) the radius of a circle, whose area is $\dfrac{1}{4}$ that of the given circle.

Solution

(a) Let r cm be the radius of the circle.
$$2\pi r = 12\pi$$
$$r = 6$$
The radius is 6 cm.

(b) Area of the circle = $\pi \times 6^2$
$$= 36\pi \text{ cm}^2$$

(c) Let R cm be the radius of the required circle.
$$\pi R^2 = \dfrac{1}{4} \times 36\pi$$
$$R^2 = 9$$
$$R = \sqrt{9}$$
$$= 3$$
The required radius is 3 cm.

Section 12.3

5. In the figure, $PQRS$ is a parallelogram, $RS = 12$ cm, $PS = 6$ cm, and $SM = 5$ cm.
   Find
   (a) the area of the parallelogram,
   (b) the length of RN.

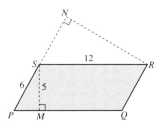

Find
   (a) the area of the parallelogram,
   (b) the length of RN.

Solution

(a) Area of $PQRS = RS \times SM$
$$= 12 \times 5$$
$$= 60 \text{ cm}^2$$

(b) $PS \times RN$ = Area of $PQRS$
$$6 \times RN = 60$$
$$RN = 10 \text{ cm}$$

6. In the figure, $ABCD$ is a parallelogram and $BC = 12$ cm. If the area of $\triangle ABE$ is $\frac{1}{5}$ that of parallelogram $ABCD$, find the length of BE.

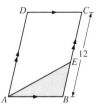

Solution

Let h cm be the height from A to the base BC.

Area of $\triangle ABE = \frac{1}{5} \times$ Area of $ABCD$

$$\frac{1}{2} \times BE \times h = \frac{1}{5} \times 12 \times h$$

$$BE = \frac{24}{5}$$

$$= 4.8 \text{ cm}$$

Section 12.4

7. In the figure, $PQRS$ is a trapezoid in which $PQ = 14$ cm, $SR = 8$ cm, and $PS = 10$ cm. Find the area of $PQRS$.

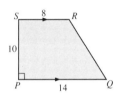

Solution

Area of $PQRS = \frac{1}{2} \times (8 + 14) \times 10$

$$= 110 \text{ cm}^2$$

8. The figure shows a shed with a uniform cross-section in which $ABCD$ is a trapezoid with AD parallel to BC, $AB = 2.5$ m, and $BC = 3$ m.
(a) Sketch the cross-section of the shed and label its dimensions.
(b) Find the length of AD if the area of $ABCD$ is 5.5 m².

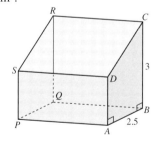

Solution

(a)

(b) Area of $ABCD = \frac{1}{2} \times (AD + 3) \times 2.5$

$$\frac{1}{2} \times (AD + 3) \times 2.5 = 5.5$$

$$AD + 3 = 4.4$$

Length of $AD = 1.4$ m

Section 12.5

9. In the figure, $AD = 6$ cm, $EC = 5$ cm, $AE = 4$ cm, and $EB = 3$ cm. Find the area of the quadrilateral $ABCD$.

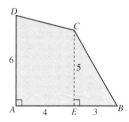

Solution

Area of $ABCD$
= Area of trapezoid $AECD$ + Area of $\triangle BCE$
$= \frac{1}{2} \times (6 + 5) \times 4 + \frac{1}{2} \times 3 \times 5$
$= 29.5 \text{ cm}^2$

10. In the figure, STP is a semicircle of diameter 30 cm and $PQRS$ is a parallelogram with $PQ = 16$ cm and $SU = 15$ cm. Find
(a) the perimeter,
(b) the area
of the figure.
(Take π as 3.142)

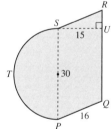

Solution

(a) Perimeter of the figure
= Semicircle STP + PQ + QR + RS
$= \frac{1}{2} \times \pi \times 30 + 16 + 30 + 16$
$= 15(3.142) + 62$
$= 109.13$ cm (corect to 2 d.p.)

(b) Area of the figure
= Area of semicircle STP
  + Area of parallelogram $PQRS$
$= \frac{1}{2} \times \pi \times 15^2 + 30 \times 15$
$= 803.475$
$= 803.48 \text{ cm}^2$ (correct to 2 d.p.)

11. The figure shows the cross-section of a stool in which $AD = 40$ cm, $EH = 30$ cm, $BC = 24$ cm, and $FG = 16$ cm. The distances of BC and FG from the ground are 25 cm and 15 cm respectively. Find the area of the cross-section of the stool.

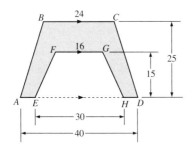

Solution

Area of $ABCD = \dfrac{1}{2} \times (24 + 40) \times 25$

$\qquad\qquad = 800$ cm^2

Area of $EHGF = \dfrac{1}{2} \times (16 + 30) \times 15$

$\qquad\qquad = 345$ cm^2

Area of the cross-section of the stool
$= 800 - 345$
$= 455$ cm^2

Exercise 12.1

Basic Practice

1. Find the area and the perimeter of each square whose length is given in inches.

   (a)

   (b)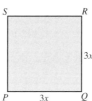

   Solution
   (a) Area of $ABCD = 5 \times 5$
   $= 25$ in.^{2}
   Perimeter of $ABCD = 4 \times 5$
   $= 20$ in.
   (b) Area of $PQRS = 3x \times 3x$
   $= 9x^2$ in.^{2}
   Perimeter of $PQRS = 4 \times 3x$
   $= 12x$ in.

2. Find the area and the perimeter of each rectangle whose dimensions are given in centimeters.

   (a)

   (b)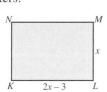

   Solution
   (a) Area of $ABCD = 5 \times 4$
   $= 20$ cm^2
   Perimeter of $ABCD = 2(5 + 4)$
   $= 18$ cm
   (b) Area of $KLMN = (2x - 3) \times x$
   $= x(2x - 3)$ cm^2
   Perimeter of $KLMN = 2[(2x - 3) + x]$
   $= 2(3x - 3)$
   $= (6x - 6)$ cm

3. Find the area of each shaded triangle whose dimensions are given in centimeters.

   (a)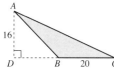

   (b)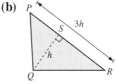

   Solution
   (a) Area of $\triangle ABC = \dfrac{1}{2} \times 20 \times 16$
   $= 160$ cm^2
   (b) Area of $\triangle PQR = \dfrac{1}{2} \times 3h \times h$
   $= \dfrac{3}{2}h^2$ cm^2
   $= 1\dfrac{1}{2}h^2$ cm^2

Further Practice

4. The perimeter of a square is 24 cm. Find
   (a) the length of a side,
   (b) the area of the square.

   Solution
   (a) Length of a side $= \dfrac{24}{4}$
   $= 6$ cm
   (b) Area of the square $= 6^2$
   $= 36$ cm^2

5. The area of a square is 529 cm^2. Find
   (a) the length of a side,
   (b) the perimeter of the square.

   Solution
   (a) Length of a side $= \sqrt{529}$
   $= 23$ cm
   (b) Perimeter of the square $= 4 \times 23$
   $= 92$ cm

6. The area of a rectangle is 120 m^2. If the width is 7.5 m, find
   (a) the length,
   (b) the perimeter
   of the rectangle.

   Solution
   (a) Length of the rectangle $= \dfrac{120}{7.5}$
   $= 16$ m
   (b) Perimeter of the rectangle $= 2(7.5 + 16)$
   $= 47$ m

7. The rectangle has a perimeter of 98 cm and its length is two and a half times as long as its width. Find
   (a) the width,
   (b) the area
   of the rectangle.

   Solution
   (a) Let x cm be the width of the rectangle.
   Hence, the length of the rectangle $= 2.5x$ cm.
   Since its perimeter is 98 cm,
   $2(2.5x + x) = 98$
   $3.5x = 49$
   $x = 14$
   ∴ the width of the rectangle is 14 cm.
   (b) Area of the rectangle $= 2.5x \times x$
   $= 2.5 \times 14 \times 14$
   $= 490$ cm^2

8. In the figure, $BC = 9$ cm, $AC = 6$ cm, and the area of $\triangle ABC$ is 15 cm^2. Find the value of
(a) h,
(b) k.

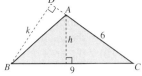

Solution

(a) $\frac{1}{2} \times 9 \times h = 15$

        $h = \frac{10}{3}$

         $= 3\frac{1}{3}$

(b) $\frac{1}{2} \times 6 \times k = 15$

        $k = 5$

Math@Work

9. A picture frame 30 cm by 21 cm has a picture centrally placed in it, leaving a uniform border of 2 cm around it. Find
(a) the perimeter of the picture,
(b) the area of the border.

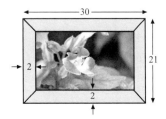

Solution

(a) Length of the picture $= 30 - 2 \times 2$
                         $= 26$ cm
    Width of the picture $= 21 - 2 \times 2$
                       $= 17$ cm
    Perimeter of the picture $= 2(26 + 17)$
                            $= 86$ cm

(b) Area of the border $= 30 \times 21 - 26 \times 17$
                      $= 188$ cm^2

10. A garden $ABCDEF$, as shown in the figure, has a triangular-shaped pond in it. The dimensions are given in meters.
(a) Find the area of the garden.
(b) What is the percentage of the garden that is occupied by the pond? Give your answer correct to 1 decimal place.

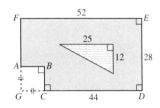

Solution

(a) Length of a side of square $ABCG = 52 - 44$
                                    $= 8$ m
    Area of the garden
    $=$ Area of rectangle $DEFG$ – Area of square $ABCG$
    $= 52 \times 28 - 8 \times 8$
    $= 1{,}392$ m^2

(b) Area of the pond $= \frac{1}{2} \times 25 \times 12$
                      $= 150$ m^2
    Require percentage $= \frac{150}{1{,}392} \times 100\%$
                              $= 10.8\%$ (correct to 1 d.p.)

11. A workman has two pieces of wire, each of length 26 m. One piece is to be bent into a square. The other piece is to be bent into a rectangle whose width is 3 m shorter than its length.
(a) What is the length of a side of the square?
(b) What are the dimensions of the rectangle?
(c) Which shape has the greater area?

Solution

(a) Length of a side of the square $= \frac{26}{4}$
                                         $= 6.5$ m

(b) Let x m be the length of the rectangle.
    Hence, the width of the rectangle is $(x - 3)$ m.

    Since the perimeter of the rectangle $= 26$ m,
        $2[x + (x - 3)] = 26$
               $2x - 3 = 13$
                 $2x = 16$
                   $x = 8$
             $x - 3 = 5$
    $\therefore$ the dimensions of the rectangle are 8 m $\times$ 5 m.

(c) Area of the square $= 6.5^2$
                       $= 42.25$ m^2
    Area of the rectangle $= 8 \times 5$
                         $= 40$ m^2
    $\therefore$ the square has the greater area.

Brainworks

12. Draw two triangles whose areas are 12 cm^2 each.

Solution

Some possible triangles whose areas are 12 cm^2 each are shown below.

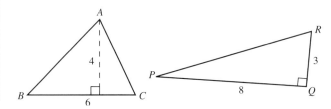

13. **(a)** Find the prime factorization of 420.

(b) A rectangle measures x cm by y cm, where x cm and y cm are relatively prime integers. The area of the rectangle is 420 cm². Find two possible dimensions of the rectangle.

Solution

(a)

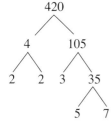

$\therefore\ 420 = 2^2 \times 3 \times 5 \times 7$

(b) Some possible dimensions of the rectangle are:

4 cm × 105 cm
12 cm × 35 cm
20 cm × 21 cm
60 cm × 7 cm

14. The figure shows a square *ABCD*.

(a) Suggest how you can draw two line segments from vertex *A* to divide the area of *ABCD* into three equal parts.

(b) Where are the other end points of these segments?

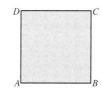

Solution

(a)

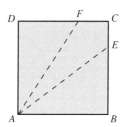

(b) Let *AB* be x cm long.

$$\text{Area of } \triangle ABE = \frac{1}{3} \times \text{Area of } ABCD$$

$$\frac{1}{2} \times x \times BE = \frac{1}{3} \times x^2$$

$$BE = \frac{2}{3}x$$

Similarly, $\quad DF = \frac{2}{3}x$.

Exercise 12.2

Round the answers to 2 decimal places if they are not exact values.

Basic Practice

1. Find the area and the circumference of each circle whose dimensions are given in cm. Leave your answer in terms of π.

(a)   **(b)**

Solution

(a) Area of the circle $= \pi \times 10^2$
$\qquad\qquad\qquad\quad = 100\pi$ cm²
Circumference of the circle $= 2\pi \times 10$
$\qquad\qquad\qquad\qquad\qquad = 20\pi$ cm

(b) Area of the circle $= \pi \times \left(\dfrac{6x}{2}\right)^2$
$\qquad\qquad\qquad\quad = 9\pi x^2$ cm²
Circumference of the circle $= \pi \times 6x$
$\qquad\qquad\qquad\qquad\qquad = 6\pi x$ cm

2. Find the area and the circumference of each circle with the given measurement.

(a) Diameter of 22 mm, taking π as 3.14

(b) Radius of 3.5 m, taking π as $\dfrac{22}{7}$

(c) Radius of 6 in., taking the value of π from your calculator

Solution

(a) Area of the circle $= \pi \times \left(\dfrac{22}{2}\right)^2$
$\qquad\qquad\qquad\quad = 3.14 \times 121$
$\qquad\qquad\qquad\quad = 379.94$ mm²
Circumference of the circle $= \pi \times 22$
$\qquad\qquad\qquad\qquad\qquad = 3.14 \times 22$
$\qquad\qquad\qquad\qquad\qquad = 69.08$ mm

(b) Area of the circle $= \pi \times 3.5^2$
$\qquad\qquad\qquad\quad = \dfrac{22}{7} \times 12.25$
$\qquad\qquad\qquad\quad = 38.5$ m²
Circumference of the circle $= 2\pi \times 3.5$
$\qquad\qquad\qquad\qquad\qquad = 2 \times \dfrac{22}{7} \times 3.5$
$\qquad\qquad\qquad\qquad\qquad = 22$ m

(c) Area of the circle $= \pi \times 6^2$
$\qquad\qquad\qquad\quad = 113.10$ in.² (correct to 2 d.p.)
Circumference of the circle
$= 2\pi \times 6$
$= 37.70$ in. (correct to 2 d.p.)

Further Practice

3. The circumference of a circle is 28.26 cm. Find
   (a) the diameter,
   (b) the area
   of the circle.

Solution
(a) Diameter of the circle

$$= \frac{28.26}{\pi}$$

$= 8.99544$ (correct to 5 d.p.)
$= 9.00$ cm (correct to 2 d.p.)

(b) Radius of the circle $= \left(\frac{1}{2} \times 8.99544\right)$ cm

Area of the circle

$$= \pi \times \left(\frac{1}{2} \times 8.99544\right)^2$$

$= 63.55280$ (correct to 5 d.p.)
$= 63.55$ cm (correct to 2 d.p.)

4. The area of a circle is 616 cm². Find
   (a) the radius,
   (b) the circumference
   of the circle.

Solution
(a) Let r cm be the radius of the circle.
   $\pi r^2 = 616$
   $r^2 = 196.07889$ (correct to 5 d.p.)
   $r = 14.003$ (correct to 3 d.p.)
   $= 14.00$ cm (correct to 2 d.p.)

   The radius of the circle is 14.00 cm.

(b) Circumference of the circle
   $= 2\pi \times 14.003$
   $= 87.98344$ (correct to 5 d.p.)
   $= 87.98$ cm (correct to 2 d.p.)

5. The diameter of a semicircle is 3.9 m. What is the perimeter and area of the semicircle?

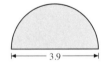

Solution
Radius of the semicircle $= \frac{1}{2} \times 3.9$

$= 1.95$ m

Perimeter of the semicircle $= \pi \times 1.95 + 3.9$
$= 10.03$ m (correct to 2 d.p.)

Area of the semicircle $= \frac{1}{2} \times \pi \times 1.95^2$

$= 5.97$ m² (correct to 2 d.p.)

6. The figure is made up of two semicircles.
   Taking π as $= \frac{22}{7}$, find its
   (a) perimeter,
   (b) area.
   The unit of length is mm.

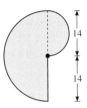

Solution
(a) Radius of the large semicircle = 14 mm

   Radius of the small semicircle = 7 mm

   Required perimeter $= \pi \times 14 + \pi \times 7 + 14$
   $= 79.97$ mm (correct to 2 d.p.)

(b) Required area $= \frac{1}{2} \times \pi \times 14^2 + \frac{1}{2} \times \pi \times 7^2$

   $= 384.85$ mm² (correct to 2 d.p.)

7. The area of a circular pond is 15 m². It is surrounded by a circular path 0.5 m wide. Find
   (a) the radius of the pond,
   (b) the circumference of the pond,
   (c) the area of the path.

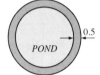

Solution
(a) Let r m be the radius of the pond.
   $\pi r^2 = 15$

   $$r = \sqrt{\frac{15}{\pi}}$$

   $= 2.18510$ (correct to 5 d.p.)
   $= 2.19$ (correct to 2 d.p.)

   The radius of the pond is 2.19 m.

(b) Circumference of the pond
   $= 2\pi \times 2.18510$
   $= 13.73$ m (correct to 2 d.p.)

(c) Area of the path
   $= \pi(2.18510 + 0.5)^2 - 15$
   $= 7.65$ m² (correct to 2 d.p.)

8. There are two pieces of wires, each of length 66 cm. One wire is bent into a square and the other wire is bent into a circle. Find
   (a) the area of the square,
   (b) the area of the circle.

Solution
(a) Length of a side of the square $= \frac{66}{4}$

   $= 16.5$ cm

   Area of the square $= 16.5^2$
   $= 272.25$ cm²

(b) Let r cm be the radius of the circle.
$$2\pi r = 66$$
$$r = \frac{66}{2\pi}$$
$$r = 10.50423 \quad \text{(correct to 5 d.p.)}$$
Area of the circle
$$= \pi r^2$$
$$= 346.64 \text{ cm}^2 \quad \text{(correct to 2 d.p.)}$$

Math@Work

9. A circular dance floor has a radius of 9.5 m. The floor is to be waxed. A can of wax will cover an area of 10 m^2. How many cans of wax would be needed?

Solution
Area of the dance floor $= \pi \times 9.5^2$
$$= 283.52874 \text{ m}^2 \text{ (correct to 5 d.p.)}$$
Let the required number of cans of wax be x.
Hence, $10x \geqslant 283.52874$
$$x \geqslant 28.352874$$
$\therefore$ 29 cans of wax would be needed.

10. The diameter of a bicycle wheel is 19 inches. What is the distance in miles covered if the wheel makes 600 complete turns? (1 mi = 5,280 ft)

Solution
Circumference of the wheel $= 19\pi$ in.
Required distance $= (600 \times 19\pi)$ in.
$$= \frac{600 \times 19\pi}{12} \text{ ft} \quad \text{1 ft = 12 in.}$$
$$= \frac{600 \times 19\pi}{12 \times 5,280} \text{ mi} \quad \text{1 mi = 5,280 ft}$$
$$= 0.57 \text{ mi} \quad \text{(correct to 2 d.p.)}$$

11. A lawn sprinkler sprays water over a distance of x meters in every direction as it rotates. Mrs. Ford wishes to install one such lawn sprinkler that will sprinkle at least 80 m^2 of her lawn. What is the least value of x that will meet Mrs. Ford's requirement?

Solution
The area covered by the sprinkler would be a circle with radius x m.
Area of the circle $\geqslant 80$ m^2
$$\pi x^2 \geqslant 80$$
$$x \geqslant \sqrt{\frac{80}{\pi}}$$
$$x \geqslant 5.05 \quad \text{(correct to 2 d.p.)}$$
The least value of x that will meet Mrs. Ford's requirement is 5.05.

Brainworks

12. Circles, arcs, and curves are often used to create beautiful designs. In the following figures, the squares are of the same size and the curved lines are all arcs of circles. Which of the following shaded figures has the greatest area? Which has the greatest perimeter?

(a) **(b)**

(c) **(d)**

(e) **(f)**

Solution
Assume that the length of a side of each square is 1 unit.

(a) 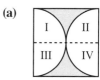 **(b)**

(c) 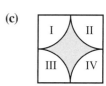 **(d)**

(e) 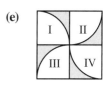 **(f)**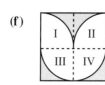

Notice that area of each shaded figure
$$= \text{area of the square} - 4 \times \text{area of the quadrant}$$
$\therefore$ all the shaded figures have the same area.
Note: Half of a semicircle is called a quadrant.

Perimeter of shaded figure **(a)**
$$= 2 \times 1 + 2 \times (\pi \times 0.5)$$
$$= 5.14 \text{ units (correct to 2 d.p.)}$$

Perimeter of shaded figure **(b)**
$$= 4 \times 1 + 2\pi \times 0.5$$
$$= 7.14 \text{ units (correct to 2 d.p.)}$$

Perimeter of shaded figure **(c)**
$$= 4 \times \left(\frac{1}{4} \times 2\pi \times 0.5 \right)$$
$$= 3.14 \text{ units (correct to 2 d.p.)}$$

Perimeter of shaded figure (d)

$$= 2 \times \left(\frac{1}{4} \times 2\pi \times 0.5 \right) + \pi \times 0.5 + 2 \times 0.5$$

= 4.14 units (correct to 2 d.p.)

Perimeter of shaded figure (e)

$$= 4 \times \left(\frac{1}{4} \times 2\pi \times 0.5 \right) + 8 \times 0.5$$

= 7.14 units (correct to 2 d.p.)

Perimeter of shaded figure (f)

$$= 2 \times \left(\frac{1}{4} \times 2\pi \times 0.5 \right) + \pi \times 0.5 + 1 + 4 \times 0.5$$

= 6.14 units (correct to 2 d.p.)

∴ shaded figures (b) and (e) have the greatest perimeter.

Exercise 12.3
Basic Practice

In this exercise, the unit of length is centimeters (cm) unless stated otherwise.

1. Find the area of each parallelogram.

(a) 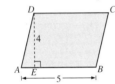 (b)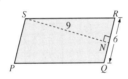

(b) 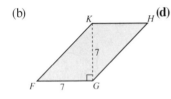 (d)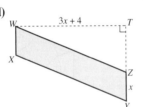

Solution

(a) Area of $ABCD = 5 \times 4$
$$= 20 \text{ cm}^2$$

(b) Area of $PQRS = 6 \times 9$
$$= 54 \text{ cm}^2$$

(c) Area of $FGHK = 7 \times 7$
$$= 49 \text{ cm}^2$$

(d) Area of $WXYZ = x(3x + 4)$
$$= (3x^2 + 4x) \text{ cm}^2$$

2. In the figure, $ABCD$ is a trapezoid. Copy and complete the table using the given measurements.

	AB	DE	BC	DE	Area of ABCD
(a)	10	6	8		
(b)	18		9	12	
(c)	15	8		10	
(d)		9	6		72

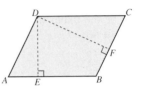

Solution

	AB	DE	BC	DE	Area of ABCD
(a)	10	6	8	7.5	60
(b)	18	8	9	12	108
(c)	15	8	12	10	120
(d)	8	9	6	12	72

Further Practice

3. In the figure, $ABCD$ is a parallelogram of area 20 cm².
   (a) Find the area of $ABEF$.
   (b) If $AB = 5$ cm, find the length of AF.

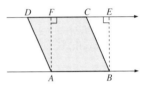

Solution

(a) Area of $ABEF$ = Area of $ABCD$
$$= 20 \text{ cm}^2$$

(b) Length of $AF = \dfrac{20}{5}$
$$= 4 \text{ cm}$$

4. In the figure, $ABCD$ is a parallelogram, $AB = 4$ cm, and $EF = 6$ cm.
   (a) Find the ratio of the area of $\triangle EFG$ to that of $ABCD$.
   (b) If the area of $\triangle EFG$ is 24 cm², find the area of $ABCD$.

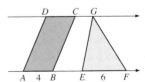

Solution

(a) Let h cm be the height from D to AB.
     Area of $\triangle EFG$: Area of $ABCD$
$$= \frac{1}{2} \times 6 \times h : 4 \times h$$
$$= 3 : 4$$

(b) Area of $ABCD = 24 \times \dfrac{4}{3}$
$$= 32 \text{ cm}^2$$

5. In the figure, $ABCD$ is a parallelogram and $AD = 18$ cm. The area of $\triangle ABE$ is $\dfrac{5}{6}$ that of $ABCD$.

(a) Find the length of DE.

(b) If the area of $ABCD$ is 450 cm², find the height from B to AD.

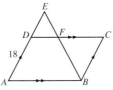

Solution

(a) Let h cm be the height from B to AD.

$$\text{Area of } \triangle ABE = \frac{5}{6} \times \text{Area of } ABCD$$

$$\frac{1}{2} \times (18 + DE) \times h = \frac{5}{6} \times 18 \times h$$

$$18 + DE = 30$$

$$\text{Length of } DE = 12 \text{ cm}$$

(b) $18h = 450$

$h = 25$

The height is 25 cm.

6. In the figure, $ABCD$ is a rhombus, $AD = 13$ cm, $AC = 24$ cm, and $BD = 10$ cm. Find

(a) the measure of $\angle AED$,

(b) the area of $ABCD$,

(c) the height from B to AD.

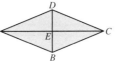

Solution

(a) $m\angle AED = 90°$ (diagonals of rhombus)

(b) Area of $ABCD$

$= 2 \times$ Area of $\triangle ACD$

$= 2 \times \dfrac{1}{2} \times 24 \times 5$

$= 120$ cm²

(c) Let h cm be the height from B to AD.

$13h = 120$

$h = \dfrac{120}{13}$

$= 9\dfrac{3}{13}$

The height is $9\dfrac{3}{13}$ cm.

Math@Work

7. In the figure, $ABCD$ is a vertical wall 2 m high. It casts a shadow $ABEF$ on the ground. $ABEF$ is a parallelogram in which the height EN is $1\dfrac{1}{2}$ times the height of the wall.

(a) Find the height EN.

(b) If the area of the wall is 7.6 m², find the area of the shadow.

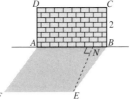

Solution

(a) The height $EN = 2 \times 1\dfrac{1}{2}$

$= 3$ m

(b) $AB = \dfrac{7.6}{2}$

$= 3.8$ m

Area of the shadow $= 3.8 \times 3$

$= 11.4$ m²

8. In the figure, $ABCD$ is a square board of area 3.24 m², M is the midpoint of BC, and $AM \mathbin{/\!/} NC$. The shape $AMCN$ is cut off from the board. Find

(a) the lengths of MC and AN,

(b) the area of $AMCN$,

(c) the ratio of the area of $\triangle ABM$ to that of $AMCN$.

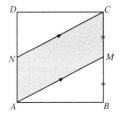

Solution

(a) Area of $ABCD = 3.24$ m²

Length of a side of $ABCD = \sqrt{3.24}$

$= 1.8$ m

$MC = BM$

$= \dfrac{1}{2} \times 1.8$

$= 0.9$ m

Since $AM \mathbin{/\!/} NC$ and $AN \mathbin{/\!/} MC$, $AMCN$ is a parallelogram.

$\therefore AN = MC$ (opp. sides of //gram)

$= 0.9$ m

(b) Area of $AMCN = MC \times AB$

$= 0.9 \times 1.8$

$= 1.62$ m²

(c) Area of $\triangle ABM = \dfrac{1}{2} \times 1.8 \times 0.9$

$= 0.81$ m²

Area of $\triangle ABM$: Area of $AMCN$

$= 0.81 : 1.62$

$= 1 : 2$

Brainworks

9. The figure shows a square grid in which the area of each small square is 1 cm². Copy the grid and draw two parallelograms on it such that the area of each figure is 6 cm².

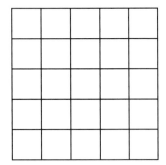

Solution

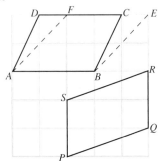

In the above diagram, *ABCD*, *ABEF*, and *PQRS* are parallelograms of areas 6 cm² each.

10. The figure shows one way to divide a parallelogram into two equal parts by a line segment. Find as many other ways as possible to divide the parallelogram into two equal parts.

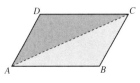

Solution

The following diagrams show some ways to divide a parallelogram *ABCD* into two equal parts.

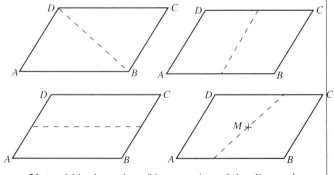

Note: *M* is the point of intersection of the diagonals.

11. The illustration and argument shown on the top of page 71 work well for the given parallelogram there, but do not seem to work with a parallelogram like the one shown on the right.

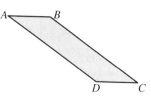

Draw parallelogram *ABCD* on a sheet of paper. Cut this parallelogram into smaller parallelograms. Investigate how you can derive the area of parallelogram *ABCD*. You may take *b* to be the length of the base of parallelogram *ABCD* and *h* to be its corresponding height.

Solution

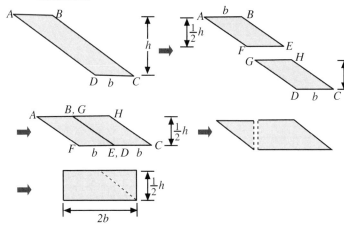

By cutting and rearranging the parallelogram given, we can form a rectangle with the length $2b$ and height $\frac{1}{2}h$ as shown.

Hence, area of the parallelogram given
$$= \text{area of the rectangle formed}$$
$$= 2b \times \frac{1}{2}h$$
$$= bh$$

Exercise 12.4
Basic Practice

In this exercise, the unit of length is centimeters (cm) unless stated otherwise.

1. Find the area of each trapezoid.

(a)

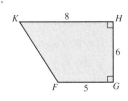

(b)

(c)

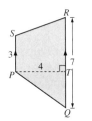

(d)

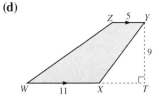

Solution

(a) Area of $ABCD = \dfrac{1}{2}(10 + 14) \times 9$

$= 108 \text{ cm}^2$

(b) Area of $FGHK = \dfrac{1}{2}(5 + 8) \times 6$

$= 39 \text{ cm}^2$

(c) Area of $PQRS = \dfrac{1}{2}(3 + 7) \times 4$

$= 20 \text{ cm}^2$

(d) Area of $WXYZ = \dfrac{1}{2}(5 + 11) \times 9$

$= 72 \text{ cm}^2$

2. In the figure, $ABCD$ is a trapezoid. Copy and complete the table using the given measurements.

	a	b	c	Area of $ABCD$
(a)	7	10	8	
(b)	5	9		42
(c)	13		14	231
(d)		11	10	85

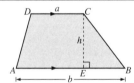

Solution

	a	b	h	Area of $ABCD$
(a)	7	10	8	68
(b)	5	9	6	42
(c)	13	20	14	231
(d)	6	11	10	85

Further Practice

3. In the figure, $ABCD$ is a trapezoid, $AE = 3$ in., $EB = 5$ in., $BC = 5$ in., and AE is one and a half times as long as DC. Find
(a) the length of DC,
(b) the ratio of the area of $AECD$ to that of $ABCD$.

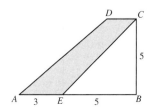

Solution

(a) $1\dfrac{1}{2} \times DC = AE$

$\dfrac{3}{2} \times DC = 3$

$\therefore \quad DC = 2 \text{ in.}$

(b) Area of $AECD = \dfrac{1}{2}(3 + 2) \times 5$

$= 12.5 \text{ in.}^2$

Area of $ABCD = \dfrac{1}{2}[(3 + 5) + 2] \times 5$

$= 25 \text{ in.}^2$

$\therefore$ area of $AECD$: area of $ABCD = 12.5 : 25$

$= 1 : 2$

4. In the figure, $ABCD$ is a parallelogram, M is the midpoint of AB and $CD = 10$ cm.
(a) Find the length of AM.
(b) If the area of $ABCD$ is 60 cm², find the area of $AMCD$.

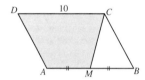

Solution

(a) $\qquad AB = DC$ (opp. sides of //gram)

$\therefore 2AM = 10$

Length of $AM = 5$ cm

(b) Let h cm be the height from A to DC.

$10h = 60$

$h = 6$

Area of $AMCD = \dfrac{1}{2}(5 + 10) \times h$

$= \dfrac{1}{2}(5 + 10) \times 6$

$= 45 \text{ cm}^2$

5. In the figure, $ABCD$ is a parallelogram, $AN = 6$ cm, $NB = 12$ cm, and M is the midpoint of CD.
(a) Find the length of CM.
(b) Find the ratio of the area of $ANMD$ to that of $NBCM$.
(c) If the area of $ABCD$ is 200 cm², find the area of $ANMD$.

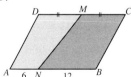

Solution

(a) $CD = BA$ (opp. sides of //gram)

$2CM = 6 + 12$

Length of $CM = 9$ cm

(b) Let h cm be the height from D to AB.

Area of $ANMD$: Area of $NBCM$

$= \frac{1}{2}(6 + 9) \times h : \frac{1}{2}(12 + 9) \times h$

$= 15 : 21$

$= 5 : 7$

(c) Area of $ANMD = 200 \times \dfrac{5}{5 + 7}$

$= 83\frac{1}{3}$ cm^2

6. In the figure, $ABCD$ is a trapezoid, $AB = 18$ cm, and $CD = 10$ cm. The area of $\triangle ACD = 75$ cm^2. Find the area of $ABCD$.

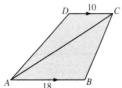

Solution

Area of $\triangle ACD$: Area of $\triangle ABC = DC : AB$

$\dfrac{75}{\text{Area of } \triangle ABC} = \dfrac{10}{18}$

$\therefore$ area of $\triangle ABC = 75 \times \dfrac{18}{10}$

$= 135$ cm^2

Area of $ABCD$ = Area of $\triangle ACD$ + Area of $\triangle ABC$

$= 75 + 135$

$= 210$ cm^2

Math@Work

7. The figure shows a window $ABCD$.

(a) Find the perimeter of the frame.

(b) Find the area enclosed by the frame.

(c) If the cost of the frame is $30 per meter and the cost of the glass panel used to fit the window is $150 per square meter, find the cost of making the window.

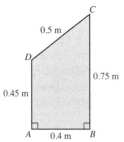

Solution

(a) Perimeter of the frame

$= 0.4 + 0.75 + 0.5 + 0.45$

$= 2.1$ m

(b) Area enclosed by the frame

$= \frac{1}{2}(0.45 + 0.75) \times 0.4$

$= 0.24$ m^2

(c) The cost of making the window

$= \$(30 \times 2.1 + 150 \times 0.24)$

$= \$99$

8. In the figure, $ABCD$ is a rectangular board that measures 20 ft by 15 ft, and $AE = BF = x$ ft. A trapezoid $CDEF$ is cut out from the rectangular board.

(a) Express EF in terms of x.

(b) If the area of $CDEF$ is $\frac{3}{4}$ that of $ABCD$, find

   (i) the area of $CDEF$,

   (ii) the value of x.

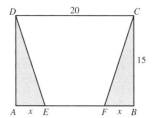

Solution

(a) $EF = 20 - x - x$

$= (20 - 2x)$ ft

(b) **(i)** Area of $CDEF = \dfrac{3}{4} \times$ Area of $ABCD$

$= \dfrac{3}{4} \times 20 \times 15$

$= 225$ ft^2

(ii) $\dfrac{1}{2}[20 + (20 - 2x)] \times 15 = 225$

$40 - 2x = 30$

$2x = 10$

$x = 5$

Brainworks

9. Draw two trapezoids whose areas are 12 cm^2 each.

Solution

Two possible trapezoids whose areas are 12 cm^2 each are as shown below.

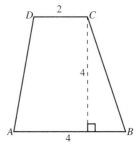
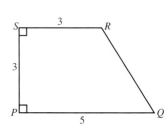

10. You are given four identical table tops, each in the shape of a trapezoid as shown.
   (a) Sketch the shapes that can be formed if they are arranged together to form a large table.
   (b) Find the perimeter of each shape formed.

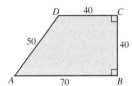

Solution
(a) The following are some possible shapes.
   (i) rectangle

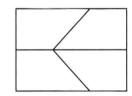

   (ii) two parallelograms

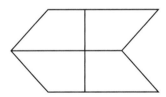

   (iii) two trapezoids

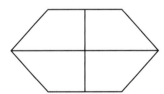

   (iv) parallelogram

(b) The perimeters of the figures are:
   (i) 380 cm   **(ii)** 420 cm
   (iii) 360 cm   **(iv)** 540 cm

Exercise 12.5
Basic Practice
In this exercise, the unit of length is cm unless stated otherwise.
   1. Find the perimeter and area of each figure.
   (a)

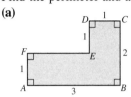

   (b)

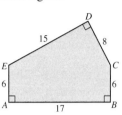

   (c)

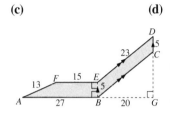

   (d)

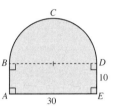

(Take π as 3.142)

   (e)

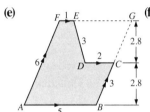

   (f)

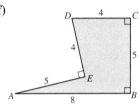

Solution
(a)

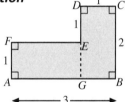

Produce *DE* to meet *AB* at *G*.
$FE = 3 - 1$
    $= 2$ cm
Perimeter of the figure
$= 3 + 2 + 1 + 1 + 2 + 1$
$= 10$ cm

Area of the figure
$=$ Area of *AGEF* + Area of *GBCD*
$= 2 \times 1 + 2 \times 1$
$= 4$ cm^2

(b)

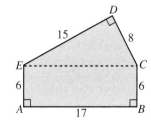

Join C and E.

Perimeter of the figure
$= 17 + 6 + 8 + 15 + 6$
$= 52$ cm

Area of the figure
$=$ Area of $ABCE$ + Area of $\triangle CDE$
$= 17 \times 6 + \dfrac{1}{2} \times 8 \times 15$
$= 162$ cm^2

(c) Perimeter of the figure
$= 27 + 23 + 5 + 23 + 15 + 13$
$= 106$ cm

Area of the figure
$=$ Area of $ABEF$ + Area of $BCDE$
$= \dfrac{1}{2}(15 + 27) \times 5 + 5 \times 20$
$= 205$ cm^2

(d) Perimeter of the figure
$= 30 + 10 + \pi \times 15 + 10$
$= 50 + 15\pi$
$= 50 + 15(3.142)$
$= 97.13$ cm   (correct to 2 d.p.)

Area of the figure
$=$ Area of $AEDB$ + Area of semicircle BDC
$= 30 \times 10 + \dfrac{1}{2} \times \pi \times 15^2$
$= 300 + 112.5\pi$
$= 300 + 112.5(3.142)$
$= 653.48$ cm^2 (correct to 2.d.p.)

(e) Perimeter of the figure
$= 5 + 3 + 2 + 3 + 1 + 6$
$= 20$ cm

Area of the figure
$=$ Area of parallelogram $ABGF$
$\quad$ – Area of trapezoid $CGED$
$= 5 \times 5.6 - \dfrac{1}{2}(2 + 4) \times 2.8$
$= 19.6$ cm^2

(f) Perimeter of the figure
$= 8 + 5 + 4 + 4 + 5$
$= 26$ cm

Area of the figure
$=$ Area of trapezoid $ABCD$ – Area of $\triangle AED$
$= \dfrac{1}{2}(8 + 4) \times 5 - \dfrac{1}{2} \times 5 \times 4$
$= 20$ cm^2

2. Each solid below has a uniform cross-section.
(i) Sketch and label the cross-section of each solid.
(ii) Hence, find the perimeter and area of each cross-section.

(a)

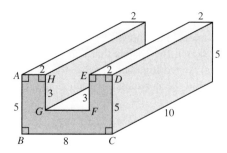

(b) Take π as 3.142 and give your answer correct to 2 decimal places.

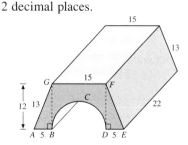

Solution

(a) **(i)**

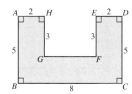

(ii) $GF = 8 - 2 - 2$
$\qquad = 4$ cm

Perimeter of the cross-section
$= 8 + 5 + 2 + 3 + 4 + 3 + 2 + 5$
$= 32$ cm

Area of the cross-section
$=$ Area of $ABCD$ – Area of $EFGH$
$= 8 \times 5 - 4 \times 3$
$= 28$ cm^2

(b) **(i)**

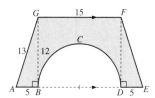

(ii) Perimeter of the cross-section
$= 5 + \pi \times 7.5 + 5 + 13 + 15 + 13$
$= 51 + 7.5\pi$
$= 74.56$ cm   (correct to 2 d.p.)

$AE = 5 + 15 + 5$
$\quad = 25$ cm

Area of the cross-section
$=$ Area of trapezoid $AEFG$
$\quad$ – Area of semicircle BCD
$= \dfrac{1}{2}(25 + 15) \times 12 - \dfrac{1}{2} \times \pi \times 7.5^2$
$= 240 - 28.125\pi$
$= 151.64$ cm^2 (correct to 2 d.p.)

Further Practice

3. Find the area of each figure.

(a)

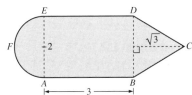

(b)

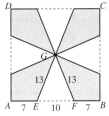

Solution

(a) Area of the figure
$$= \frac{1}{2} \times 10 \times 15 + \frac{1}{2}(15 + 25) \times 17 + \frac{1}{2} \times 12 \times 25$$
$$= 75 + 340 + 150$$
$$= 565 \text{ cm}^2$$

(b) $HC = GD = FE = 16$ cm
Area of the figure
$$= \frac{1}{2}(36 + 16) \times 8 + 16 \times 8 + 16 \times 5$$
$$= 208 + 128 + 80$$
$$= 416 \text{ cm}^2$$

4. In the figure, the shape is made up of a semicircle AFE, a rectangle $ABDE$, and an equilateral triangle BCD. If $AE = 2$ cm, $AB = 3$ cm, and the height from C to BD is $\sqrt{3}$ cm, find
   (a) the perimeter,
   (b) the area
   of the shape. Round your answers correct to 2 decimal places.

Solution

(a) Perimeter of the shape
$$= 3 + 2 + 2 + 3 + \pi \times 1$$
$$= 10 + \pi$$
$$= 13.14 \text{ cm} \quad \text{(correct to 2 d.p.)}$$

(b) Area of the shape
$$= \frac{1}{2} \times \pi \times 1^2 + 3 \times 2 + \frac{1}{2} \times 2 \times \sqrt{3}$$
$$= 0.5\pi + 6 + \sqrt{3}$$
$$= 9.30 \text{ cm}^2 \quad \text{(correct to 2 d.p.)}$$

5. In the figure, four identical triangles such as $\triangle GEF$ are cut off from a square $ABCD$ to form a symmetrical shape. If $EF = 10$ cm, $AE = FB = 7$ cm, and $GE = GF = 13$ cm, find
   (a) the perimeter,
   (b) the area
   of the shape formed.

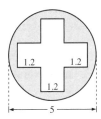

Solution

(a) Perimeter of the shape
$$= 4 \times (7 + 13 + 13 + 7)$$
$$= 160 \text{ cm}$$

(b) Height from G to EF
$$= \frac{1}{2}BC$$
$$= \frac{1}{2}(7 + 10 + 7)$$
$$= 12 \text{ cm}$$
Area of $\triangle GEF = \frac{1}{2} \times 10 \times 12$
$$= 60 \text{ cm}^2$$
Area of the shape
$$= \text{Area of } ABCD - 4 \times \text{Area of } \triangle GEF$$
$$= 24 \times 24 - 4 \times 60$$
$$= 336 \text{ cm}^2$$

Math@Work

6. The figure shows a cross slot on a circular plate where a joystick stands. Each side of the cross and the diameter of the plate are 1.2 in. and 5 in. respectively. Find
   (a) the perimeter of the cross,
   (b) the area of the cross,
   (c) the area of the plate, giving your answer correct to 2 decimal places.

Solution

(a) Perimeter of the cross $= 12 \times 1.2$
$$= 14.4 \text{ in.}$$

(b) Area of the cross $= 5 \times 1.2^2$
$$= 7.2 \text{ in.}^2$$

(c) Area of the plate
$$= \text{Area of the circle} - \text{Area of the cross}$$
$$= \pi \times 2.5^2 - 7.2$$
$$= 12.43 \text{ in.}^2 \quad \text{(correct to 2 d.p.)}$$

7. The figure shows a cross-section of an iron rail. The top part consists of a rectangle and two semicircles at the ends. The bottom part is a trapezoid. These two parts are joined by a rectangle in the middle. Find
   (a) the perimeter,
   (b) the area
   of the cross-section.
   (Take π as 3.142)

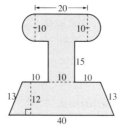

Solution

(a) Perimeter of the cross-section
$$= 40 + 13 + 10 + 15 + 5 + 2\pi \times 5 + 20 + 5 + 15$$
$$+ 10 + 13$$
$$= 146 + 10\pi$$
$$= 146 + 10 \times 3.142$$
$$= 177.42 \text{ cm}$$

(b) Area of the cross-section
$$= \frac{1}{2}(40 + 30) \times 12 + 10 \times 15 + 20 \times 10 + \pi \times 5^2$$
$$= 770 + 25\pi$$
$$= 770 + 25 \times 3.142$$
$$= 848.55 \text{ cm}^2$$

Brainworks

8. Name two items in our daily life which are composite plane figures and describe what shapes each of them is composed of.

   Solution

   An oval sports field is composed of a rectangle and two semicircles.
   A direction arrow on a lane of a road is composed of a triangle and a rectangle.

9. (a) Sketch some closed plane figures with right-angled vertices which you can form using 12 toothpicks.
   (b) Suppose each toothpick is 5 cm long, find the perimeter and the area of each figure formed.
   (c) What is the maximum area obtained among your figures?

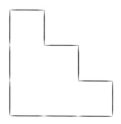

Solution
(a) (i)

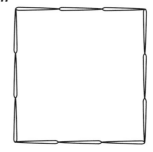

(ii)

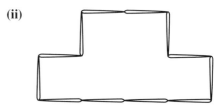

(iii)

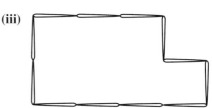

(b) The perimeter of each figure $= 5 \times 12$
$$= 60 \text{ cm}$$
Area of figure (i) $= 15 \times 15$
$$= 225 \text{ cm}^2$$
Area of figure (ii) $= 20 \times 5 + 10 \times 5$
$$= 150 \text{ cm}^2$$
Area of figure (iii) $= 15 \times 10 + 5 \times 5$
$$= 175 \text{ cm}^2$$

(c) The maximum area $= 225 \text{ cm}^2$

Review Exercise 12

1. In the figure, $ABCD$ is a rectangle, $AB = 32$ cm, $BE = 13$ cm, $EC = 8$ cm, and $CF = 15$ cm. Find
   (a) the perimeter of $ABCD$,
   (b) the area of $ABCD$,
   (c) the area of $\triangle AEF$.

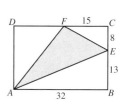

Solution
(a) $AD = 8 + 13$
$$= 21 \text{ cm}$$
Perimeter of $ABCD = 2(32 + 21)$
$$= 106 \text{ cm}$$

(b) Area of $ABCD = 32 \times 21$
$$= 672 \text{ cm}^2$$

(c) $DF = 32 - 15$
  $= 17$ cm
  Area of $\triangle AEF$
  $=$ Area of $ABCD$ – Area of $\triangle ABE$
  $\quad$ – Area of $\triangle CEF$ – Area of $\triangle ADF$
  $= 672 - \dfrac{1}{2} \times 32 \times 13 - \dfrac{1}{2} \times 8 \times 15$
  $\quad - \dfrac{1}{2} \times 21 \times 17$
  $= 672 - 208 - 60 - 178.5$
  $= 225.5$ cm^2

2. A circular pie was cut into five equal pieces. Each piece of pie has an area of 63 cm^2. Find the perimeter of each piece of pie, giving your answer correct to 2 decimal places.

Solution
Area of the circular pie $= 5 \times 63$
$\qquad\qquad\qquad\qquad = 315$ cm^2
Let x cm be the radius of the circular pie.
$\qquad \pi x^2 = 315$
$\qquad\quad x = \sqrt{\dfrac{315}{\pi}}$
$\qquad\qquad = 10.01337$ (correct to 5 d.p.)
Perimeter of the circular pie
$= 2\pi \times 10.01337$
$= 62.91586$ cm (correct to 5 d.p.)
Perimeter of each piece of pie
$= 2 \times 10.01337 + \dfrac{62.91586}{5}$
$= 32.61$ cm (correct to 2 d.p.)

3. In the figure, the shaded region is formed by three semicircles with $AB = 12$ cm and $BC = 6$ cm. Find, in terms of π,
(a) the perimeter,
(b) the area
of the shaded region.

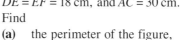

Solution
(a) The radii of the semicircles are 9 cm, 6 cm, and 3 cm.
  Perimeter of the shaded region
  $= \pi \times 9 + \pi \times 6 + \pi \times 3$
  $= 18\pi$ cm
(b) Area of the shaded region
  $= \dfrac{1}{2}\pi \times 9^2 - \dfrac{1}{2}\pi \times 6^2 - \dfrac{1}{2}\pi \times 3^2$
  $= 18\pi$ cm^2

4. The figure shows a semicircle of area 308 cm^2 formed by a piece of wire.
(a) Find the radius of the semicircle.
(b) Find the perimeter of the semicircle.
(c) If the semicircle is cut at A and bent into a circle, find the radius of the circle.
Round your answers to 2 decimal places.

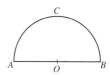

Solution
(a) Let r cm be the radius of the semicircle.
  $\qquad \dfrac{1}{2}\pi r^2 = 308$
  $\qquad\qquad r^2 = \dfrac{308 \times 2}{\pi}$
  $\qquad\qquad\; r = \sqrt{\dfrac{308 \times 2}{\pi}}$
  $\qquad\qquad\quad = 14.00282$ (correct to 5 d.p.)
  $\qquad\qquad\quad = 14.00$ (correct to 2 d.p.)
  The required radius is 14.00 cm.

(b) Perimeter of the semicircle
  $= \pi r + 2r$
  $= \pi \times 14.00282 + 2 \times 14.00282$
  $= 71.99680$ cm (correct to 5 d.p.)
  $= 72.00$ cm (correct to 2 d.p.)

(c) Let R cm be the radius of the circle.
  $\qquad 2\pi R = 71.99680$
  $\qquad\quad R = \dfrac{71.99680}{2\pi}$
  $\qquad\qquad = 11.46$ cm (correct to 2 d.p.)
  The required radius is 11.46 cm.

5. In the figure, $ABEF$ and $BCDE$ are two parallelograms. $CD = 24$ cm, $DE = EF = 18$ cm, and $AC = 30$ cm. Find
(a) the perimeter of the figure,
(b) the area of the figure,
(c) the perpendicular distance from F to AB.

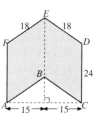

Solution
(a) Perimeter of the figure
  $= 24 \times 2 + 18 \times 4$
  $= 120$ cm

(b) Area of the figure $= 2 \times 24 \times 15$
  $\qquad\qquad\qquad = 720$ cm^2

(c) Let h cm be the perpendicular distance from F to AB.

$$18 \times h = 24 \times 15$$
$$h = 20$$

The perpendicular distance from F to AB is 20 cm.

6. The figure shows the innermost line of a 400-meter running track, with two straight sides of length 100 m each and two semicircles of length 100 m each. Find

(a) d, the distance between the two straight sides,

(b) the area enclosed by the track.

Round your answers to 2 decimal places.

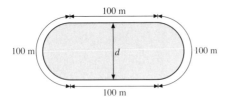

Solution

(a) Radius of the semicircle $= \dfrac{d}{2}$

$$\pi \times \frac{d}{2} = 100 \text{ m}$$
$$d = \frac{200}{\pi} \text{ m}$$
$$= 63.66198 \text{ m} \quad \text{(correct to 5 d.p.)}$$
$$= 63.66 \text{ m} \quad \text{(correct to 2 d.p.)}$$

(b) Radius of the semicircle $= \dfrac{63.66198}{2}$
$$= 31.83099 \text{ m}$$

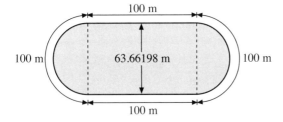

Area enclosed by the track
= 2 × Area of the semicircle + Area of the rectangle

$$= 2 \times \left(\frac{1}{2} \times \pi \times 31.83099^2 \right) + 63.66198 \times 100$$

$$= 9{,}549.30 \text{ m}^2 \quad \text{(correct to 2 d.p.)}$$

7. The figure shows a solid with a uniform cross-section. $CD = DE = FG = GH = 1$ cm, $AH = 2$ cm, and $EF = 3$ cm.

(a) Sketch and label the cross-section of the solid.

(b) Find the perimeter and area of the cross-section.

(c) If a square has the same area as the cross-section of the given solid, what is the length of a side of the square? Round your answer to 2 decimal places.

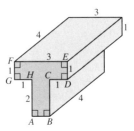

Solution

(a)

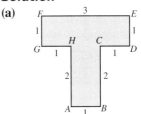

(b) $AB = 3 - 1 - 1$
$$= 1 \text{ cm}$$

Perimeter of the cross-section
$$= 1 + 2 + 1 + 1 + 3 + 1 + 1 + 2$$
$$= 12 \text{ cm}$$

Area of the cross-section
= Area of $ABCH$ + Area of $DEFG$
$$= 2 \times 1 + 1 \times 3$$
$$= 5 \text{ cm}^2$$

(c) Length of a side of the square
$$= \sqrt{5}$$
$$= 2.24 \text{ cm} \quad \text{(correct to 2 d.p.)}$$

8. The figure shows the internal part of a thermal bottle. The uniform cross-section of the bottle consists of a trapezoid, a rectangle, and a semicircle. $AB = GF = 13$ cm, $CE = 20$ cm, $EF = 25$ cm, $AG = 10$ cm, and $AN = 12$ cm.

(a) Draw and label the cross-section $ABCDEFG$ of the bottle.

(b) Find the perimeter and area of the cross-section, giving your answer correct to the nearest integer.

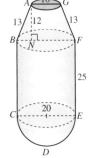

Solution

(a)

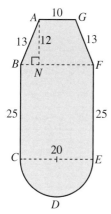

(b) Perimeter of the cross-section
$$= 13 \times 2 + 25 \times 2 + 10 + \pi \times 10$$
$$= 86 + 10\pi$$
$$= 117.42 \text{ cm} \quad \text{(correct to 2 d.p.)}$$

Area of the cross-section
$$= \frac{1}{2}(10 + 20) \times 12 + 25 \times 20 + \frac{1}{2} \times \pi \times 10^2$$
$$= 680 + 50\pi$$
$$= 837.08 \text{ cm}^2 \quad \text{(correct to 2 d.p.)}$$

(d) Let h cm be the height from A to CD.

Area of $\triangle ADE$: Area of $ABCE$
$$= \frac{1}{2} \times 10 \times h : \frac{1}{2}(30 + 20) \times h$$
$$= 10 : 50$$
$$= 1 : 5$$

Alternatively,
Area of $\triangle ADE$: Area of $ABCE$
$$= 90 : 450$$
$$= 1 : 5$$

Note: Area of $\triangle ADE = \frac{1}{2} \times 10 \times h$
$$= \frac{1}{2} \times 10 \times 18$$
$$= 90 \text{ cm}^2$$

9. In the figure, $ABCD$ is a parallelogram in which $AB = 30$ cm, $AD = 20$ cm, $DE = 10$ cm, and $CN = 27$ cm. Find

(a) the perimeter of $ABCD$,
(b) the area of $ABCD$,
(c) the area of $ABCE$,
(d) the ratio of the area of $\triangle ADE$ to the area of $ABCE$.

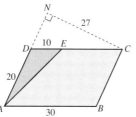

Solution

(a) Perimeter of $ABCD = 2(30 + 20)$
$$= 100 \text{ cm}$$

(b) Area of $ABCD = 20 \times 27$
$$= 540 \text{ cm}^2$$

(c) Let h be the height from A to CD.

Area of $\triangle ADE$ + Area of $ABCE = 540$ cm^2
$$\frac{1}{2} \times 10 \times h + \frac{1}{2}(30 + 20) \times h = 540$$
$$5h + 25h = 540$$
$$h = \frac{540}{30}$$
$$= 18$$

Area of $ABCE = \frac{1}{2}(30 + 20) \times 18$
$$= 450 \text{ cm}^2$$

Chapter 13 Volumes And Surface Areas Of Solids

Class Activity 1

Objective: To recognize the relationship between nets and the solids formed from the nets.

Tasks

- Copy the given nets on a sheet of paper.
- Cut each of them out along the solid lines.
- Fold each of them up along the dotted lines to form solids.

(a)

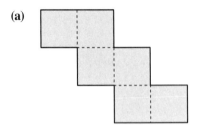

(b)

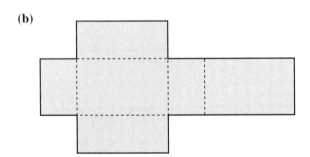

(c)

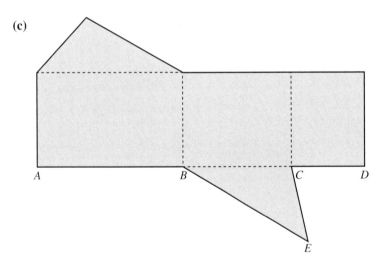

Questions

1. What is the solid of each net in **(a)**, **(b)**, and **(c)**?

   (a) _____Cube_____

   (b) _____Cuboid_____

   (c) _____Triangular prism_____

2. What is the relationship between *AB* and *BE*, and between *CD* and *CE* in the figure in **(c)**?

AB = BE and *CD = CE*

3. State a common property of these solids.

Each solid has a uniform cross-section between two faces.

4. Can a solid have different nets? Sketch other possible nets for each of the solids formed.

Yes. Different nets for each of the solids formed are shown below.

(a)

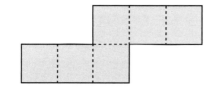 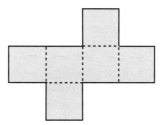

(b)

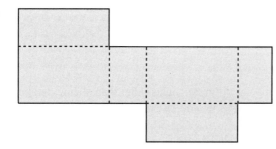

(c)

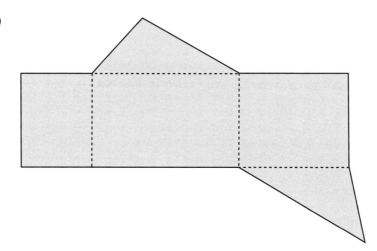

Discuss

Page 103

1. How do you arrange 100 square pieces of area 1 cm^2 each to form a big square?
What is the area of the big square in square meters (m^2)?

We can arrange these 100 square pieces into a big square of side 10 cm.
The area of the big square is 100 cm^2.

2. How do you arrange 1,000 cubes of volume 1 cm^3 each to form a big cube? What is the volume of the big cube in cubic meters (m^3)?

We can arrange these 1,000 cubes into a big cube of side 10 cm.
The volume of the big cube is 1,000 cm^3.

Extend Your Learning Curve

Slicing Solids

A cross-section is the face you get when you make one slice through an object. The figure on the right is a sample slice through a cube, showing one of the cross sections you can get.

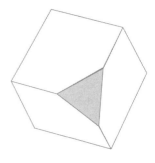

The polygon formed by the slice is the cross-section. The cross-section cannot contain any piece of the original face; it all comes from "inside" the solid. In this figure, only the shaded shape is a cross-section.

1. What shapes do you think you can get if you slice the solid cube at different angles other than slicing parallel to the end face? Record which of the shapes you are able to create and explain how you can make the following cross-sections by slicing a cube:

    (a) a rectangle,   **(b)** a parallelogram,

    (c) a triangle that is not equilateral.

One example is shown above. An equilateral triangle cross-section can be obtained by cutting a cube through the midpoints of the 3 edges originating from any one vertex.

2. Sketch the two-dimensional shape you would get if you slice the following solids as indicated.

(a)

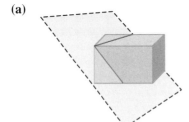

(b)

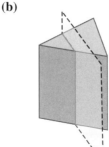

You can find out more about slicing solids on the following websites:
* http://www.learner.org/courses/learningmath/geometry/session9/part_c/index.html#c2
* http://nlvm.usu.edu/en/nav/frames_asid_126_g_3_t_3.html?open=instructions

Suggested Answer:

1. **(a)** One way to obtain a rectangle is by cutting the cube with a plane perpendicular to one of its faces (but not perpendicular to the edges of that face), and parallel to the four, in this case, vertical edges.

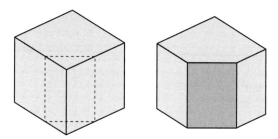

(b) To create a parallelogram, slice with a plane from the top face to the bottom. The slice cannot be parallel to any side of the top face, and the slice must not be vertical. This allows the cut to form no 90° angles. One example is to cut through the top face at a corner and a midpoint of a non-adjacent side, and cut to a different corner and midpoint in the bottom face.

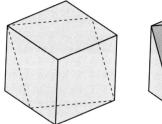 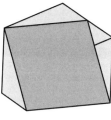

(c) Pick a vertex, let's say A, and consider the three edges meeting at the vertex. Construct a plane that contains a point near a vertex (other than vertex A) on one of the three edges, a point in the middle of another one of the edges, and a third point that is neither in the middle nor coinciding with the first point. Slicing the cube with this plane creates a cross-section that is a triangle, but not an equilateral triangle; it is a scalene triangle. Notice that if any two selected points are equidistant from the original vertex, the cross-section would be an isosceles triangle.

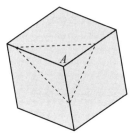 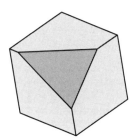

2. **(a)** The cross-section is a rhombus.

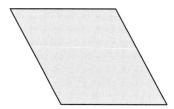

(b) The cross-section is a rectangle.

Try It!

Section 13.1

1. Find the volume and the total surface area of a cube of side 4 cm.

Solution

Volume of the cube = 4^3
$\qquad\qquad\qquad\quad = 64$ cm^3
Total surface area of the cube = 6×4^2
$\qquad\qquad\qquad\qquad\qquad\qquad\quad = 96$ cm^2

2. The surface area of a cube is 294 cm^2. Find
   (a) the length of a side of the cube,
   (b) the volume of the cube.

Solution

(a) Let the length of a side of the cube be x cm.
$\qquad 6x^2 = 294$
$\qquad\quad x^2 = 49$
$\qquad\quad\: x = 7$
   The length of a side of the cube is 7 cm.
(b) Volume of the cube = 7^3
$\qquad\qquad\qquad\qquad\quad = 343$ cm^3

3. A rectangular block of copper is 10 cm by 9 cm by 4 cm.
   (a) Find the volume of the copper block.
   (b) Find the total surface area of the copper block.
   (c) If the copper block is melted and recast into a cube, find the length of a side of the cube, giving your answer correct to 2 decimal places.

Solution

(a) Volume of the block = $10 \times 9 \times 4$
$\qquad\qquad\qquad\qquad\qquad = 360$ cm^3
(b) Total surface area of the block
$\qquad = 2 \times (10 \times 9 + 9 \times 4 + 10 \times 4)$
$\qquad = 332$ cm^2
(c) Let the length of a side of the cube be x cm.
$\qquad\quad x^3 = 360$
$\qquad\quad\: x = \sqrt{360}$
$\qquad\qquad = 7.11$ (correct to 2 d.p.)
   The length of a side of the cube is 7.11 cm.

4. A cuboid is 13 cm long and 6 cm high. Its volume is 624 cm^3. Find
   (a) its width, **(b)** its total surface area.

Solution

(a) Let the width of the cuboid be y cm.
$\qquad 13 \times y \times 6 = 624$
$\qquad\qquad\qquad\: y = 8$
   The width of the cuboid is 8 cm.

(b) Total surface area of the cuboid
$\qquad = 2 \times (13 \times 8 + 13 \times 6 + 8 \times 6)$
$\qquad = 460$ cm^2

Section 13.2

5. The figure shows a triangular prism in which $AB = 14$ cm, $CN = 6$ cm, and $BE = 8$ cm. Find the volume of the prism.

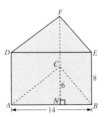

Solution

Area of $\triangle ABC = \frac{1}{2} \times 14 \times 6$
$\qquad\qquad\qquad\quad = 42$ cm^2
Volume of the prism = 42×8
$\qquad\qquad\qquad\qquad\quad = 336$ cm^3

6. The figure shows a swimming pool with a rectangular surface $ABCD$ (not drawn to scale). It is 25 m long and 18 m wide. Its depth is 3 m at the deep end and 2 m at the shallow end. Find the volume of the swimming pool.

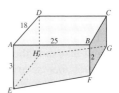

Solution

Base area = Area of $ABFE$
$\qquad\qquad = \frac{1}{2} \times (3 + 2) \times 25$
$\qquad\qquad = 62.5$ m^2
Volume of the swimming pool = 62.5×18
$\qquad\qquad\qquad\qquad\qquad\qquad\quad = 1{,}125$ m^3

7. The figure shows a triangular prism in which $m\angle BAC = 90°$, $AB = 5$ cm, $BC = 13$ cm, $AC = 12$ cm, and $BE = 14$ cm.
   (a) Draw a net of the prism.
   (b) Find the volume of the prism.
   (c) Find its total surface area.

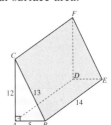

Solution

(a)

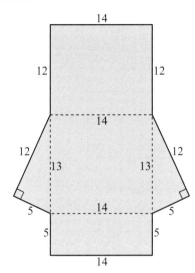

(b) Base area = Area of $\triangle ABC$

$$= \frac{1}{2} \times 5 \times 12$$

$$= 30 \text{ cm}^2$$

Volume of the prism = 30×14

$$= 420 \text{ cm}^3$$

(c) Perimeter of the base = Perimeter of $\triangle ABC$

$$= 5 + 12 + 13$$

$$= 30 \text{ cm}$$

Total surface area of the prism

$$= 30 \times 14 + 2 \times 30$$

$$= 480 \text{ cm}^2$$

8. The figure shows a sauce dish shaped like a trapezoidal prism in which $AB = 10$ cm, $BC = AD = 5$ cm, $CD = 16$ cm, $BF = 18$ cm, and the depth of the dish is 4 cm.
   (a) Find the volume of the dish.
   (b) Find the external surface area of the dish.
   (c) If the material for the dish costs $0.02 per cm^2, find the cost of material used in making the dish.

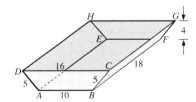

Solution

(a) Base area = Area of $ABCD$

$$= \frac{1}{2} \times (10 + 16) \times 4$$

$$= 52 \text{ cm}^2$$

Volume of the dish = 52×18

$$= 936 \text{ cm}^3$$

(b) $DA + AB + BC = 5 + 10 + 5$

$$= 20 \text{ cm}$$

External surface area of the dish

$$= 20 \times 18 + 2 \times 52$$

$$= 464 \text{ cm}^2$$

(c) The required cost of material = 0.02×464

$$= \$9.28$$

Section 13.3

9. The internal dimensions of a rectangular storage container are 7.20 m by 4.88 m by 5.67 m. Find
   (a) its total internal surface area
      (i) in square meters,
      (ii) in square centimeters,
   (b) its internal volume
      (i) in cubic meters,
      (ii) in cubic centimeters.
Round your answers correct to the nearest hundred.

Solution

(a) **(i)** Total surface area of the container

$$= 2 \times (7.20 \times 4.88 + 4.88 \times 5.67 + 7.20 \times 5.67)$$

$$= 207.2592 \text{ m}^2$$

$$= 200 \text{ m}^2 \text{ (correct to the nearest hundred)}$$

   (ii) Total surface area of the container

$$= 207.2592 \times 10,000 \text{ cm}^2 \quad 1 \text{ m}^2 = 10,000 \text{cm}^2$$

$$= 2,072,592 \text{ cm}^2$$

$$= 2,072,600 \text{ cm}^2$$

$$\text{(correct to the nearest hundred)}$$

(b) **(i)** Internal volume of the container

$$= 7.20 \times 4.88 \times 5.67$$

$$= 199.22112 \text{ m}^3$$

$$= 200 \text{ m}^3 \text{ (correct to the nearest hundred)}$$

   (ii) Internal volume of the container

$$= 199.22112 \times 1,000,000 \text{ cm}^2 \quad 1 \text{m}^3 = 1,000,000 \text{cm}^3$$

$$= 199,221,120 \text{ cm}^3$$

$$= 199,221,100 \text{ cm}^3$$

$$\text{(correct to the nearest hundred)}$$

10. A solid metal bar has a uniform cross-section as shown. Given that $PQ = 2.1$ cm, $QR = 2.8$ cm, $PR = 3.5$ cm, and the length of the metal bar is 3.9 m, find
   (a) its total surface area
      (i) in square centimeters,
      (ii) in square meters,
   (b) its volume
      (i) in cubic centimeters,
      (ii) in cubic meters.
Round your answers correct to 4 decimal places where appropriate.

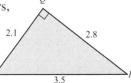

Solution

(a) (i) Length of the metal bar
= 3.9 m
= 390 cm

Total surface area of the metal bar
= Perimeter of the cross-section × Length
+ 2 × Cross-section area
= (2.1 + 2.8 + 3.5) × 390
$$+ 2 \times \left(\frac{1}{2} \times 2.1 \times 2.8 \right)$$
= 3,281.88 cm²

(ii) Total surface area of the metal bar
$$= 3{,}281.88 \times \frac{1}{10{,}000} \text{ m}^2$$
= 0.328188 m²
= 0.3282 m² (correct to 4 d.p.)

(b) (i) Volume of the metal bar
= Area of cross-section × Length
$$= \left(\frac{1}{2} \times 2.1 \times 2.8 \right) \times 390$$
= 1,146.6 cm³

(ii) Volume of the metal bar
$$= 1{,}146.6 \times \frac{1}{1{,}000{,}000} \text{ m}^3$$
= 0.0011466 m³
= 0.0011 m³ (correct to 4 d.p.)

11. The figure shows a right pentagonal prism in which
$AB = 8$ in., $BC = 15$ in., $AF = 6$ in., $IJ = 17$ in., and
$AJ = CI = 25$ in. Find
(a) the perimeter of the face $ABCIJ$,
(b) the area of the face $ABCIJ$,
(c) the total surface area of the prism,
(d) the volume of the prism.

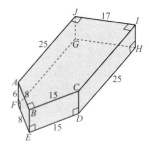

Solution

(a) Perimeter of the face $ABCIJ$
= $AB + BC + CI + IJ + JA$
= 8 + 15 + 25 + 17 + 25
= 90 in.

(b)

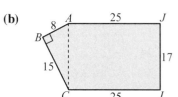

Area of the face $ABCIJ$
= Area of $\triangle ABC$ + Area of rectangle $CIJA$
$$= \frac{1}{2} \times 8 \times 15 + 25 \times 17$$
= 485 in.²

(c) Total surface area of the prism
= Perimeter of the face $ABCIJ$
× Height of the prism
+ 2 × Area of the face $ABCIJ$
= 90 × 6 + 2 × 485
= 1,510 in.²

(d) Volume of the prism
= Area of the face $ABCIJ$ × Height of the prism
= 485 × 6
= 2,910 in.³

12. The figure shows a prism whose cross-section is formed
by cutting out $\triangle CDF$ from the parallelogram $ABFE$.
$AB = 25$ cm, $DE = 15$ cm, and $BH = 30$ cm. The heights
from C to EF and AB are 8 cm and 10 cm respectively.
Find the volume of the prism.

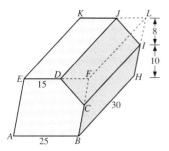

Solution

Area of the cross-section of the prism
$$= 25 \times 18 - \frac{1}{2} \times 10 \times 8$$
= 410 cm²
Volume of the prism = 410 × 30
= 12,300 cm³

Exercise 13.1

Basic Practice

1. Determine whether each of the following is a net of a cube.

   (a)

   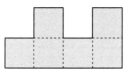

   (b)

   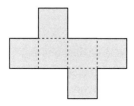

   Solution
   (a) No
   (b) Yes

2. Draw two possible nets of the cuboid shown below, where the unit of length is centimeter.

   Solution
   The possible nets of the cuboid are shown below.

   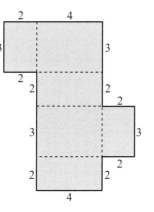

3. Sketch the solid that can be formed by each of the following nets.

   (a)

   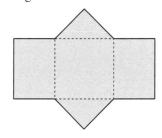

   (b)

   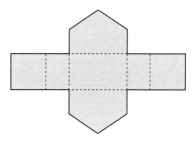

   Solution

   (a)

   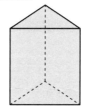

   (b)

   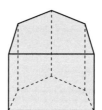

4. Find the volume and the total surface area of a cube whose side is
   (a) 6 cm,
   (b) 11 in.,
   (c) 1.3 m.

   Solution
   (a) Volume of the cube = 6^3
   $\qquad = 216$ cm^3

   Total surface area of the cube = 6×6^2
   $\qquad = 216$ cm^2

   (b) Volume of the cube = 11^3
   $\qquad = 1,331$ in.^{3}

   Total surface area of the cube = 6×11^2
   $\qquad = 726$ in.^{2}

   (c) Volume of the cube = 1.3^3
   $\qquad = 2.197$ m^3

   Total surface area of the cube = 6×1.3^2
   $\qquad = 10.14$ m^2

5. Find the volume and the total surface area of a cuboid whose dimensions are
(a)   12 cm by 8 cm by 5 cm,
(b)   10 in. by 7 in. by 6 in.,
(c)   4 ft by 3 ft by 2 ft.

Solution
(a)   Volume of the cuboid
      $= 12 \times 8 \times 5$
      $= 480$ cm^3
      Total surface area of the cuboid
      $= 2 \times (12 \times 8 + 12 \times 5 + 8 \times 5)$
      $= 392$ cm^2

(b)   Volume of the cuboid
      $= 10 \times 7 \times 6$
      $= 420$ in.^{3}
      Total surface area of the cuboid
      $= 2 \times (10 \times 7 + 10 \times 6 + 7 \times 6)$
      $= 344$ in.^{2}

(c)   Volume of the cuboid
      $= 4 \times 3 \times 2$
      $= 24$ ft^3
      Total surface area of the cuboid
      $= 2 \times (4 \times 3 + 4 \times 2 + 3 \times 2)$
      $= 52$ ft^2

Further Practice

6. Draw a net of the solid shown below, where the unit of length is centimeter.

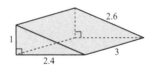

Solution
The net of the solid is shown below.

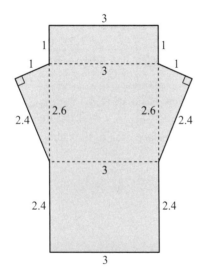

7. The area of a face of a cube is 169 cm^2. Find
(a)   the length of a side,
(b)   the total surface area,
(c)   the volume
of the cube.

Solution
(a)   Let the length of a side of the cube be x cm.
      $x^2 = 169$
      $x = \sqrt{169}$
      $\quad = 13$
      The length of a side of the cube is 13 cm.

(b)   Total surface area of the cube $= 6 \times 169$
                                    $= 1,014$ cm^2

(c)   Volume of the cube $= 13^3$
                         $= 2,197$ cm^3

8. The total surface area of a cube is 486 cm^2. Find
(a)   the length of a side,
(b)   the volume
of the cube.

Solution
(a)   Let the length of a side of the cube be x cm.
      $6x^2 = 486$
      $x^2 = 81$
      $x = 9$
      The length of a side of the cube is 9 cm.

(b)   Volume of the cube $= 9^3$
                         $= 729$ cm^3

9. Copy and complete the following table for cuboids.

	Length	Width	Height	Volume	Total surface area
(a)	9 cm	6 cm		270 cm^3	
(b)		8 cm	5 cm	440 cm^3	
(c)	14 cm		6 cm		608 cm^2

Solution

	Length	Width	Height	Volume	Total surface area
(a)	9 cm	6 cm	5 cm	270 cm^3	258 cm^2
(b)	11 cm	8 cm	5 cm	440 cm^3	366 cm^2
(c)	14 cm	11 cm	6 cm	924 cm^3	608 cm^2

(a) Height = $\dfrac{270}{9 \times 6}$

= 5 cm

Total surface area

= $2 \times (9 \times 6 + 9 \times 5 + 6 \times 5)$

= 258 cm^2

(b) Length = $\dfrac{440}{8 \times 5}$

= 11 cm

Total surface area

= $2 \times (11 \times 8 + 11 \times 5 + 8 \times 5)$

= 366 cm^2

(c) Let the width be y cm.

$2 \times (14y + 14 \times 6 + 6y) = 608$

$20y + 84 = 304$

$20y = 220$

$y = 11$

Width = 11 cm

Volume = $14 \times 11 \times 6$

= 924 cm^3

---

10. The dimensions of a cuboid are 7 cm by 5cm by 4 cm.

    (a) Find its volume.

    (b) If a cube of side x cm has the same volume as the cuboid, find the value of x. Give your answer correct to 2 decimal places.

Solution

(a) Volume of the cuboid = $7 \times 5 \times 4$

= 140 cm^3

(b) $x^3 = 140$

$x = \sqrt[3]{140}$

= 5.19 (correct to 2 d.p.)

---

11. A rectangular copper block A measuring 10 cm by 6 cm by 5 cm, is melted and recast into a rectangular bar B, 3 cm wide and 2 cm high. Find

    (a) the length of copper bar B,

    (b) the ratio of the total surface area of block A to that of bar B.

Solution

(a) Let the length of the copper bar B be y cm.

$3 \times 2 \times y = 10 \times 6 \times 5$

$y = 50$

The length of copper bar B is 50 cm.

(b) Total surface area of block A

= $2 \times (10 \times 6 + 10 \times 5 + 6 \times 5)$

= 280 cm^2

Total surface area of bar B

= $2 \times (50 \times 3 + 50 \times 2 + 3 \times 2)$

= 512 cm^2

The required ratio = 280 : 512

= 35 : 64

Math@Work

12. A rectangular aquarium tank is 50 cm long, 30 cm wide, and 36 cm high.

    (a) Find the volume of water required to fill up the tank.

    (b) The tank is open at the top. Find the external surface area of glass required to make the tank.

    (c) If 6,000 cm^3 of water is drained from the tank, find the drop in water level.

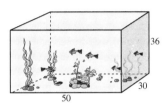

Solution

(a) The required volume of water

= $50 \times 30 \times 36$

= 54,000 cm^3

(b) External surface area of glass

= $50 \times 30 + 2 \times 30 \times 36 + 2 \times 50 \times 36$

= 7,260 cm^2

(c) Let the drop in water level be h cm.

$50 \times 30 \times h = 6,000$

$h = \dfrac{6,000}{1,500}$

= 4

The drop in water level is 4 cm.

---

13. A rectangular tin plate measures 40 cm by 30 cm. A small square of side 8 cm is cut out from each corner as shown in the figure. The plate is then folded along the dotted lines to form an open tray. Find

    (a) the external surface area,

    (b) the volume

of the tray.

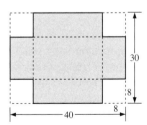

Solution

(a) External surface area of the tray

= $40 \times 30 - 4 \times 8^2$

= 944 cm^2

(b) Length of the tray = 40 – 8 – 8
                    = 24 cm
    Width of the tray = 30 – 8 – 8
                  = 14 cm
  Volume of the tray = 24 × 14 × 8
                  = 2,688 cm^3

14. The external dimensions of a wooden box are 15 cm by 10 cm by 8 cm. The thickness of the wood on each side is 1.5 cm. Find
(a) the internal dimensions of the box,
(b) the volume of wood used to make the box.

Solution
(a) Internal length = 15 – 2 × 1.5
                = 12 cm
    Internal width = 10 – 2 × 1.5
               = 7 cm
    Internal height = 8 – 2 × 1.5
               = 5 cm

(b) External volume of the box = 15 × 10 × 8
                           = 1,200 cm^3
    Internal volume of the box = 12 × 7 × 5
                       = 420 cm^3
    Volume of wood used = 1,200 – 420
                  = 780 cm^3

Brainworks

15. Suggest a way to estimate the volume of your body and then use your method to find an estimated value.

Solution
We can estimate the volume of our body by approximating it to a cuboid. The dimensions of the cuboid are
  body height × shoulder width × chest depth.

For example, if a boy is 160 cm tall, 40 cm broad, and 15 cm thick,
  his body volume ≈ 160 × 40 × 15
                  = 96,000 cm^3.

A more accurate method is by water displacement. Fill completely a large rectangular tank with water. You can fully immerse in the tank for a moment to displace water and then get out. Measure the drop in water level in the tank.

  Body volume = Length of the tank
               × Width of the tank
               × Drop in water level

Exercise 13.2
Basic Practice
1. For each of the following,
  (i) draw a net of the prism,
  (ii) find the volume and the total surface area of the prism.
The unit of measurement is centimeter (cm).

(a)   **(b)**

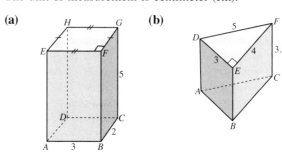

(c)   **(d)**

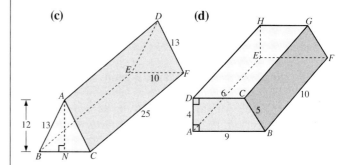

Solution
(a) **(i)**

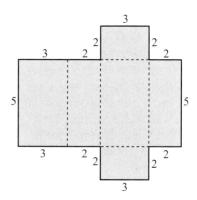

(ii) Volume of the prism = 3 × 2 × 5
                          = 30 cm^3

    Total surface area of the prism
    = 2 × (3 × 2 + 3 × 5 + 2 × 5)
    = 62 cm^2

(b) (i)

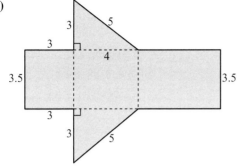

(ii) Area of $\triangle DEF = \frac{1}{2} \times 3 \times 4$

$= 6 \text{ cm}^2$

Volume of the prism $= 6 \times 3.5$

$= 21 \text{ cm}^3$

Total surface area of the prism

$= (3 + 4 + 5) \times 3.5 + 2 \times 6$

$= 54 \text{ cm}^2$

(c) (i)

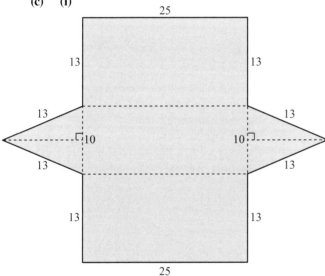

(ii) Area of $\triangle ABC = \frac{1}{2} \times 10 \times 12$

$= 60 \text{ cm}^2$

Volume of the prism $= 60 \times 25$

$= 1,500 \text{ cm}^3$

Total surface area of the prism

$= (13 + 13 + 10) \times 25 + 2 \times 60$

$= 1,020 \text{ cm}^2$

(d) (i)

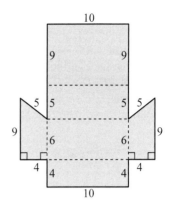

(ii) Area of $ABCD = \frac{1}{2} \times (6 + 9) \times 4$

$= 30 \text{ cm}^2$

Volume of the prism $= 30 \times 10$

$= 300 \text{ cm}^3$

Total surface area of the prism

$= (4 + 6 + 5 + 9) \times 10 + 2 \times 30$

$= 300 \text{ cm}^2$

2. The figure shows a pentagonal prism in which the area of $ABCDE$ is 150 cm^2, $AB = 10 \text{ cm}$, $BC = 6 \text{ cm}$, $CD = 11 \text{ cm}$, $DE = 13 \text{ cm}$, $EA = 8 \text{ cm}$, and $CH = 21 \text{ cm}$. Find

   (a) the volume of the prism,

   (b) the total surface area of the prism.

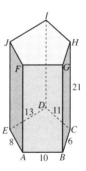

Solution

(a) Volume of the prism $= 150 \times 21$

$= 3,150 \text{ cm}^3$

(b) Total surface area of the prism

$= (10 + 6 + 11 + 13 + 8) \times 21 + 2 \times 150$

$= 1,308 \text{ cm}^2$

Further Practice

3. The figure shows a trapezoidal prism in which $AB = DC = 5$ in., $BC = 4$ in., $AD = 10$ in., and $BN = 4$ in. The volume of the prism is 210 in³. Find
   (a) the area of $ABCD$,
   (b) the length of DH,
   (c) the total surface area of the prism.

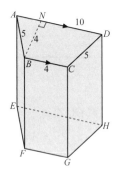

Solution

(a) Area of $ABCD = \dfrac{1}{2} \times (4 + 10) \times 4$
$= 28$ in²

(b) Volume of the prism = Length of DH × Area of $ABCD$
210 in³ = Length of DH × 28 in²
∴ length of DH = 7.5 in.

(c) Total surface area of the prism
$= (4 + 5 + 10 + 5) \times 7.5 + 2 \times 28$
$= 236$ in²

4. The figure shows a right triangular prism standing on a horizontal rectangular base $BCDE$ and $AC = FD = 25$ cm.
   (a) If the area of $BCDE$ is 480 cm², $CD = 32$ cm, and $AB = 20$ cm, find
      (i) the length of BC,
      (ii) the total surface area and volume of the prism.
   (b) If the area of $\triangle ABC$ is 84 cm², $CD = 30$ cm, and $BC = 24$ cm, find
      (i) the length of AB,
      (ii) the total surface area and volume of the prism.

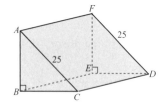

Solution

(a) **(i)** Area of $BCDE = BC \times CD$
480 cm² = $BC \times 32$ cm
∴ $BC = 15$ cm

(ii) Total surface area of the prism
$= (25 + 15 + 20) \times 32 + 2 \times \left(\dfrac{1}{2} \times 15 \times 20 \right)$
$= 2,220$ cm²
Volume of the prism
$= \left(\dfrac{1}{2} \times 15 \times 20 \right) \times 32$
$= 4,800$ cm³

(b) **(i)** Area of $\triangle ABC = \dfrac{1}{2} \times AB \times BC$
84 cm² $= \dfrac{1}{2} \times AB \times 24$ cm
$AB = 7$ cm

(ii) Total surface area of the prism
$= (25 + 24 + 7) \times 30 + 2 \times \left(\dfrac{1}{2} \times 24 \times 7 \right)$
$= 1,848$ cm²
Volume of the prism
$= \left(\dfrac{1}{2} \times 24 \times 7 \right) \times 30$
$= 2,520$ cm³

Math@Work

5. The figure shows a camping tent. The tent is closed at both ends and at the bottom. Given that $AB = AC = 1.7$ m, $BC = 1.6$ m, $AN = 1.5$ m, and $CF = 2.1$ m, find
   (a) the space inside the tent,
   (b) the surface area of the tent,
   (c) the total cost of the material used in making the tent if the material of the tent costs $30 per square meter.

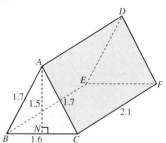

Solution

(a) Area of $\triangle ABC = \dfrac{1}{2} \times 1.6 \times 1.5$
$= 1.2$ m²
Space inside the tent $= 1.2 \times 2.1$
$= 2.52$ m³

(b) Surface area of the tent
$= (1.7 + 1.7 + 1.6) \times 2.1 + 2 \times 1.2$
$= 12.9$ m²

(c) Total cost of material $= \$30 \times 12.9$
$= \$387$

6. The figure shows a swimming pool with a rectangular surface $ABCD$ (not drawn to scale). $CD = 20$ m, $AE = 1.6$ m, $BF = 1$ m, and the area of $ABCD$ is 240 m^2. Find

   (a) the length of AD,

   (b) the volume of the pool.

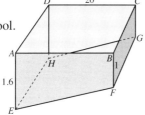

Solution

  (a) Length of $AD = \dfrac{240}{20}$

                   $= 12$ m

  (b) Area of the cross-section $ABFE$

       $= \dfrac{1}{2} \times (1.6 + 1) \times 20$

       $= 26$ m^2

       Volume of the pool $= 26 \times 12$

                          $= 312$ m^3

7. The figure shows a tray whose end faces are trapezoids. If $AB = 15$ in., $AN = 12$ in., $CD = 22$ in., $BF = 45$ in., and $BC = AD = 12.5$ in., find

   (a) the area of $ABCD$,

   (b) the volume of the tray,

   (c) the external surface area of the tray.

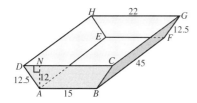

Solution

  (a) Area of $ABCD = \dfrac{1}{2} \times (15 + 22) \times 12$

                      $= 222$ in^2

  (b) Volume of the tray $= 222 \times 45$

                       $= 9,990$ in^3

  (c) External surface area of the tray

       $= (12.5 + 15 + 12.5) \times 45 + 2 \times 222$

       $= 2,244$ in^2

Brainworks

8. A manager wants to design a rectangular storage container of capacity 900 ft^3. The container should have a square base of side a ft and a height of h ft, where a and h are integers greater than 1.

   (a) Find two possible sets of dimensions for the container.

   (b) Suggest a design that uses the least material to make the container.

Solution

  (a)

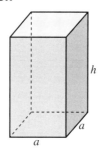

$a^2 h = 900$

When $a = 5$, $5^2 \times h = 900$

                       $h = 36$

When $a = 10$, $10^2 \times h = 900$

                       $h = 9$

Two possible sets of dimensions are:

         5 ft $\times$ 5 ft $\times$ 36 ft

and   10 ft $\times$ 10 ft $\times$ 9 ft.

  (b) Total surface area of the box $= 2a^2 + 4ah$

                            $= 2a^2 + 4a \times \dfrac{900}{a^2}$

                            $= 2a^2 + \dfrac{3,600}{a}$

Setting up a table or using a spreadsheet program, we have

a	Total surface area
5	770
6	672
7	612.3
8	578
9	562
10	560
11	569.3
12	588
13	614.9

Hence, the material used is minimum when $a = 10$. The optimal dimensions are

         10 ft $\times$ 10 ft $\times$ 9 ft.

Exercise 13.3

Basic Practice

1. Express the following areas in cm^2.

   (a) 3 m^2 **(b)** 13.6 m^2

Solution

  (a) 3 m$^2 = 3 \times 10{,}000$ cm^2

               $= 30{,}000$ cm^2

  (b) 13.6 m$^2 = 13.6 \times 10{,}000$ cm^2

                    $= 136{,}000$ cm^2

2. Express the following areas in m².

    (a) 4,000 cm²   **(b)** 25,600 cm²

Solution

    (a) 4,000 cm² = $\dfrac{4,000}{10,000}$ m²

              = 0.4 m²

    (b) 25,600 cm² = $\dfrac{25,600}{10,000}$ m²

              = 2.56 m²

3. Express the following volumes in cm³.

    (a) 2 m³   **(b)** 39.7 m³

Solution

    (a) 2 m³ = 2 × 1,000,000 cm³

           = 2,000,000 cm³

    (b) 39.7 m³ = 39.7 × 1,000,000 cm³

             = 39,700,000 cm³

4. Express the following volumes in m³.

    (a) 63,000 cm³   **(b)** 9,280,000 cm³

Solution

    (a) 63,000 cm³ = $\dfrac{63,000}{1,000,000}$ m³

              = 0.063 m³

    (b) 9,280,000 cm³ = $\dfrac{9,280,000}{1,000,000}$ m³

              = 9.28 m³

Further Practice

5. A playground is built on a rectangular plot of land 35 m long and 24 m wide. Find the area of the land
    (a) in square meters,
    (b) in square centimeters.

Solution

    (a) Area of the playground = 35 × 24

                  = 840 m²

    (b) Area of the playground = 840 × 10,000 cm²

                  = 8,400,000 cm²

6. Jane drinks eight cups of water a day. If each cup contains 250 cm³ of water, find the total amount of water she drinks per day in
    (a) cubic centimeters,
    (b) cubic meters.

Solution

    (a) Amount of water = 250 × 8 cm³

              = 2,000 cm³

    (b) Amount of water = $\dfrac{2,000}{1,000,000}$ m³

              = 0.002 m³

7. Find the total surface area and volume of each prism, where the unit of length is centimeter (cm).

    (a)

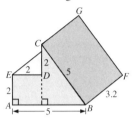

    (b)

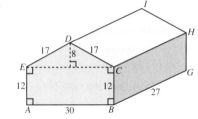

Solution

    (a) Area of the cross-section *ABCDE*

        = $2 \times 2 + \dfrac{1}{2} \times 4 \times 3$

        = 10 cm²

        Volume of the prism = 10 × 3.2

                      = 32 cm³

        Total surface area of the prism

        = (5 + 5 + 2 + 2 + 2) × 3.2 + 2 × 10

        = 71.2 cm²

    (b) Area of the cross-section *ABCDE*

        = $\dfrac{1}{2} \times 30 \times 8 + 12 \times 30$

        = 480 cm²

        Volume of the prism = 480 × 27

                      = 12,960 cm³

        Total surface area of the prism

        = (30 + 12 + 17 + 17 + 12) × 27 + 2 × 480

        = 3,336 cm²

8. Find the total surface area and volume of each prism, where the unit of length is centimeter (cm).

    (a)

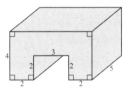

    (b)

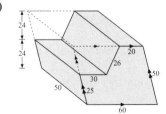

Solution

(a) Area of the cross-section
$$= 4 \times (2 + 3 + 2) - 2 \times 3$$
$$= 22 \text{ cm}^2$$

Total surface area of the prism
$$= (4 + 2 + 2 + 3 + 2 + 2 + 4 + 2 + 3 + 2) \times 5$$
$$+ 2 \times 22$$
$$= 174 \text{ cm}^2$$

Volume of the prism
$$= 22 \times 5$$
$$= 110 \text{ cm}^3$$

(b) Area of the cross-section
$$= 60 \times (24 + 24) - \frac{1}{2} \times (30 + 40) \times 24$$
$$= 2,040 \text{ cm}^2$$

Total surface area of the prism
$$= (60 + 50 + 20 + 26 + 30 + 25) \times 50 + 2 \times 2,040$$
$$= 14,630 \text{ cm}^2$$

Volume of the prism
$$= 2,040 \times 50$$
$$= 102,000 \text{ cm}^3$$

9. A cuboid measuring 10 in. by 7 in. by 12 in. has a square hole with side 2 in. drilled through it from the face *EFGH* to the face *ABCD*. Find
(a) the volume,
(b) the total surface area
of the solid.

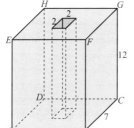

Solution

(a) Volume of the solid
$$= 10 \times 7 \times 12 - 2 \times 2 \times 12$$
$$= 792 \text{ in.}^3$$

(b) Total surface area of the solid
$$= 10 \times 12 \times 2 + 7 \times 12 \times 2 + (10 \times 7 - 2 \times 2) \times 2$$
$$+ 2 \times 12 \times 4$$
$$= 636 \text{ in.}^2$$

10. The figure shows the uniform cross-section of a solid. *ABCD* and *EFGH* are trapezoids with dimensions given in centimeters. If the length of the solid is 10 cm, find
(a) the volume,
(b) the total surface area
of the solid.

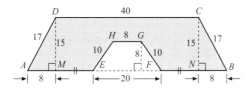

Solution

(a) $AB = 8 + 40 + 8$
$$= 56 \text{ cm}$$

Area of the cross-section
$$= \frac{1}{2} \times (40 + 56) \times 15 - \frac{1}{2} \times (8 + 20) \times 8$$
$$= 608 \text{ cm}^2$$

Volume of the solid
$$= 608 \times 10$$
$$= 6,080 \text{ cm}^3$$

(b) $ME = \frac{1}{2} \times (40 - 20)$
$$= 10$$

Total surface area of the solid
$$= (40 + 17 + 8 + 10 + 10 + 8 + 10 + 10 + 8 + 17) \times 10$$
$$+ 2 \times 608$$
$$= 2,596 \text{ cm}^2$$

Math@Work

11. A rectangular gasoline tank measures 0.7 m by 0.8 m by 2.0 m. The gasoline in it is used to fill up small cubical cans of sides 25 cm each.
(a) Find the volume of the tank
   (i) in cubic meters,
   (ii) in cubic centimeters.
(b) Find the volume of a can
   (i) in cubic centimeters,
   (ii) in cubic meters.
(c) How many complete cans can be filled if the tank is completely filled with gasoline initially?

Solution

(a) **(i)** Volume of the tank $= 0.7 \times 0.8 \times 2.0$
$$= 1.12 \text{ m}^3$$

   (ii) Volume of the tank $= 1.12 \times 1,000,000 \text{ cm}^3$
$$= 1,120,000 \text{ cm}^3$$

(b) (i) Volume of a can $= 25^3$
$$= 15,625 \text{ cm}^3$$

   (ii) Volume of a can $= \dfrac{15,625}{1,000,000} \text{ m}^3$
$$= 0.015625 \text{ m}^3$$

(c) Let n be the number of cans that can be filled with gasoline.
$$n \times 15,625 \leqslant 1,120,000$$
$$n \leqslant 71.68$$
71 cans can be filled with gasoline.

12. The figure shows the uniform cross-section of a sofa chair. Given that the dimensions are in centimeters and the length of the sofa is 1.8 m, find

   (a) the perimeter of the cross-section,

   (b) the area of the cross-section,

   (c) the total surface area of the sofa in square meters,

   (d) the volume of the sofa in cubic meters.

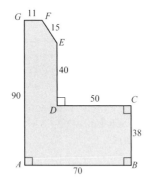

Solution

(a) Perimeter of the cross-section
$$= 90 + 70 + 38 + 50 + 40 + 15 + 11$$
$$= 314 \text{ cm}$$

(b)

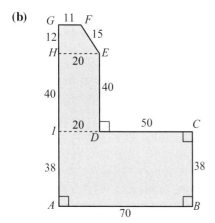

Area of the cross-section
$$= \frac{1}{2} \times (11 + 20) \times 12 + 20 \times 40 + 70 \times 38$$
$$= 3{,}646 \text{ cm}^2$$

(c) Total surface area of the sofa
$$= 314 \times 180 + 2 \times 3{,}646$$
$$= 63{,}812 \text{ cm}^2$$
$$= \frac{63{,}812}{10{,}000} \text{ m}^2$$
$$= 6.3812 \text{ m}^2$$

(d) Volume of the sofa
$$= 3{,}646 \times 180$$
$$= 656{,}280 \text{ cm}^3$$
$$= \frac{656{,}280}{1{,}000{,}000} \text{ m}^3$$
$$= 0.65628 \text{ m}^3$$

13. The figure shows a metal girder of uniform cross-section. *ABCD* is a trapezoid and *EFGH* is a square. Given that their dimensions are in feet, find

   (a) the volume of the girder,

   (b) the total surface area of the girder,

   (c) the number of such girders that can be casted using 14,000 ft³ of molten metal,

   (d) the number of cans of paint needed to coat six such girders if each can of paint can coat an area of 800 ft².

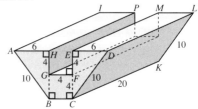

Solution

(a) Area of the cross-section *ABCDEFGH*
$$= \frac{1}{2} \times (4 + 16) \times 8 - 4 \times 4$$
$$= 64 \text{ ft}^2$$
Volume of the girder
$$= 64 \times 20$$
$$= 1{,}280 \text{ ft}^3$$

(b) Total surface area of the girder
$$= (10 + 4 + 10 + 6 + 4 + 4 + 4 + 6) \times 20 + 2 \times 64$$
$$= 1{,}088 \text{ ft}^2$$

(c) Let n be the number of girders that can be casted using 14,000 ft³ of molten metal.
$$n \times 1{,}280 \leqslant 14{,}000$$
$$n \leqslant 10.9375$$
∴ 10 girders can be casted.

(d) Let m be the number of cans of paint needed to coat six girders.
$$m \times 800 \geqslant 6 \times 1{,}088$$
$$m \geqslant 8.16$$
∴ 9 cans of paint are needed.

Brainworks

14. (a) Describe and draw two items in your home that are made up of basic solids.

   (b) Measure their dimensions and calculate their volumes and total surface areas.

Solution

For **(a)** and **(b)**, the answers vary.

Examples of items that are made up of basic solids are as follows:

A table may be in the form of a cuboid with 4 triangular prism as legs.

An ice cube tray may be in the form of a cuboid with many cubic holes.

Review Exercise 13

1. A cuboid is 3.5 cm long, 2 cm wide, and 1.5 cm high.
   (a) Draw a net of the cuboid.
   (b) Find the volume of the cuboid.
   (c) Find its total surface area.

Solution
(a) The following is a net of the cuboid.

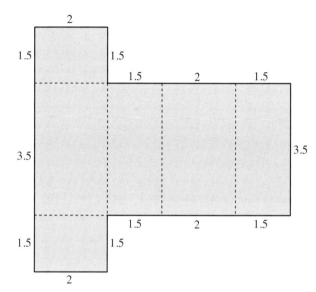

(b) Volume of the cuboid
   $= 3.5 \times 2 \times 1.5$
   $= 10.5$ cm^3

(c) Total surface area of the cuboid
   $= 2 \times (3.5 \times 2 + 3.5 \times 1.5 + 2 \times 1.5)$
   $= 30.5$ cm^2

2. The face of a cube has an area of 196 in^2. Find
   (a) the length of a side of the cube,
   (b) its total surface area,
   (c) its volume.

Solution
(a) Length of a side of the cube $= \sqrt{196}$
   $= 14$ in.

(b) Total surface area of the cube $= 6 \times 14^2$
   $= 1,176$ in^2

(c) Volume of the cube $= 14^3$
   $= 2,744$ in^3

3. The figure shows the net of a prism. $BC = PB = PC = 2$ cm, $DE = 2.5$ cm, and $PN = \sqrt{3}$ cm.
   (a) Name the prism.
   (b) Find the volume of the prism.
   (c) Find its total surface area.

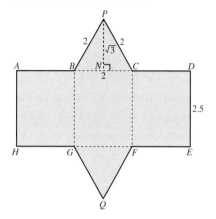

Solution
(a) The prism is a triangular prism.

(b) Area of $\triangle BCP = \frac{1}{2} \times 2 \times \sqrt{3}$
   $= \sqrt{3}$ cm^2

   Volume of the prism $= \sqrt{3} \times 2.5$
   $= 4.33$ cm^3
   (correct to 2 d.p.)

(c) Total surface area of the prism
   $= 2.5 \times 6 + 2 \times \sqrt{3}$
   $= 18.46$ cm^2 (correct to 2 d.p.)

4. Find the volume and total surface area of each prism, where the unit of length is cm.
   (a)

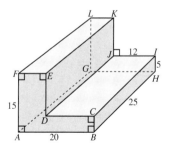

   (b)

Solution

(a) Area of the cross-section *ABCDEF*
$$= 20 \times 5 + 10 \times 8$$
$$= 180 \text{ cm}^2$$
Volume of the prism $= 180 \times 25$
$$= 4,500 \text{ cm}^3$$
Total surface area of the prism
$$= (20 + 5 + 12 + 10 + 8 + 15) \times 25 + 2 \times 180$$
$$= 2,110 \text{ cm}^2$$

(b) Area of the cross-section *ABCDE*
$$= \frac{1}{2} \times 8 \times 3 + 6 \times 8$$
$$= 60 \text{ cm}^2$$
Volume of the prism $= 60 \times 7$
$$= 420 \text{ cm}^3$$
Total surface area of the prism
$$= (5 + 5 + 6 + 8 + 6) \times 7 + 2 \times 60$$
$$= 330 \text{ cm}^2$$

5. The figure shows the cross-section *ABCD* of a prism of height 5.0 cm. *AB* = 3.6 cm, *BC* = 3.2 cm, *BD* = 6.0 cm, and $m\angle BAD = m\angle CBD = 90°$.

(a) Construct the quadrilateral *ABCD* using a protractor, a pair of compasses, and a ruler.

(b) Measure the lengths of *AD* and *CD*.

(c) Draw a net of the prism.

(d) Find the volume of the prism.

(e) Find its total surface area.

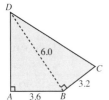

Solution

(a)

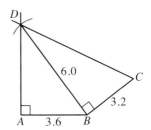

Construction Steps:
1. Draw a line segment *AB* 3.6 cm long.
2. Draw a line from *A* and perpendicular to *AB*.
3. With *B* as center and radius 6.0 cm, draw an arc to cut the ray at *D*.
4. Draw the line segment *BD*.
5. Draw *BC* 3.2 cm long and perpendicular to *BD*.
6. Draw the line segment *CD*.
7. Then *ABCD* is the required quadrilateral.

(b) Length of *AD* = 4.8 cm
Length of *CD* = 6.8 cm

(c)

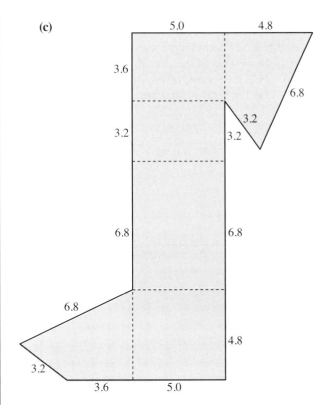

(d) Area of $ABCD = \frac{1}{2} \times 3.6 \times 4.8 + \frac{1}{2} \times 6.0 \times 3.2$
$$= 18.24 \text{ cm}^2$$
Volume of the prism $= 18.24 \times 5.0$
$$= 91.2 \text{ cm}^3$$

(e) Perimeter of $ABCD = 3.6 + 3.2 + 6.8 + 4.8$
$$= 18.4 \text{ cm}$$
Total surface area of the prism
$$= 18.4 \times 5.0 + 2 \times 18.24$$
$$= 128.48 \text{ cm}^2$$

6. The figure shows the cross-section of a solid metal prism of height 20 cm.

(a) Find the volume of the prism.

(b) If the prism is melted and recast into a cuboid of length 30 cm and width 16 cm, find the height of the cuboid.

(c) If the prism is melted and recast into a cube, find the length of a side of the cube.

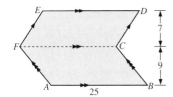

Solution

(a) Area of the cross-section
= 25 × 9 + 25 × 7
= 400 cm²
Volume of the prism = 400 × 20
= 8,000 cm³

(b) Let the height of the cuboid be h cm.
30 × 16 × h = 8,000
h = 16.67   (correct to 2 d.p.)
The height of the cuboid is 16.67 cm.

(c) Length of a side of the cube = $\sqrt[3]{8,000}$
= 20 cm

7. The figure shows a cabinet whose uniform cross-section is a triangle *CDE* on a rectangle *ABCE*. *AB* = 60 cm, *AE* = 90 cm, *DN* = 40 cm, *DC* = *DE* = 50 cm, and *BG* = 40 cm. Find
(a) the perimeter of the cross-section,
(b) the area of the cross-section,
(c) the surface area of the cabinet, not including the bottom area in contact with the floor,
  (i) in square centimeters,
  (ii) in square meters,
(d) the volume of the cabinet
  (i) in cubic centimeters,
  (ii) in cubic meters.

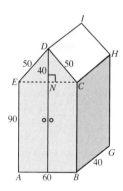

Solution

(a) Perimeter of the cross-section
= 60 + 90 + 50 + 50 + 90
= 340 cm

(b) Area of the cross-section
= 60 × 90 + $\frac{1}{2}$ × 60 × 40
= 6,600 cm²

(c) **(i)** Surface area of the cabinet
= (90 + 50 + 50 + 90) × 40 + 2 × 6,600
= 24,400 cm²

(ii) Surface area of the cabinet
= $\frac{24,400}{10,000}$ m²
= 2.44 m²

(d) **(i)** Volume of the cabinet
= 6,600 × 40
= 264,000 cm³

(ii) Volume of the cabinet
= $\frac{24,400}{10,000}$ m³
= 0.264 m³

8. In the figure, a triangular prism *CMNGPQ* is cut off from a cuboid *ABCDEFGH*. *AB* = 6 cm, *AD* = 8 cm, *BF* = 10 cm, *M* and *N* are the midpoints of *BC* and *CD* respectively.
(a) Find the volume of the cuboid.
(b) Find the volume of the triangular prism.
(c) Find the volume of the remaining prism.
(d) Find the percentage decrease in the volume of the cuboid due to the removal of the triangular prism.
(e) Is the total surface area of the remaining prism greater than that of the cuboid? Explain briefly.

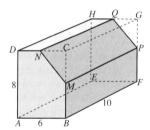

Solution

(a) Volume of the cuboid = 6 × 8 × 10
= 480 cm³

(b) Area of △*CNM* = $\frac{1}{2}$ × 4 × 3
= 6 cm²
Volume of the triangular prism = 6 × 10
= 60 cm³

(c) Volume of the remaining prism = 480 – 60
= 420 cm³

(d) Percentage decrease in volume = $\frac{60}{480}$ × 100%
= 12.5%

(e) Since *CN* + *CM* > *NM*, the surface area of the remaining prism is NOT greater than that of the cuboid.

9. The figure shows an open wooden box. Its external length, width, and height are 25 cm, 22 cm, and 20 cm respectively. The thickness of the wood is 2 cm. Find
   (a) the volume of wood used in making the box,
   (b) the total surface area of the box.

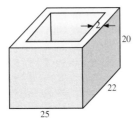

Solution
(a) External volume of the box
   $= 25 \times 22 \times 20$
   $= 11,000 \text{ cm}^3$

   Internal volume of the box
   $= 21 \times 18 \times 18$
   $= 6,804 \text{ cm}^3$

   Volume of wood used
   $= 11,000 - 6,804$
   $= 4,196 \text{ cm}^3$

(b) Total surface area of the box
   = Total surface area of a closed box with external dimensions + Sum of the areas of the 4 internal side walls
   $= 2 \times (25 \times 22 + 25 \times 20 + 20 \times 22) +$
   $\quad 2 \times (21 + 18) \times 18$
   $= 4,384 \text{ cm}^2$

10. The figure shows an open water container whose uniform cross-section is a rectangle *ABDE* on a triangle *BCD*. The length of the container is 13 cm.
   (a) Draw a net of the prism.
   (b) Find the total outer surface area and the volume of the container.
   (c) If water flows at a rate of 14 cm³/s into the empty water container, how many minutes will it take to fill the container completely?

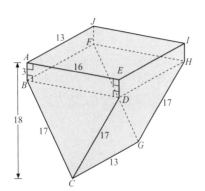

Solution
(a)

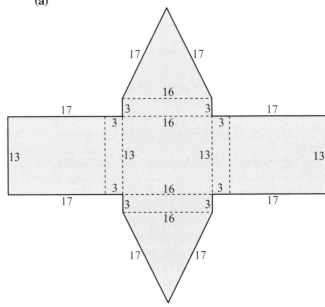

(b) Area of the cross-section *ABCDE*
   $= 16 \times 3 + \frac{1}{2} \times 16 \times 15$
   $= 168 \text{ cm}^2$
   Total outer surface area of the container
   $= (3 + 17 + 17 + 3) \times 13 + 2 \times 168$
   $= 856 \text{ cm}^2$
   Volume of the container
   $= 168 \times 13$
   $= 2,184 \text{ cm}^3$

(c) Required time $= \dfrac{2,184}{14}$
   $= 156 \text{ s}$
   $= 2.6 \text{ min}$
   It will take 2.6 minutes to fill the container completely.

Chapter 14   Proportions

Class Activity 1

Objective: To understand the idea of direct proportion.

Questions

The following table shows the relationship between the number of books bought (x) and the total cost of the books ($\$y$).

Number of books (x)	1	2	3	4	5	6
Total cost ($\$y$)	5	10	15	20	25	30

(a)   Copy and complete the following table.

x	1	2	3	4	5	6
y	5	10	15	20	25	30
$\dfrac{y}{x}$	5	5	5	5	5	5

(b)   On a sheet of graph paper, plot the corresponding points (x, y) in **(a)** using the scale for both axes as shown.

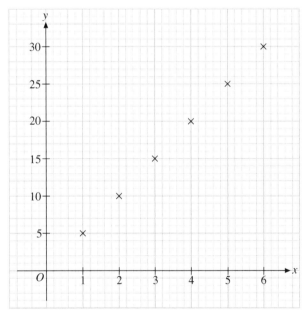

(c)   What can you say about the points you have plotted in **(b)**?

The points are on a straight line.

(d)   Write down an equation connecting x and y.

$y = 5x$

(e)   What is the value of y when $x = 8$?

When $x = 8$, $y = 5 \times 8 = 40$.

(f)   Does the graph of the equation in **(d)** pass through the origin $(0, 0)$?

Yes.

Class Activity 2

Objective: To understand the idea of inverse proportion between two quantities.

Questions

A fixed amount of water is poured into individual containers of various uniform cross-sections. The following table shows the correspondence between the cross-sectional area (x cm^2) of each container and the depth of water (y cm) in it.

Cross-sectional area (x cm^2)	10	20	30	40	50	60
Depth of water (y cm)	36	18	12	9	7.2	6

(a) Copy and complete the following table. Give the values of $\frac{1}{x}$ correct to 3 decimal places.

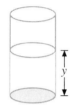

x	10	20	30	40	50	60
y	36	18	12	9	7.2	6
$\frac{1}{x}$	0.1	0.05	0.033	0.025	0.02	0.017
xy	360	360	360	360	360	360

(b) On a sheet of graph paper, plot the corresponding points (x, y) in **(a)** using the scales for both axes as shown below.

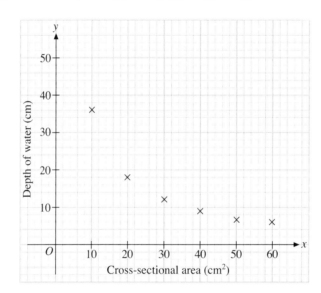

(c) What can you say about the points you have plotted in **(b)**?

The points can be joined to form a curve such that y decreases when x increases.

(d) What happens to the depth of the water as the cross-sectional area of a container increases?

When the cross-sectional area of the container increases, the depth of water decreases.

(e) On a sheet of graph paper, plot the corresponding points $\left(\dfrac{1}{x}, y\right)$ in **(a)** using the scales for both axes as shown below.

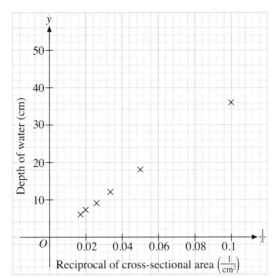

(f) What can you say about the points you have plotted in **(e)**?

The points lie on a straight line that passes through the origin. In other words, $\dfrac{y}{\frac{1}{x}}$ is a constant or $y = k\left(\dfrac{1}{x}\right)$, where k is a constant

In this case, $k = 360$.

(g) Suggest an equation connecting x and y.

$xy = 360$ or $y = \dfrac{360}{x}$

(h) What is the value of y when $x = 80$?

When $x = 80$, $y = \dfrac{360}{80} = 4.5$.

Discuss

Page 116

In this case, the scale drawing is an enlarged drawing of the actual object. Notice that the scale $1 : n$ is $1 : \dfrac{1}{2}$, that is $n = \dfrac{1}{2}$.

What can you say about the value of n? What will be the value of n if the scale drawing is a reduced drawing of the actual object?

n is smaller than 1.
For a reduced drawing, n will be greater than 1.

Page 118

In **(b)**, can we first find the area in cm^2, then multiply it by 50, and finally convert it to m^2? Explain your answers.

No. Area in the diagram : Actual area = 1 : (50 × 50) = 1 : 250, so we should multiply area by 250 instead.

1. Do you know why the numerator of a scale is usually 1?

To make it easier for the reader to calculate the actual value

2. If 1 cm on the map represents 20,000 cm on the ground, how many meters on the ground would 1 mm on the map represent?

Actual distance = $\frac{1}{10}$ × 20,000 cm = 2,000 cm = 20 m

Page 129

In the graph in Class Activity 1,

(a) what is the slope of the straight line?

5

(b) what does the slope represent?

The slope represents the increase in total price for every additional book purchased.

Page 137

In the equation $xy = 360$, what does 360 represent?

The constant value of the product of x and y

Page 141

Do you expect the intensity to be greater when the distance is less? Check to see if the answer is reasonable.

Yes.

Extend Your Learning Curve

Time Taken By A Planet To Revolve Around The Sun

In our solar system, planets revolve around the Sun in orbits. The shape of each orbit is an ellipse. This means the distance between a planet and the Sun is not a constant. The mean distance of a planet from the Sun is an average distance. The period of a planet is the time it takes to complete one orbit.

The following table gives the mean distance ($d \times 10^6$ km) and the period (p years) of the eight planets.

Planet	Mercury	Venus	Earth	Mars	Jupiter	Saturn	Uranus	Neptune
Mean distance ($d \times 10^6$ km)	57.91	108.21	149.60	227.94	778.41	1,426.73	2,870.97	4,498.25
Period (p years)	0.241	0.615	1.0	1.88	11.86	29.46	84.01	164.79

An astronomer found that d^m and p^n, where m and n are certain positive integers, have a proportional relationship. What is this relationship?

Suggested Answer:

Students are encouraged to explore the relationship between the mean distance and the period using a spreadsheet program.

Kepler's Third Law states that d^3 and p^2 are in direct proportion.

Try It!

Section 14.1

1. Express each of the following scales in the form $1 : n$.
   (a) 1 in. : 50 yd
   (b) 2 cm : 70 m
   (c) 1 ft : 3 in.

Solution
(a) 1 in. : 50 yd
$$= 1 \text{ in.} : 50 \times 3 \text{ ft}$$
$$= 1 \text{ in.} : 50 \times 3 \times 12 \text{ in.}$$
$$= 1 \text{ in.} : 1,800 \text{ in.}$$
$$= 1 : 1,800$$

(b) 2 cm : 70 m $= 2 \text{ cm} : 70 \times 100 \text{ cm}$
$$= 2 \text{ cm} : 7,000 \text{ cm}$$
$$= 1 : 3,500$$

(c) 1 ft : 3 in. $= 12 \text{ in.} : 3 \text{ in.}$
$$= 12 : 3$$
$$= \frac{12}{12} : \frac{3}{12}$$
$$= 1 : \frac{1}{4}$$

2. A tennis court measures 24 m by 11 m. It is represented by a rectangle 22 cm wide on a plan. Find
   (a) the scale of the plan,
   (b) the length of the rectangle on the plan.

Solution
(a) Scale of the plan $= 22 \text{ cm} : 11 \text{ m}$
$$= 22 \text{ cm} : 1,100 \text{ cm}$$
$$= 1 : 50$$

(b) Length of the rectangle on the plan
$$= 24 \times \frac{1}{50} \text{ m}$$
$$= 0.48 \text{ m}$$
$$= 48 \text{ cm}$$

3. The diagram shows a floor plan of a bathroom which is drawn to a scale of 1 : 40. The dimensions of the bathroom in the plan are 6 cm by 5 cm. Find the actual
   (a) dimensions of the bathroom in m,
   (b) area of the bathroom in m^2.

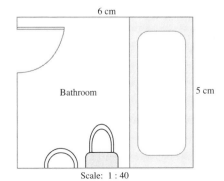

Scale: 1 : 40

Solution
(a) Actual length of the bathroom $= 6 \times 40 \text{ cm}$
$$= 240 \text{ cm}$$
$$= 2.4 \text{ m}$$
Actual width of the bathroom $= 5 \times 40 \text{ cm}$
$$= 200 \text{ cm}$$
$$= 2 \text{ m}$$

(b) Actual area of the bathroom $= 24 \times 2$
$$= 4.8 \text{ m}^2$$

4. A rectangular living room $PQRS$ has length $PQ = 9$ m and width $QR = 7.5$ m. A cable runs from P to the midpoint M of PQ, and then runs from M to the corner R.
   (a) Draw a plan of the living room, using a scale of 1 : 150.
   (b) Measure MR on the plan, correct to the nearest 0.1 cm.
   (c) Hence, estimate the length of the cable, correct to the nearest meter.

Solution
(a) Length of the living room on the plan
$$= 9 \times \frac{1}{150} \text{ m}$$
$$= 0.06 \text{ m}$$
$$= 6 \text{ cm}$$
Width of the living room on the plan
$$= 7.5 \times \frac{1}{150} \text{ m}$$
$$= 0.05 \text{ m}$$
$$= 5 \text{ cm}$$
Hence, the plan of the living room can be drawn as shown below.

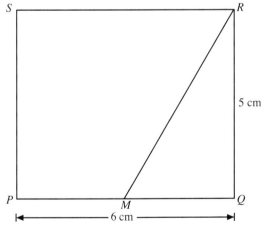

Scale: 1 : 150

(b) By measurement, MR on the plan $= 5.8$ cm
(correct to 0.1 cm)

(c) Actual length of the cable
$$= PM + MR$$
$$= (3 + 5.8) \times 150 \text{ cm}$$
$$= 1,320 \text{ cm}$$
$$= 13.2 \text{ m}$$
$$= 13 \text{ m} \quad \text{(correct to the nearest meter)}$$

Section 14.2

5. A distance of 4 in. on a map represents an actual distance of 5 mi.

  (a) Express the scale of the map in the form $\dfrac{1}{r}$.

  (b) If the distance between two cafes on the map is 6 in., find the actual distance between the two cafes.

  (c) What is the distance between two supermarkets on the map when their actual distance apart is 6 mi?

Solution

(a) Map scale
  = 4 in. : 5 mi
  = 4 in. : 5 × 12 × 5,280 in.   1 mi = 5,280 ft
  = 4 in. : 316,800 in.
  = 1 : 79,200
  The scale of the map is $\dfrac{1}{79,200}$.

(b) Actual distance between the two cafes
  = 6 × 79,200 in.
  = 475,200 in.
  = $\dfrac{475,000}{12 \times 5,280}$ mi
  = 7.5 mi

(c) Distance between the supermarkets on the map
  = $\dfrac{6}{79,200}$ mi
  = $\dfrac{6}{79,200} \times 12 \times 5,280$ in.
  = 4.8 in.

6. The scale of a map is 1 : 40,000. A rectangular field is 3 cm by 2 cm on the map.

  (a) Find the actual area of the field in km^2.

  (b) If the actual area of the region that is covered with bush is 2 km^2, find its area on the map in cm^2.

Solution

(a) Scale of the map = 1 : 40,000
  = 1 cm : 40,000 cm
  = 1 cm : 0.4 km

  $\dfrac{\text{Area on the map}}{\text{Actual area}} = \dfrac{1 \ cm^2}{0.4^2 \ km^2}$

  $= \dfrac{1 \ cm^2}{0.16 \ km^2}$

  $= 1 \ cm^2 : 0.16 \ km^2$

  Actual area of the field = $(3 \times 2) \times 0.16 \ km^2$
  = 0.96 km^2

(b) Area on the map = $\dfrac{2}{0.16}$
  = 12.5 cm^2

Section 14.3

7. The following table shows the number of hours (t) worked and the corresponding wages ($\$w$) of a worker.

Number of hours worked (t)	10	20	30	40	50
Wages ($\$w$)	150	300	450	600	750

  (a) Show that t and w are in direct proportion.

  (b) Draw the graph of w against t.

  (c) Find the equation connecting t and w.

  (d) If the worker worked 35 hours, find his wages.

  (e) If the wages of a worker were $675, find the number of hours he worked.

Solution

(a) Since $\dfrac{1}{w} = \dfrac{1}{15}$ for all pairs of values of t and w in the table, t and w are in direct proportion.

(b) The graph of w against t is shown below.

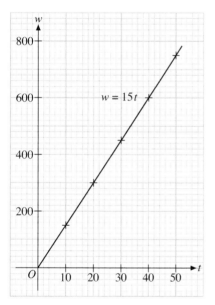

(c) $\dfrac{1}{w} = \dfrac{1}{15}$
  $\therefore \ w = 15t$

(d) When $t = 35$,
  $w = 15 \times 35$
  $= 525$
  His wages was $525.

(e) When $w = 675$,
  $675 = 15$
  $t = \dfrac{675}{15}$
  $= 45$
  He worked 45 hours.

8. The number of pieces, n, of chocolate and their total mass, M grams, are in direct proportion. The mass of 15 pieces of chocolate is 180 g. Find the mass in grams of 20 pieces of chocolate.

Solution

$$\frac{n_1}{M_1} = \frac{n_2}{M_2}$$

When $n_1 = 15$, $M_1 = 180$, $n_2 = 20$,

$$\frac{15}{180} = \frac{20}{M_2}$$

$$M_2 = 20 \times \frac{180}{15}$$

$$= 240$$

∴ the mass of 20 pieces of chocolate is 240 g.

9. The mass of a square piece of glass panel is directly proportional to the square of the length of its side. When its side is 20 cm, the mass is 1,000 g. Find the mass in grams of a glass panel of side 30 cm.

Solution

Let the mass of a glass panel of side x cm be y grams.
Then $y = kx^2$, where k is a constant.

When $x = 20$, $y = 1,000$,
$$1,000 = k \times 20^2$$
$$k = 2.5$$

When $x = 30$,
$$y = 2.5 \times 30^2$$
$$= 2,250$$

The required mass is 2,250 g.

Section 14.4

10. The following table shows the corresponding volume (V cm^3) of air inside a syringe when the air pressure is P units.

Pressure (P units)	1	2	3	4	5	6
Volume (V cm³)	120	60	40	30	24	20

(a) Show that P and V are in inverse proportion.

(b) Draw the graph of V against P.

(c) Draw the graph of V against $\frac{1}{p}$.

(d) Find the equation connecting P and V.

(e) Find the volume of air when the air pressure is 8 units.

Solution

(a) Since $PV = 120$ for all pairs of values of P and V in the table, P and V are in inverse proportion.

(b) The diagram below shows the graph of V against P.

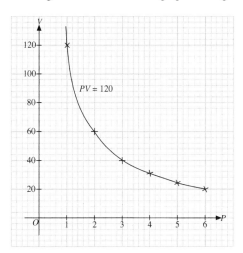

(c)

P	1	2	3	4	5	6
V	120	60	40	30	24	20
$\frac{1}{p}$	1	0.5	0.33	0.25	0.2	0.17

The diagram below shows the graph of V against $\frac{1}{p}$.

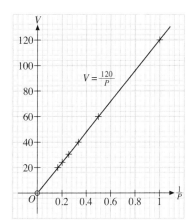

(d) The equation connecting P and V is $PV = 120$ or $V = \frac{120}{p}$.

(e) When $P = 8$,
$$8V = 120$$
$$V = 15$$
The volume of air is 15 cm^3.

11. A big bottle of orange juice is shared equally among n boys. Each boy drinks V cm^3 of the juice. It is known that n and V are in inverse proportion. If there are 6 boys sharing the drink, each boy has 250 cm^3 of it. How much can each boy drink when there are 10 boys?

Solution

$$n_1 V_1 = n_2 V_2$$

When $n_1 = 6$, $V_1 = 250$, $n_2 = 10$,

$$6 \times 250 = 10 V_2$$
$$V_2 = 150$$

Each boy can drink 150 cm^3 of orange juice.

12. When a fixed amount of water is poured into a cylinder, the depth of water is inversely proportional to the square of the base radius of the cylinder. When the radius is 3 in., the depth of water is 24 in. Find the depth when the radius is 6 in.

Solution

Let the depth of water be d in. and the base radius of the cylinder be r in.

Then $dr^2 = k$, where k is a constant.

When $r = 3$, $d = 24$,

$$24 \times 3^2 = k$$
$$k = 216$$

When $r = 6$, $d \times 6^2 = 216$

$$36d = 216$$
$$d = 6$$

The required depth is 6 in.

Exercise 14.1

Basic Practice

1. Express each of the following scales in the form 1 : n.
   (a) 1 in. : 20 ft   (b) 1 cm : 200 m
   (c) 1 ft : 2 in.   (d) 5 cm : 20 m

   Solution
   (a) 1 in : 20 ft
        = 1 in. : 20 × 12 in.
        = 1 in. : 240 in.
        = 1 : 240
   (b) 1 cm : 200 m
        = 1 cm : 200 × 100 cm
        = 1 cm : 20,000 cm
        = 1 : 20,000
   (c) 1 ft : 2 in.
        = 12 in. : 2 in.
        = 12 : 2
        = 1 : $\frac{1}{6}$
   (d) 5 cm : 20 m
        = 5 cm : 20 × 100 cm
        = 5 cm : 2,000 cm
        = 5 : 2,000
        = 1 : 400

2. On a scale drawing, 100 ft is represented by 3 in.
   (a) Find the scale of the drawing in the form 1 : n.
   (b) What is the actual length of a wall if its length is 1.8 in. on the drawing?

   Solution
   (a) Scale of the drawing = 3 in. : 100 ft
        = 3 in. : 100 × 12 in.
        = 3 : 1,200
        = 1 : 400
   (b) Actual length = 1.8 × 400 in.
        = 720 in.
        = 60 ft

3. The scale of a drawing is 5 cm to 30 m.
   (a) Find the scale of the drawing in the form 1 : n.
   (b) If a building is 75 m tall, find its height on the drawing.

   Solution
   (a) Scale of the drawing = 5 cm : 30 m
        = 5 cm : 3,000 cm
        = 1 : 600

   (b) Height of the building on the drawing
        = 75 × $\frac{1}{600}$ m
        = 0.125 m
        = 12.5 cm

4. On a scale drawing of insects, a beetle is drawn 7.5 cm long when its actual length is 1.5 cm.
   (a) Find the scale of the drawing in the form 1 : n.
   (b) If the actual length of a beetle is 5 cm, find its length on the drawing.

   Solution
   (a) Scale of the drawing = 7.5 cm : 1.5 cm
        = 5 : 1
        = 1 : $\frac{1}{5}$

   (b) Length of the beetle on the drawing
        = 5 × 5 cm
        = 25 cm

Further Practice

5. The scale used for drawing a plant is 2 : 1.
   (a) The diameter of a flower is 3 inches. What is its diameter on the drawing?
   (b) The length of a leaf on the same drawing is 7 inches. What is the actual length of the leaf?

   Solution
   (a) Diameter of the flower on the drawing
        = 3 × $\frac{2}{1}$ in.
        = 6 in.

   (b) Actual length of the leaf = 7 × $\frac{1}{2}$ in.
        = 3.5 in.

6. The scale of a car drawing is 1 : 20. The actual length and width of the car are 4.5 m and 1.75 m respectively. Find the length and width of the car on the drawing, in centimeters.

   Solution
   Length of the car on the drawing = 4.5 × $\frac{1}{20}$ m
        = 0.225 m
        = 22.5 cm

   Width of the car on the drawing = 1.75 × $\frac{1}{20}$ m
        = 0.0875 m
        = 8.75 cm

7. The length of a room on a drawing with scale 1 : 50 is 9.2 cm. If the scale is changed to 1 : 40, what is the length of the room on the new drawing?

Solution
Actual length of the room = 9.2 × 50 cm
$$= 460 \text{ cm}$$
If the scale is 1 : 40,
length of the room on drawing = $460 \times \dfrac{1}{40}$ cm
$$= 11.5 \text{ cm}$$

Math@Work

8. The Fountain of Wealth in Suntec City, Singapore, is supposedly the world's largest fountain that is made of bronze as recorded in the 1998 edition of the Guinness Book of Records. Four 13.8 m bronze legs support a huge bronze ring measuring 21 m in diameter. On a design drawing, each leg is 27.6 cm high. Find
  (a) the scale of the drawing in the form 1 : n,
  (b) the diameter of the ring on the drawing.

Solution
(a) Scale of the drawing = 27.6 cm : 13.8 m
$$= 27.6 : 1,380$$
$$= 1 : 50$$
(b) Diameter of the ring on the drawing
$$= 21 \times \dfrac{1}{50} \text{ m}$$
$$= 0.42 \text{ m}$$
$$= 42 \text{ cm}$$

9. The diameter of the face of a watch is 36 mm and the length of its minute-hand is 11 mm. On a scale drawing, the diameter of the watch is 180 mm. Find
  (a) the scale of the drawing in the form 1 : n,
  (b) the length of the minute-hand on the drawing.

Solution
(a) Scale of the drawing = 180 mm : 36 mm
$$= 5 : 1$$
$$= 1 : \dfrac{1}{5}$$
(b) Length of the minute-hand on the drawing
$$= 11 \times 5 \text{ mm}$$
$$= 55 \text{ mm}$$

10. The diagram shows a floor plan of an apartment. The scale of the plan is 1 : 200.
  (a) Find the actual dimensions, in meters, of
    (i) Bedroom 1,
    (ii) the kitchen.

(b) Find the actual area, in square meters, of
  (i) the apartment,
  (ii) the living room.

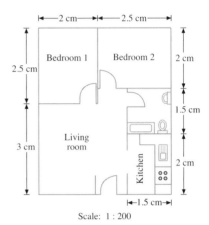

Scale: 1 : 200

Solution
(a) **(i)** For Bedroom 1,
actual length = 2.5 × 200 cm
$$= 500 \text{ cm}$$
$$= 5 \text{ m}$$
actual width = 2 × 200 cm
$$= 400 \text{ cm}$$
$$= 4 \text{ m}$$

(ii) For the kitchen,
actual length = 2 × 200 cm
$$= 400 \text{ cm}$$
$$= 4 \text{ m}$$
actual width = 1.5 × 200 cm
$$= 300 \text{ cm}$$
$$= 3 \text{ m}$$

(b) **(i)** For the apartment,
actual length = (3 + 2.5) × 200 cm
$$= 1,100 \text{ cm}$$
$$= 11 \text{ m}$$
actual width = (2 + 2.5) × 200 cm
$$= 900 \text{ cm}$$
$$= 9 \text{ m}$$
∴ actual area = 11 × 9
$$= 99 \text{ m}^2$$

(ii) For the living room,
actual length = 3 × 200 cm
$$= 600 \text{ cm}$$
$$= 6 \text{ m}$$
actual width = (4.5 − 1.5) × 200 cm
$$= 600 \text{ cm}$$
$$= 6 \text{ m}$$
∴ actual area = 6 × 6
$$= 36 \text{ m}^2$$

Brainworks

11. (a) Measure the dimensions of your classroom and of the structures like the doors and windows in the room.

(b) Choose a suitable scale such that the floor plan of your classroom can be drawn to fit on an entire sheet of letter-size paper.

(c) Draw the floor plan of your classroom on the sheet of paper.

Solution

The floor plan of your classroom depends on the dimensions of your classroom. A suitable scale may be 1 : 50 or 1 : 100.

Exercise 14.2
Basic Practice

1. Express each map scale in the form 1 : r.

(a) 1 in. : 5,000 yd   **(b)** 0.5 in. : 3 mi

(c) 3 cm : 900 m   **(d)** 5 cm : 20 km

Solution

(a) Map scale = 1 in. : 5,000 yd
$$= 1 \text{ in.} : 5{,}000 \times 3 \times 12 \text{ in.}$$
$$= 1 : 180{,}000$$

(b) Map scale = 0.5 in. : 3 mi
$$= 0.5 \text{ in.} : 3 \times 5{,}280 \times 12 \text{ in.}$$
$$= 0.5 : 190{,}080$$
$$= 1 : 380{,}160$$

(c) Map scale = 3 cm : 900 m
$$= 3 \text{ cm} : 90{,}000 \text{ cm}$$
$$= 1 : 30{,}000$$

(d) Map scale = 5 cm : 20 km
$$= 5 \text{ cm} : 20 \times 1{,}000 \times 100 \text{ cm}$$
$$= 1 : 400{,}000$$

2. Express each map scale in the form $\dfrac{1}{r}$.

(a) 1 in. : 1 mi   **(b)** 2 in. : 5 mi

(c) 4 cm : 1 km   **(d)** 7 cm : 28 km

Solution

(a) Map scale = 1 in. : 1 mi
$$= 1 \text{ in.} : 5{,}280 \times 12 \text{ in.}$$
$$= \frac{1}{63{,}360}$$

(b) Map scale = 2 in. : 5 mi
$$= 2 \text{ in.} : 5 \times 5{,}280 \times 12 \text{ in.}$$
$$= \frac{1}{158{,}400}$$

(c) Map scale = 4 cm : 1 km
$$= 4 \text{ cm} : 1{,}000 \times 100 \text{ cm}$$
$$= \frac{1}{25{,}000}$$

(d) Map scale = 7 cm : 28 km
$$= 7 \text{ cm} : 28 \times 1{,}000 \times 100 \text{ cm}$$
$$= \frac{1}{400{,}000}$$

3. Study the map of Ubin Island below.

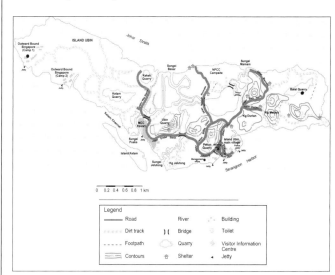

(a) Express the scale of the map in the form $\dfrac{1}{r}$.

(b) What is the actual direct distance between Outward Bound Singapore (Camp 1) and Balai Quarry?

Solution

(a) Map scale = 2 cm : 1 km
$$= 2 \text{ cm} : 1{,}000 \times 100 \text{ cm}$$
$$= 1 : 50{,}000$$
$$= \frac{1}{50{,}000}$$

(b) Distance on the map = 12 cm
Actual distance = 12 × 50,000 cm
$$= 600{,}000 \text{ cm}$$
$$= 6 \text{ km}$$
The actual direct distance between Outward Bound Singapore (Camp 1) and Balai Quarry is 6 km.

4. (a) The scale of a road map is 1 : 5,000. How many meters is a distance 7 cm on the map?

(b) Another road map has a scale of 1 : 63,360. How many miles is a distance of 7 in. on this map?

Solution

(a) Actual distance = 7 × 5,000 cm
= 35,000 cm
= 350 m

(b) Actual distance = 7 × 63,360 in.
= 443,520 in.
$$= \frac{443,520}{12 \times 5,280} \text{ mi}$$
= 7 mi

5. The scale of a district map is $\frac{1}{10,000}$. Find the distance on the map, in centimeters, for each of the following actual distances.

(a) 800 m   **(b)** 5 km

Solution

(a) Distance on the map = $800 \times \frac{1}{10,000}$ m
= 0.08 m
= 8 cm

(b) Distance on the map = $5 \times \frac{1}{10,000}$ km
$$= 5 \times \frac{1,000 \times 100}{10,000} \text{ cm}$$
= 50 cm

6. The scale of a detailed map is 1 : 2,000. Find the actual area, in m², for each of the following areas on the map.

(a) 1 cm²   **(b)** 5 cm²

Solution

(a) Map scale = 1 : 2,000
= 1 cm : 2,000 cm
= 1 cm : 20 m
Area on the map : Actual area = 1 cm² : 20² m²
= 1 cm² : 400 m²
Actual area = 400 m²

(b) Actual area = 5 × 400 m²
= 2,000 m²

7. The scale of a city map is 1 : 50,000. Find the area on the map, in cm², for each of the following actual areas.

(a) 1 km²   **(b)** 15 km²

Solution

(a) Map scale = 1 : 50,000
= 1 cm : 50,000 cm
= 1 cm : 0.5 km
Area on the map : Actual area = 1 cm² : 0.5² km²
= 1 cm² : 0.25 km²
Area on the map = $\frac{1}{0.25}$ cm²
= 4 cm²

(b) Area on the map = 4 × 15 cm²
= 60 cm²

Further Practice

8. An actual ground distance of 6 km is represented by a distance of 2 cm on a map.

(a) Express the scale of the map in the form $\frac{1}{r}$.

(b) If the distance between two banks on the map is 5 cm, find their actual distance apart in kilometers.

Solution

(a) Map scale = 2 cm : 6 km
$$= \frac{2 \text{ cm}}{6 \text{ km}}$$
$$= \frac{2 \text{ cm}}{6 \times 1,000 \times 100 \text{ cm}}$$
$$= \frac{1}{300,000}$$

(b) Actual distance apart = 5 × 300,000 cm
$$= 5 \times \frac{300,000}{1,000 \times 100} \text{ km}$$
= 15 km

9. Suppose that 3 cm on a map represents 1.2 km on the ground.

(a) Express the scale of the map in the form 1 : r.

(b) If the area of a lake is 0.32 km², what is its area on the map in cm²?

Solution

(a) Map scale = 3 cm : 1.2 km
= 3 cm : 1.2 × 1,000 × 100 cm
= 3 cm : 120,000 cm
= 1 : 40,000

(b) Map scale = 1 cm : 0.4 km
Area on the map : Actual area = 1 cm² : 0.4² km²
= 1 cm² : 0.16 km²
Area on the map = $\frac{0.32}{0.16}$ cm²
= 2 cm²

10. A map is drawn to a scale of $1 : 316,800$.
- **(a)** How many miles is a distance of 5 in. on this map?
- **(b)** What area, in square inches, on the map would represent a nature reserve of area 50 square miles?

Solution
- **(a)** Actual distance $= 5 \times 316,800$ in.
$$= \frac{5 \times 316,800}{12 \times 5,280} \text{ mi}$$
$$= 25 \text{ mi}$$

- **(b)** Map scale $= 1 : 316,800$
$$= 1 \text{ in.} : 316,800 \text{ in.}$$
$$= 1 \text{ in.} : 5 \text{ mi}$$
Area on the map : Actual area
$$= 1 \text{ in.}^2 : 5^2 \text{ mi}^2$$
$$= 1 \text{ in.}^2 : 25 \text{ mi}^2$$
Area on the map $= \dfrac{50}{25} \text{ in.}^2$
$$= 2 \text{ in.}^2$$

11. A street 250 yd long is represented by a distance of 6 in. on a map.
- **(a)** Express the scale of the map in the form $1 : r$.
- **(b)** What is the distance on the map that represents another street which is 400 yd long?
- **(c)** Find the actual area of a park, in square feet, if its area on the map is 0.6 in.^{2}

Solution
- **(a)** Map scale $= 6 \text{ in.} : 250 \text{ yd}$
$$= 6 \text{ in.} : 250 \times 3 \times 12 \text{ in.}$$
$$= 6 \text{ in.} : 9,000 \text{ in.}$$
$$= 1 : 1,500$$

- **(b)** Distance on the map $= 400 \times \dfrac{1}{1,500} \text{ yd}$
$$= 400 \times \dfrac{3 \times 12}{1,500} \text{ in.}$$
$$= 9.6 \text{ in.}$$

- **(c)** Map scale $= 6 \text{ in.} : 250 \text{ yd}$
$$= 6 \text{ in.} : 750 \text{ ft}$$
$$= 1 \text{ in.} : 125 \text{ ft}$$
Area on the map : Actual area $= 1 \text{ in.}^2 : 125^2 \text{ ft}^2$
$$= 1 \text{ in.}^2 : 15,625 \text{ ft}^2$$
Actual area $= 0.6 \times 15,625 \text{ ft}^2$
$$= 9,375 \text{ ft}^2$$

Math@Work

12. An actual region of area 18 km^2 is represented by an area of 2 cm^2 on a map.
- **(a)** Express the scale of the map in the form $\dfrac{1}{r}$.
- **(b)** If the area of a farm is 0.25 cm^2 on the map, find its ground area in km^2.

Solution
- **(a)** Area on the map : Actual area $= 2 \text{ cm}^2 : 18 \text{ km}^2$
$$= 1 \text{ cm}^2 : 9 \text{ km}^2$$
Map scale $= 1 \text{ cm} : \sqrt{9} \text{ km}$
$$= 1 \text{ cm} : 3 \text{ km}$$
$$= 1 \text{ cm} : 3 \times 1,000 \times 100 \text{ cm}$$
$$= \dfrac{1}{300,000}$$

- **(b)** Ground area $= 0.25 \times 9 \text{ km}^2$
$$= 2.25 \text{ km}^2$$

13. The figure shows a piece of land in which $AB = 45$ m, $BC = 24$ m, and $AD = 16$ m.

- **(a)** Find the area of the land.
- **(b)** Find the length of AB and the area of the land on a map if the scale of the map is
  - **(i)** 1 cm to 5 m,
  - **(ii)** $1 : 200$,
  - **(iii)** $\dfrac{1}{2,500}$.

Solution
- **(a)** Area of the land $= \dfrac{1}{2}(16 + 24) \times 45$
$$= 900 \text{ m}^2$$

- **(b)** **(i)** Map scale $= 1 \text{ cm} : 5 \text{ m}$
  Length of AB on the map $= 45 \div 5 \text{ cm}$
  $$= 9 \text{ cm}$$
  Area on the map : Actual area
  $$= 1 \text{ cm}^2 : 5^2 \text{ m}^2$$
  $$= 1 \text{ cm}^2 : 25 \text{ m}^2$$
  Area of the land on the map
  $$= 900 \div 25 \text{ cm}^2$$
  $$= 36 \text{ cm}^2$$

  (ii) Map scale $= 1 : 200$
  Length of AB on the map $= 45 \times \dfrac{1}{200} \text{ m}$
  $$= 0.225 \text{ m}$$
  $$= 22.5 \text{ cm}$$
  Area on the map : Actual area
  $$= 1^2 : 200^2$$
  $$= 1 : 40,000$$
  Area of the land on the map
  $$= 900 \times \dfrac{1}{40,000} \text{ m}^2$$
  $$= 0.0225 \text{ m}^2$$
  $$= 225 \text{ cm}^2$$

(iii) Map scale = $\dfrac{1}{2,500}$

Length of AB on the map $= 45 \times \dfrac{1}{2,500}$ m

$= 0.018$ m

$= 1.8$ cm

Area on the map : Actual area $= \dfrac{1}{2,500^2}$

$= \dfrac{1}{6,250,000}$

Area of the land on the map

$= 900 \times \dfrac{1}{6,250,000}$ m^2

$= 900 \times \dfrac{10,000}{6,250,000}$ cm^2

$= 1.44$ cm^2

14. The scale of a map of Asia is 1 : 25,000,000. The actual distance between Singapore and Beijing is 4,457 km. The total area of Taiwan is 36,000 km^2. Find
(a) the distance between Singapore and Beijing on the map,
(b) the total area of Taiwan on the map.
Give your answers correct to 2 decimal places.

Solution
(a) Map scale = 1 : 25,000,000
$= 1$ cm : 25,000,000 cm
$= 1$ cm : 250 km
Distance between Singapore and Beijing on the map
$= 4,457 \div 250$ cm
$= 17.83$ cm (correct to 2 d.p.)

(b) Area on the map : Actual area
$= 1$ cm^2 : 250^2 km^2
$= 1$ cm^2 : 62,500 km^2
Total area of Taiwan on the map
$= 36,000 \div 62,500$ cm^2
$= 0.576$ cm^2
$= 0.58$ cm^2 (correct to 2 d.p.)

15. The actual distance between New York City and Los Angeles is 3,935 km. The total area of Alaska is 1,717,850 km^2. A map is drawn to the scale of 1 : 15,000,000. Determine, correct to 1 decimal place,
(a) the distance between New York City and Los Angeles on the map,
(b) the total area of Alaska on the map,
(c) the actual distance between Dallas and Detroit if their distance apart on this map is 10.7 cm.

Solution
(a) Required distance on the map
$= 3,935 \times \dfrac{1}{15,000,000}$ km
$= 3,935 \times \dfrac{1,000 \times 100}{15,000,000}$ cm
$= 26.2$ cm (correct to 1 d.p.)

(b) Map scale = 1 : 15,000,000
$= 1$ cm : 15,000,000 cm
$= 1$ cm : 150 km
Area on the map : Actual area
$= 1$ cm^2 : 150^2 km^2
$= 1$ cm^2 : 22,500 km^2
Total area of Alaska on the map
$= \dfrac{1,717,850}{22,500}$ cm^2
$= 76.3$ cm^2 (correct to 1 d.p.)

(c) Actual distance between Dallas and Detroit
$= 10.7 \times 150$ km
$= 1,605$ km

Brainworks

16. California, the third largest state in the United States, has an east-west dimension of 480 km.
(a) A map of California, drawn with a scale of 1 : 1,500,000, fits exactly from north to south inside a rectangle of length 84 cm. What is the north-south dimension of California?
(b) If you sketch a map of California on a piece of paper 21 cm by 28 cm, what is an appropriate scale you would choose such that the map fits inside a rectangle with a uniform border of 1 cm around the sides of the paper?

Solution

(a) Map scale = 1 : 1,500,000

= 1 cm : 1,500,000 cm

= 1 cm : 15 km

Actual north-south dimension of California

= 84 × 15 km

= 1,260 km

(b) Actual east-west dimension of California

= 480 km

= 480 × 1,000 × 100 cm

= 48,000,000 cm

Actual north-south dimension of California

= 1,260 km

= 1,260 × 1,000 × 100 cm

= 126,000,000 cm

Let the scale of the required map be 1 : n.

We should have

$(21 - 2 \times 1)n > 48,000,000$

and $(28 - 2 \times 1)n > 126,000,000$,

i.e., $n > 2,526,315.79$ and $n > 4,846,153.85$.

Hence, one appropriate scale would be 1 : 5,000,000.

Exercise 14.3

Basic Practice

1. In each of the following tables, determine whether x and y are in direct proportion.

(a)

x	1	2	3	4
y	3	6	9	12

(b)

x	2	4	6	8
y	10	20	25	40

(c)

x	3	6	7	10
y	21	42	49	70

(d)

x	8	12	15	20
y	30	48	60	80

Solution

(a) $\frac{1}{3} = \frac{2}{6} = \frac{3}{9} = \frac{4}{12}$

∴ x and y are in direct proportion.

(b) $\frac{2}{10} \neq \frac{6}{25}$

∴ x and y are NOT in direct proportion.

(c) $\frac{3}{21} = \frac{6}{42} = \frac{7}{49} = \frac{10}{70}$

∴ x and y are in direct proportion.

(d) $\frac{8}{30} \neq \frac{12}{48}$

∴ x and y are NOT in direct proportion.

2. In each of the following graphs, determine whether x and y are in direct proportion.

(a)

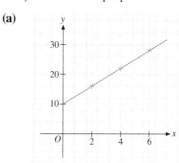

(b)

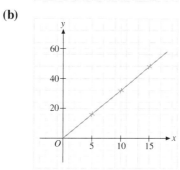

Solution

(a) The straight line graph does not pass through the origin.

∴ x and y are NOT in direct proportion.

(b) The straight line graph passes through the origin.

∴ x and y are in direct proportion.

3. In each of the following equations, determine whether x and y are in direct proportion.

(a) $y = 4x$ **(b)** $y = x + 2$

(c) $y = x^2$ **(d)** $y = \frac{1}{2}x$

Solution

(a) $y = 4x$ is in the form of $y = kx$ with $k = 4$.

∴ x and y are in direct proportion.

(b) $y = x + 2$ cannot be written as $y = kx$.

∴ x and y are NOT in direct proportion.

(c) $y = x^2$ cannot be written as $y = kx$.

∴ x and y are NOT in direct proportion.

(d) $y = \frac{1}{2}x$ is in the form of $y = kx$ with $k = \frac{1}{2}$.

∴ x and y are in direct proportion.

4. If two quantities, x and y, are in direct proportion, find the values of p and q in the following table.

x	12	18	q
y	8	p	24

Solution

$$\frac{12}{8} = \frac{18}{p}$$

$$\therefore p = 18 \times \frac{8}{12}$$

$$= 12$$

$$\frac{12}{8} = \frac{n}{24}$$

$$q = 24 \times \frac{12}{8}$$

$$= 36$$

5. It is given that w is directly proportional to t. When $t = 4$, $w = 20$. Find
(a) the value of w when $t = 6$,
(b) the value of t when $w = 45$.

Solution
(a) Let $w = kt$, where k is a constant.
When $t = 4$, $w = 20$.
$$20 = k \times 4$$
$$k = 5$$
$$w = 5t$$
When $t = 6$,
$$w = 5 \times 6$$
$$= 30$$

(b) When $w = 45$,
$$45 = 5t$$
$$t = 9$$

6. It is given that A is directly proportional to r^2 and $r > 0$. When $r = 5$, $A = 75$. Find
(a) the value of A when $r = 4$,
(b) the value of r when $A = 147$.

Solution
(a) Let $A = kr^2$, where k is a constant.
When $r = 5$, $A = 75$.
$$75 = k \times 5^2$$
$$k = 3$$
$$\therefore A = 3r^2$$
When $r = 4$,
$$A = 3 \times 4^2$$
$$= 48$$

(b) When $A = 147$,
$$147 = 3r^2$$
$$r^2 = 49$$
$$r = \sqrt{49}$$
$$= 7$$

Further Practice

7. The following table shows the total price ($\$P$) for x copies of books.

Copies of books (x)	1	2	3	4	5
Total price ($\$P$)	15	30	45	60	75

(a) Show that x and P are in direct proportion.
(b) Draw the graph of P against x.
(c) Describe the graph in **(b)**.
(d) Find the equation connecting x and P.
(e) Hence, find the total price for 8 copies of books.

Solution
(a) $$\frac{1}{15} = \frac{2}{30} = \frac{3}{45} = \frac{4}{60} = \frac{5}{75}$$
$$\therefore \ x \text{ and } P \text{ are in direct proportion.}$$

(b) The diagram below shows the graph of P against x.

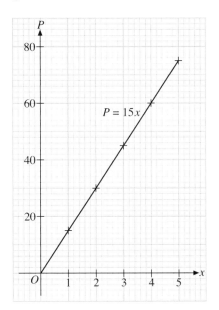

(c) The graph in **(b)** is a straight line that passes through the origin and its slope is positive.

(d) As $\dfrac{x}{P} = \dfrac{1}{15}$,

$$P = 15x.$$

(e) When $x = 8$,

$$P = 15 \times 8$$
$$= 120$$

The total price for 8 copies of books is $120.

---

8. The following table shows the mass (m g) of a pinewood cube of side x cm.

Length of a side (x cm)	2	4	5	8	10
Mass (m g)	5.2	41.6	81.25	332.8	650

(a) Is m proportional to x?

(b) Is m proportional to x^3?

(c) Find an equation connecting m and x.

(d) Hence, find the mass in grams of a pinewood cube of side 9 cm.

Solution

(a) $\dfrac{2}{5.2} \neq \dfrac{4}{41.6}$

$\therefore$ m is NOT proportional to x.

(b) $\dfrac{5.2}{2^3} = \dfrac{41.6}{4^3} = \dfrac{81.25}{5^3} = \dfrac{332.8}{8^3} = \dfrac{650}{10^3} = 0.65$

$\therefore$ m is proportional to x^3.

(c) $\dfrac{P_1}{n_1} = 0.65$

$\therefore$ $m = 0.65x^3$

(d) When $x = 9$,

$$m = 0.65 \times 9^3$$
$$= 473.85$$

The required mass is 473.85 g.

Math@Work

9. The cost of renting a car is directly proportional to the number of days the car is being rented for. The cost of renting a car for 4 days is $240. Find the cost of renting a car for 7 days.

Solution

Let the price of renting a car for n days be $P.

Then $\dfrac{P_1}{n_1} = \dfrac{P_2}{n_2}$.

When $n_1 = 4$, $P_1 = 240$, $n_2 = 7$,

$$\dfrac{240}{4} = \dfrac{P_2}{7}$$

$$P_2 = 7 \times \dfrac{240}{4}$$

$$= 420$$

The cost of renting a car for 7 days is $420.

---

10. The mass of a metal plate is directly proportional to its volume. When its volume is 20 cm^3, its mass is 210 g. If the volume of the metal plate is 50 cm^3, what is its mass?

Solution

Let the mass of a metal plate of V cm^3 be m g.

Then $\dfrac{V_1}{m_1} = \dfrac{V_2}{m_2}$.

When $V_1 = 20$, $m_1 = 210$, $V_2 = 50$,

$$m_2 = 50 \times \dfrac{210}{20}$$

$$= 525$$

The mass of the metal plate of volume 50 cm^3 is 525 g.

---

11. When a car is traveling steadily along a highway, its consumption of gasoline is directly proportional to the distance traveled. A car travels 100 mi on 2.7 gal of gasoline. Find, giving your answer correct to 1 decimal place,

(a) the gasoline consumption of the car for a distance of 74 mi,

(b) the maximum distance that the car can travel with 1 gal of gasoline.

Solution

(a) Let the consumption of gasoline be y gal when the distance traveled is d mi.

Then $y = kd$, where k is a constant.

When $d = 100$, $y = 2.7$.

$$2.7 = k(100)$$
$$k = 0.027$$
$$\therefore y = 0.027d$$

When $d = 74$,

$$y = 0.027 \times 74$$
$$= 2.0 \quad \text{(correct to 1 d.p.)}$$

The required gasoline consumption is 2.0 gal.

(b) When $y = 1$,

$$1 = 0.027d$$
$$d = 37.0 \quad \text{(correct to 1 d.p.)}$$

The required maximum distance traveled is 37.0 mi.

12. The period (the time taken for one complete oscillation) of a simple pendulum is directly proportional to the square root of its length. When its length is 1.02 m, its period is 2.01 seconds. Find
   (a) the period of the pendulum when its length is 0.8 m,
   (b) the length of the pendulum when its period is 1.0 second.
   Give your answers correct to 2 decimal places.

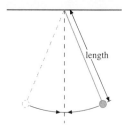

Solution
(a) Let the period of a simple pendulum of length L cm be T seconds.

Then $T = k\sqrt{L}$, where k is a constant.

When $L = 1.02$, $T = 2.01$.

$$2.01 = k\sqrt{1.02}$$

$$k = \frac{2.01}{\sqrt{1.02}}$$

i.e., $T = \frac{2.01}{\sqrt{1.02}}\sqrt{L}$

When $L = 0.8$,

$$T = \frac{2.01}{\sqrt{1.02}} \times \sqrt{0.8}$$

$$= 1.78 \quad \text{(correct to 2 d.p.)}$$

The required period of the pendulum is 1.78 seconds.

(b) When $T = 1$,

$$1 = \frac{2.01}{\sqrt{1.02}}\sqrt{L}$$

$$\sqrt{L} = \frac{\sqrt{1.02}}{2.01}$$

$$L = \frac{1.01}{2.01^2}$$

$$= 0.25 \quad \text{(correct to 2 d.p.)}$$

The required length of the pendulum is 0.25 m.

13. The vertical falling distance of a ball is directly proportional to the square of the time of falling. The ball falls 80 m in 4 s.
   (a) Find the vertical falling distance of the ball when the time taken is 6 s.
   (b) If the ball is dropped from a height of 245 m, find the time it takes to hit the ground.

Solution
(a) Let the vertical falling distance be y m in t seconds.
   Then $y = kt^2$, where k is a constant.
   When $t = 4$, $y = 80$.

$$80 = k \times 4^2$$
$$k = 5$$
$$\therefore \ y = 5t^2$$

When $t = 6$,
$$y = 5 \times 6^2$$
$$= 180$$

The required vertical falling distance is 180 m.

(b) When $y = 245$,
$$245 = 5t^2$$
$$t^2 = 49$$
$$t = \sqrt{49}$$
$$= 7$$

The required time taken is 7 seconds.

Brainworks

14. **(a)** In our daily life, we often encounter a wide variety of quantities involving direct proportion. Describe two such quantities.
   (b) Draw a graph to show their relationship.
   (c) Find an equation connecting the quantities.

Solution
(a) If the admission fee per person for a concert is $40, then the total admission fee, T, is directly proportional to the number of people, n, attending the concert.

(b) The graph of T against n is shown below.

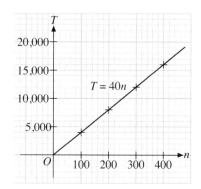

(c) The equation connecting T and n is $T = 40n$.
   Note: Students may provide other relevant cases.

15. Jordan's height and weight increase as he grows bigger. Do you think his height and weight are in direct proportion? Give reasons for your answer.

Solution
In general, when the height of a boy increases, his weight also increases. But the height and the weight may not increase at the same rate. Hence, they are not in direct proportion.

Exercise 14.4
Basic Practice

1. In each of the following tables of values, determine whether x and y are in inverse proportion.

(a)

x	1	2	3	4
y	12	10	8	6

(b)

x	2	4	6	8
y	12	6	4	3

(c)

x	10	20	25	40
y	60	30	24	15

(d)

x	12	15	18	24
y	30	24	18	15

Solution
(a) $1 \times 12 \neq 2 \times 10$
x and y are NOT in inverse proportion.
(b) $2 \times 12 = 4 \times 6 = 6 \times 4 = 8 \times 3$
x and y are in inverse proportion.
(c) $10 \times 60 = 20 \times 30 = 25 \times 24 = 40 \times 15$
x and y are in inverse proportion.
(d) $12 \times 30 \neq 18 \times 18$
x and y are NOT in inverse proportion.

2. In each of the following graphs, determine whether x and y are in inverse proportion.

(a)

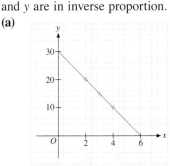

(b)

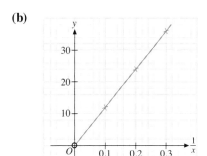

Solution
(a) $(2, 20)$ and $(3, 15)$ are two points on the graph. But $2 \times 20 \neq 3 \times 15$, hence x and y are NOT in inverse proportion.

(b) As the graph of y against $\frac{1}{x}$ is part of a straight line that passes through the origin, x and y are in inverse proportion.

3. In each of the following equations, determine whether x and y are in inverse proportion.
(a) $xy = 20$ **(b)** $x - y = 20$
(c) $y = \dfrac{18}{x}$ **(d)** $y = \dfrac{1}{x} + 1$

Solution
(a) $xy = 20$ is in the form $xy = k$ with $k = 20$.
∴ x and y are in inverse proportion.
(b) $x - y = 20$ is not in the form $xy = k$.
∴ x and y are NOT in inverse proportion.
(c) $y = \dfrac{18}{x}$ can be written as $xy = 18$.
∴ x and y are in inverse proportion.
(d) $y = \dfrac{1}{x} + 1$ cannot be expressed in the form $xy = k$.
∴ x and y are NOT in inverse proportion.

4. If two quantities, x and y, are in inverse proportion, find the values of p and q in the following table.

x	32	20	q
y	5	p	16

Solution
$20 \times p = 32 \times 5$
$p = \dfrac{32 \times 5}{20}$
$= 8$
$q \times 16 = 32 \times 5$
$q = 10$

5. It is given that z is inversely proportional to t. When $t = 9$, $z = 28$. Find
   (a)   the value of z when $t = 12$,
   (b)   the value of t when $z = 36$.

Solution
   (a)   Let $zt = k$, where k is a constant.
         When $t = 9$, $z = 28$.
         $28 \times 9 = k$
         $\quad\quad k = 252$
         $\therefore zt = 252$
         When $t = 12$,
         $z \times 12 = 252$
         $\quad\quad z = 21$
   (b)   When $z = 36$,
         $36 \times t = 252$
         $\quad\quad t = 7$

6. It is given that D is inversely proportional to $\sqrt{m}$. When $m = 9$, $D = 64$. Find
   (a)   the value of D when $m = 4$,
   (b)   the value of m when $D = 32$.

Solution
   (a)   Let $D = \dfrac{k}{\sqrt{m}}$, where k is a constant.
         When $m = 9$, $D = 64$.
         $64 = \dfrac{k}{\sqrt{9}}$
         $k = 192$
         $\therefore D = \dfrac{192}{\sqrt{m}}$
         When $m = 4$,
         $D = \dfrac{192}{\sqrt{4}}$
         $\quad = 96$
   (b)   When $D = 32$,
         $32 = \dfrac{192}{\sqrt{m}}$
         $\sqrt{m} = 6$
         $m = 6^2$
         $\quad = 36$

Further Practice

7. The diagram shows a lever system with a load that is balanced by a weight m grams at a distance d cm from the fulcrum.

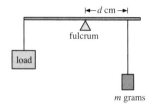

The following table shows various pairs of values of d and m.

d (cm)	10	20	30	40	50
m (g)	60	30	20	15	12

   (a)   Show that d and m are in inverse proportion.
   (b)   Draw the graph of m against d.
   (c)   Draw the graph of m against $\dfrac{1}{d}$.
   (d)   Find the equation connecting d and m.
   (e)   Find the value of m when $d = 25$.

Solution
   (a) $10 \times 60 = 20 \times 30 = 30 \times 20 = 40 \times 15 = 50 \times 12$
         $\therefore$ d and m are in inverse proportion.
   (b)   The diagram below shows the graph of m against d.

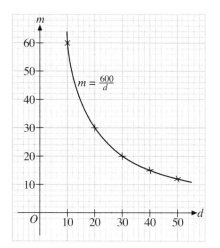

   (c)

d	10	20	30	40	50
m	60	30	20	15	12
$\dfrac{1}{d}$	0.1	0.05	0.033	0.025	0.02

The diagram below shows the graph of m against $\dfrac{1}{d}$.

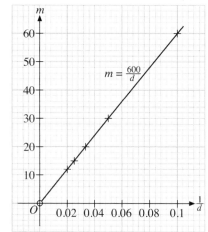

(d) The equation connecting d and m is $m = \dfrac{600}{d}$.

(e) When $d = 25$,

$$m = \frac{600}{25}$$
$$= 24$$

8. The following table shows the number of trees (y) required to be planted on a hillside when the distance between two adjacent trees is x meters.

x	1	2	3	5	6
y	900	225	100	36	25

(a) Is y inversely proportional to x?
(b) Is y inversely proportional to x^2?
(c) Find an equation connecting x and y.
(d) Find the number of trees required when $x = 1.5$.

Solution
(a) $1 \times 900 \ne 2 \times 225$
∴ y is NOT inversely proportional to x.

(b)

x	1	2	3	5	6
y	900	225	100	36	25
x^2	1	4	9	25	36
x^2y	900	900	900	900	900

x^2y = constant
∴ y is inversely proportional to x^2.

(c) The equation connecting x and y is $x^2y = 900$.

(d) When $x = 1.5$,

$$(1.5)^2 y = 900$$
$$y = 400$$

The number of trees required is 400.

9. Given that y is inversely proportional to the cube of x, and $y = 30$ when $x = 2$. Find
(a) the value of y when $x = 5$,
(b) the value of x when $y = 3.75$.

Solution
(a) Let $x^3y = k$, where k is a constant.
When $x = 2$, $y = 30$.

$$2^3 \times 30 = k$$
$$k = 240$$
∴ $x^3y = 240$

When $x = 5$,

$$5^3 \times y = 240$$
∴ $y = 1.92$

(b) When $y = 3.75$,

$$x^3 \times 3.75 = 240$$
$$x^3 = 64$$
∴ $x = 4$

10. It is given that S is inversely proportional to t^n for the values given in the following table.

t	1	3	5	
S	90	10		0.9

(a) Find the value of n.
(b) Copy and complete the given table.

Solution
(a) Let $St^n = k$, where k is a constant.
When $t = 1$, $S = 90$.

$$90 \times 1^n = k$$
$$k = 90$$
∴ $St^n = 90$

When $t = 3$, $S = 10$.

$$10 \times 3^n = 90$$
$$3^n = 9$$
∴ $n = 2$

Hence, $St^2 = 90$.

(b) When $t = 5$,

$$S \times 5^2 = 90$$
∴ $S = 3.6$

When $S = 0.9$,

$$0.9 \times t^2 = 90$$
$$t^2 = 100$$
∴ $t = 10$

We can complete the table as shown below.

t	1	3	5	10
S	90	10	3.6	0.9

Math@Work

11. The time taken, t minutes, to download a file from a computer is inversely proportional to the Internet connection speed, v kB/s. When the speed is 64 kB/s, the time taken is 12 minutes. Find the time taken when the speed is 512 kB/s.

Solution
Let $vt = k$, where k is a constant.
When $v = 64$, $t = 12$.

$$64 \times 12 = k$$
$$k = 768$$
∴ $vt = 768$

When $v = 512$,
$$512t = 768$$
$$t = 1.5$$
The required time taken is 1.5 minutes.

12. The rate of water delivered and the time taken to fill up a pool are in inverse proportion. If the rate is 16 gal/min, the time taken is 20 minutes. What is the time taken when the rate is 40 gal/min?

Solution

Let the time taken to fill up the tank be t minutes when the rate is r gal/min.
Then $rt = k$, where k is a constant.
When $r = 16$, $t = 20$.
$$16 \times 20 = k$$
$$k = 320$$
$$\therefore \ rt = 320$$
When $r = 40$,
$$40t = 320$$
$$t = 8$$
The required time taken is 8 minutes.

13. The frequency of sound produced by a string is inversely proportional to the length of the string. When the string is 50 cm long, the frequency of sound is 256 Hz. Find
(a) the frequency of sound when the string is 40 cm long,
(b) the length of the string when the frequency of sound is 400 Hz.

Solution

(a) Let the frequency of sound be f Hz when the length is L cm.
Then $fL = k$, where k is a constant.
When $L = 50$, $f = 256$.
$$256 \times 50 = k$$
$$k = 12,800$$
$$\therefore \ fL = 12,800$$
When $L = 40$,
$$f \times 40 = 12,800$$
$$f = 320$$
The required frequency of sound is 320 Hz.

(b) When $f = 400$,
$$400 \times L = 12,800$$
$$L = 32$$
The required length is 32 cm.

14. The force of attraction between two magnets is inversely proportional to the square of the distance between them. When their distance apart is 3 in., the force of attraction is 56 units. Find
(a) the force of attraction when the distance apart is 2 in.,
(b) the distance apart when the force of attraction is 14 units.

Solution

(a) Let the force of attraction between two magnets be F units when they are d in. apart.
Then $F = \dfrac{k}{d^2}$, where k is a constant.
When $d = 3$, $F = 56$.
$$56 = \dfrac{1}{2}$$
$$k = 504$$
$$\therefore \ F = \dfrac{504}{d^2}$$
When $d = 2$,
$$F = \dfrac{504}{d^2}$$
$$= 126$$
The required force is 126 units.

(b) When $F = 14$,
$$14 = \dfrac{504}{d^2}$$
$$d^2 = 36$$
$$d = \sqrt{36}$$
$$= 6$$
The required distance apart is 6 in.

15. The speed of a bullet fired from a gun is inversely proportional to the square root of its mass. When the mass is 49 g, the speed is 640 m/s. Find
(a) the speed when its mass is 36 g,
(b) the mass when its speed is 560 m/s.

Solution

(a) Let the speed of a bullet be v m/s when its mass is m grams.
Then $v = \dfrac{k}{\sqrt{m}}$, where k is a constant.

When $m = 49$, $v = 640$.
$$640 = \dfrac{k}{\sqrt{49}}$$
$$k = 4,480$$
$$\therefore \ v = \dfrac{4,480}{\sqrt{m}}$$

When $m = 36$,

$$v = \frac{4{,}480}{\sqrt{36}}$$

$$= 746\frac{2}{3}$$

The required speed is $746\frac{2}{3}$ m/s.

(b) When $v = 560$,

$$560 = \frac{4{,}480}{\sqrt{m}}$$

$$\sqrt{m} = 8$$

$$m = 64$$

The required mass is 64 g.

Brainworks

16. In your science laboratory studies, you would have come across two quantities that are in inverse proportion. Show how these quantities are related, using a graph.

Solution

For a given quantity of heat, the temperature rise T °C of a piece of metal is inversely proportional to its mass m kg.

If $mT = 100$, the graph of T against $\frac{1}{m}$ is part of a straight line that passes through the origin with slope 100.

Note: Students may give other examples.

17. If 12 workers take 100 days to build a house, is it true that 1,200 workers will take one day to build the house? Explain briefly.

Solution

It is very unlikely that 1200 workers can build the house in one day. As the skills of the workers and the rate at which they work are different, the number of days taken to build the house is NOT inversely proportional to the number of workers.

Review Exercise 14

1. The shaft of a gardening tool has a length of 25 cm and a diameter of 3.8 cm. It is drawn 5 cm long in a mechanical drawing. Find
   (a) the scale of the drawing,
   (b) the diameter of the shaft in the drawing.

Solution
(a) Scale of the drawing = 5 cm : 25 cm
$$= 1 : 5$$
(b) Diameter of the shaft in the drawing
$$= 3.8 \times \frac{1}{5} \text{ cm}$$
$$= 0.76 \text{ cm}$$

2. The diagram shows a part of the floor plan of an apartment. The actual length of the wall, *AB*, of the living room is 8 m.

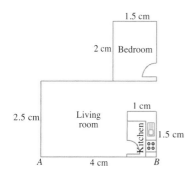

   (a) the scale of the floor plan,
   (b) the actual width of the living room,
   (c) the actual dimensions of the bedroom.

Solution
(a) Scale of the plan = 4 cm : 8 m
$$= 4 : 800$$
$$= 1 : 200$$

(b) Actual width of the living room
$$= 2.5 \times 200 \text{ cm}$$
$$= 500 \text{ cm}$$
$$= 5 \text{ m}$$

(c) For the bedroom,
its actual length $= 2 \times 200$ cm
$$= 400 \text{ cm}$$
$$= 4 \text{ m}$$
its actual width $= 1.5 \times 200$ cm
$$= 300 \text{ cm}$$
$$= 3 \text{ m}$$
Its actual dimensions are 4 m by 3 m.

3. The scale of a floor plan is 1 in. to $16\frac{2}{3}$ ft. Find
   (a) the scale of the plan,
   (b) the length of a hallway on the plan if its actual length is 50 ft,
   (c) the actual area of a rectangular garden if its dimensions on the plan are 3 in. by $1\frac{1}{2}$ in.

Solution

(a) Scale of the plan $= 1$ in. $: 16\frac{2}{3}$ ft

$\qquad\qquad\qquad\quad = 1$ in. $: \dfrac{50}{3} \times 12$ in.

$\qquad\qquad\qquad\quad = 1 : 200$

(b) Length of the hallway on the plan

$\qquad = 50 \times \dfrac{1}{200}$ ft

$\qquad = 50 \times \dfrac{12}{200}$ in.

$\qquad = 3$ in.

(c) Area of the rectangular garden on the plan

$\qquad = 3 \times 1\frac{1}{2}$

$\qquad = 4.5$ in.^{2}

Area on the map : Actual area $= 1$ in.$^2 : 200^2$ in.^{2}

$\qquad\qquad\qquad\qquad\qquad\quad = 1$ in.$^2 : 40,000$ in.^{2}

Actual area of the rectangular garden

$\qquad = 4.5 \times 40,000$ in.^{2}

$\qquad = 180,000$ in.^{2}

$\qquad = \dfrac{180,000}{12 \times 12}$ ft^2

$\qquad = 1,250$ ft^2

4. A map is drawn to the scale $1 : 4,000$.
  (a) The length of a road on the map is 3.5 cm. Find its actual length in meters.
  (b) The area of a garden is 20,000 m^2. Find the area of the garden on the map in square centimeters.

Solution

(a) Actual length $= 3.5 \times 4,000$ cm

$\qquad\qquad\qquad = 14,000$ cm

$\qquad\qquad\qquad = 140$ m

(b) Map scale $= 1 : 4,000$

$\qquad\qquad\quad = 1$ cm $: 4,000$ cm

$\qquad\qquad\quad = 1$ cm $: 40$ m

Area on the map : Actual area

$\qquad = 1$ cm$^2 : 40^2$ m^2

$\qquad = 1$ cm$^2 : 1,600$ m^2

Area of a garden on the map $= 20,000 \div 1,600$ cm^2

$\qquad\qquad\qquad\qquad\qquad\qquad = 12.5$ cm^2

5. The scale of map A is $1 : 5,000$ and the scale of map B is $1 : 3,000$.
  (a) The distance between two schools on map A is 6 cm. Find their distance apart on map B.
  (b) The area of a lake on map B is 18 cm^2. Find
    (i) the actual area of the lake in m^2,
    (ii) the area of the lake on map A.

Solution

(a) Scale of map $A = 1 : 5,000$
Scale of map $B = 1 : 3,000$
Actual distance between two schools
$\qquad = 6 \times 5,000$ cm
$\qquad = 30,000$ cm
Distance apart on map $B = 30,000 \times \dfrac{1}{3,000}$ cm
$\qquad\qquad\qquad\qquad\qquad = 10$ cm

(b) **(i)** Scale of map $B = 1 : 3,000$
$\qquad\qquad\qquad\qquad\quad = 1$ cm $: 3,000$ cm
$\qquad\qquad\qquad\qquad\quad = 1$ cm $: 30$ m
Area on map B : Actual area
$\qquad = 1$ cm$^2 : 30^2$ m^2
$\qquad = 1$ cm$^2 : 900$ m^2
Actual area of the lake $= 18 \times 900$ m^2
$\qquad\qquad\qquad\qquad\qquad = 16,200$ m^2

  (ii) Scale of map $A = 1 : 5,000$
$\qquad\qquad\qquad\qquad\quad = 1$ cm $: 5,000$ cm
$\qquad\qquad\qquad\qquad\quad = 1$ cm $: 50$ m
Area on map A : Actual area
$\qquad = 1$ cm$^2 : 50^2$ m^2
$\qquad = 1$ cm$^2 : 2,500$ m^2
Area of the lake on map A
$\qquad = 16,200 \div 2,500$ cm^2
$\qquad = 6.48$ cm^2

6. A carat is a measure of mass used for gemstones. The following table shows the conversion between carats and grams.

Gram (x)	2	4	6	8	10
Carat (y)	10	20	30	40	50

  (a) Show that x and y are in direct proportion.
  (b) Draw the graph of y against x.
  (c) Find the equation connecting x and y.
  (d) The mass of a piece of diamond is 7 g. How many carats is this?

Solution

(a) $\dfrac{2}{10} = \dfrac{4}{20} = \dfrac{6}{30} = \dfrac{8}{40} = \dfrac{10}{50}$

$\therefore$ x and y are in direct proportion.

(b) The diagram below shows the graph of y against x.

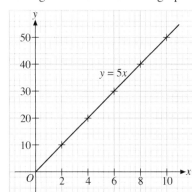

(c) $\dfrac{x}{y} = \dfrac{2}{10}$

$\therefore \ y = 5x$

(d) When $x = 7$,

$\quad y = 5 \times 7$

$\quad\quad = 35$

The mass is 35 carats.

7. The cost $C of a metal wire is directly proportional to its length x in. When the length is 3 in., its cost is $0.20.
   (a) Find the length of the wire if its cost is $15.
   (b) Metal wire is used to make the frame of a rectangular prism that measures 25 in. by 20 in. by 15 in. Find the total cost of the wire used.

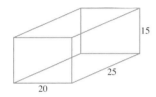

Solution

(a) Let $C = kx$, where k is a constant.

When $x = 3$, $C = 0.2$.

$\quad 0.2 = k(3)$

$\quad\quad k = \dfrac{1}{15}$

$\therefore \ C = \dfrac{1}{15}x$

When $C = 15$,

$\quad 15 = \dfrac{1}{15}x$

$\quad\quad x = 225$

The length of the metal wire is 225 in.

(b) Total length of the metal wire used

$= 4 \times (25 + 20 + 15)$

$= 240$ in.

Total cost $= \$\left(240 \times \dfrac{1}{15}\right)$

$\quad\quad\quad = \$16$

The total cost of the wire used is $16.

8. The mass of a model car is directly proportional to the cube of its length. When the length is 6 cm, its mass is 96 g.
   (a) Find the length of the model car when its mass is 324 g.
   (b) The model car is made using a scale of 1 : 50. The length of the real car is 4 m. Find
   (i) the length of the model car in centimeters,
   (ii) the mass of the model car, correct to the nearest gram.

Solution

(a) Let the mass of a model car be m grams when its length is x cm.

Then $m = kx^3$, where k is a constant.

When $x = 6$, $m = 96$.

$\quad 96 = k \times 6^3$

$\quad\quad k = \dfrac{4}{9}$

$\therefore \ m = \dfrac{4}{9}x^3$

When $m = 324$,

$\quad 324 = \dfrac{4}{9}x^3$

$\quad\quad x^3 = 729$

$\quad\quad x = \sqrt[3]{729}$

$\quad\quad\ = 9$

The length of the model car is 9 cm.

(b) (i) Scale of model car = 1 : 50

Length of the model car $= 4 \times \dfrac{1}{50}$ m

$\quad\quad\quad\quad\quad\quad\quad = 0.08$ m

$\quad\quad\quad\quad\quad\quad\quad = 8$ cm

(ii) When $x = 8$,

$\quad m = \dfrac{4}{9} \times 8^3$

$\quad\quad\ = 228$ g (correct to the nearest gram)

The required mass is 228 g.

9. The following table shows some corresponding values of two quantities, x and y.

x	0	1	2	3	4
y	0	2	8	18	32

(a) Draw the graph of y against x.
(b) Draw the graph of y against x^2.
(c) State the relationship between x and y.
(d) Write down an equation connecting x and y.
(e) Find the value of y when $x = 2.5$.

Solution

(a) The diagram below shows the graph of y against x.

(b)

x	0	1	2	3	4
y	0	2	8	18	32
x^2	0	1	4	9	16

The diagram below shows the graph of y against x^2.

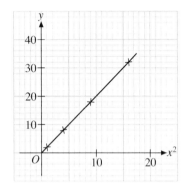

(c) Since the graph of y against x^2 is a straight line passing through the origin, y is directly proportional to x^2.

(d) $\dfrac{y}{x^2} = \dfrac{2}{1}$

$\therefore\ y = 2x^2$

(e) When $x = 2.5$,
$$y = 2(2.5)^2$$
$$= 12.5$$

10. Suppose the amount of food served to each person at a party is inversely proportional to the number of people who attend the party. When there are 25 people at the party, each person will have 1.2 kg of food.
   (a) If there are 60 people, find the amount of food each person is served.
   (b) How many people are there at the party if each person is served 0.4 kg of food?

Solution
(a) Let the amount of food served to each person be m kg.
   If there are n persons,
   then $m = \dfrac{k}{n}$, where k is a constant.
   When $n = 25$, $m = 1.2$.
   $$1.2 = \dfrac{k}{25}$$
   $$k = 30$$
   $$\therefore\ m = \dfrac{30}{n}$$

When $n = 60$,
$$m = \dfrac{30}{60}$$
$$= 0.5$$
The amount of food served to each person is 0.5 kg.

(b) When $m = 0.4$,
$$0.4 = \dfrac{30}{n}$$
$$n = 75$$
There are 75 people at the party.

11. The dimensions of a rectangle are x in. by y in. It is known that x and y are in inverse proportion. When $x = 36$, $y = 20$.
   (a) Find the equation connecting x and y.
   (b) Find the value of y when $x = 24$.
   (c) Find the value of x when $y = 15$.
   (d) What can you say about the area of the rectangle?

Solution
(a) Let $y = \dfrac{k}{x}$, where k is a constant.

   When $x = 36$, $y = 20$.
   $$20 = \dfrac{k}{36}$$
   $$k = 720$$
   $$\therefore\ y = \dfrac{720}{x}$$

(b) When $x = 24$,
   $$y = \dfrac{720}{24}$$
   $$= 30$$

(c) When $y = 15$,
   $$15 = \dfrac{720}{x}$$
   $$x = 48$$

(d) As the value of xy is a constant, i.e., $xy = 720$, the area of the rectangle is always 720 cm^2.

12. The intensity of radiation is inversely proportional to the square of the distance from a radioactive source. When the distance is 4 m, the intensity of radiation is 900 units. Find
   (a) the intensity of radiation when the distance from its source is 5 m,
   (b) the distance from the source if its intensity of radiation is 1,600 units.

Solution

(a) Let the intensity be I units when the distance is d m.

Then $I = \dfrac{k}{d^2}$, where k is a constant.

When $d = 4$, $I = 900$.

$$900 = \frac{k}{4^2}$$
$$k = 14{,}400$$
$$\therefore I = \frac{14{,}400}{d^2}$$

When $d = 5$,

$$I = \frac{14{,}400}{5^2}$$
$$= 576$$

The required intensity of radiation is 576 units.

(b) When $I = 1{,}600$,

$$1{,}600 = \frac{14{,}400}{d^2}$$
$$d^2 = 9$$
$$d = \sqrt{9}$$
$$= 3$$

The required distance is 3 m.

---

13. 6 men take 6 hours to complete a job. The time required to complete the job, T hours, is inversely proportional to the number of workers, x.

  (a) Find the time taken to complete the job when there are 9 workers.

  (b) How many workers are required if the job has to be completed in 45 minutes?

Solution

(a) Let $T = \dfrac{k}{x}$, where k is a constant.

When $x = 6$, $T = 6$.

$$6 = \frac{k}{6}$$
$$k = 36$$
$$\therefore T = \frac{36}{x}$$

When $x = 9$,

$$T = \frac{36}{9}$$
$$= 4$$

The required time taken to complete the job is 4 hours.

(b) When $T = \dfrac{45}{60} = \dfrac{3}{4}$,

$$\frac{3}{4} = \frac{36}{x}$$
$$x = 48$$

The number of required workers is 48.

---

14. In kick boxing, it is found that the force needed to break a board is inversely proportional to the length of the board. If it takes 6 lb of pressure to break a board 2 ft long, how many pounds of pressure will it take to break a board that is 5 ft long?

Solution

Let the force needed to break a board be y lb when the length of the board is x ft.

Then $y = \dfrac{k}{x}$, where k is a constant.

When $x = 2$, $y = 6$.

$$6 = \frac{k}{2}$$
$$k = 12$$
$$\therefore y = \frac{12}{x}$$

When $x = 5$,

$$y = \frac{12}{5}$$
$$= 2.4$$

The required force to break the board is 2.4 lb.

Chapter 15   Data Handling

Class Activity 1

Objective: To observe patterns of distributions revealed by dot plots.

Questions

1. The dot plot below displays the scores of the students from Class A in a math quiz. The maximum possible number of points of the quiz is 20.

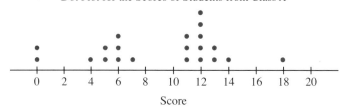

Dot Plot for the Scores of Students from Class A

Score

(a)   How many students are there?

21 students

(b)   What is the range of the data?

The data vary from 0 to 18.

(c)   At which values do the scores cluster around?

6 and 12

2. The dot plot below displays the scores of the students from Class B in the same math quiz.

Dot Plot for the Scores of Students from Class B

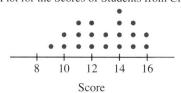

Score

(a)   How many students are there?

20 students

(b)   Briefly describe the distribution of the scores.

From the dot plot, we observe that
– the data vary from 9 to 16,
– the data are spread out between 10 and 16.

(c)   Compare the dot plot for Class A with that for Class B. What do you notice? What conclusions can you draw?

Dot plot for Class B is more clustered together. Hence, the variation of students' scores is less than that in the dot plot for Class A.

3. (a)   Record the pulse rates (beats per minute) of 10 classmates who are resting or sitting and plot the data on a dot plot.
    (b)   Record the pulse rates of 10 classmates who are moving around and plot the data on another dot plot.
    (c)   Analyze and compare the two distributions. What conclusions can you draw?

Answers vary.

Class Activity 2

Objective: To compare between mean, median, and mode.

Questions

1. Consider the data set $A = \{3, 3, 7, 8, 9\}$.
   (a) Find its mean, median, and mode.

   $\text{Mean} = \dfrac{3+3+7+8+9}{5} = 6, \quad \text{Median} = 7, \quad \text{Mode} = 3$

   (b) If the number 54 is included in the set, find the new mean, median, and mode.

   $\text{New mean} = \dfrac{3+3+7+8+9+54}{6} = 14, \quad \text{New median} = \dfrac{7+8}{2} = 7.5, \quad \text{New mode} = 3$

   (c) Which measure in (a) is most affected by the addition of a large number?

   The mean is the most affected by the addition of a large number.

   (d) Which measure in (a) do you recognize to be the most appropriate representation of the center of the data set A? Explain your choice briefly.

   Since the mean involves all the data and there are no extreme values in the data set A, it is the most appropriate representation of the center of the data set A.

2. Consider the data set $B = \{1, 1, 3, 6\}$ and $C = \{1, 1, 4, 10, 10, 10\}$.
   (a) Find the mean, median, and mode of data set B, data set C, and the combined data set D of data sets B and C. Copy and complete the following table.

Measure of Center	Mean	Median	Mode
Data set B	2.75	2	1
Data set C	6	7	10
Combined data set D	4.7	3.5	1

   (b) Which measure of center involves all the data of a data set in its calculation?

   The mean involves all the data of a data set in its calculation.

   (c) Suppose you are given only the numbers of items for sets B and C, and their individual measures of center. Which measure can you derive for the combined data set D from the given values?

   The mean can be derived for the combined data set D from the given values as follows: mean $= \dfrac{4 \times 2.75 + 6 \times 6}{4 + 6} = 4.7$.

Discuss

Page 150

Do you know the purpose of conducting a population census?

To gather information about the people living in a certain region

Page 166

If we know the number of apples and the median masses for apples in basket A and basket B, can we derive the overall median mass?

No.

Extend Your Learning Curve

Weighted Mean

Suppose in one academic semester, there are three tests and one examination on mathematics. The maximum point for each test or examination is 100. If the test points are x_1, x_2, and x_3, and the examination point is x_4, the overall mathematics point in the term is given by the **weighted mean** W, where

$$W = \frac{x_1 + x_2 + x_3 + 2x_4}{1 + 1 + 1 + 2}.$$

(a) If Wendy's points in the three tests are 62, 80, and 73, and her examination point is 65, find her weighted mean.

(b) Check the definition of weighted mean and write it down.

(c) For what purpose do you think we need to use the weighted mean?

Suggested Answer:

(a) Wendy's weighted mean point $= \dfrac{62 + 80 + 73 + 2 \times 65}{1 + 1 + 1 + 2}$

$= 69$

(b) For a data set $\{x_1, x_2, \dots x_N\}$,

the weighted mean $= \dfrac{w_1 x_1 + w_2 x_2 + \dots + w_N x_N}{w_1 + w_2 + \dots + w_N}$

where $w_1, w_2, \dots, w_N$ are weights assigned to the items $x_1, x_2, \dots, x_N$ respectively.

(c) When different items in a data set have different levels of importance in working out the average value of the data set, we will use the weighted mean. For example, weighted means are used to calculate index numbers such as consumer price index and index for a stock market.

Try It!

Section 15.2

1. The midnight temperatures in degrees Celsius in Miami during the same two-week period were as follows:

Midnight Temperatures

18	14	15	17	28	20	16
12	19	30	15	20	19	18

(a) Represent the data on a dot plot.
(b) Briefly describe the distribution of the data.
(c) Compare the distribution of the data for the noon temperatures and midnight temperatures. What conclusions can you draw?

Solution

(a)

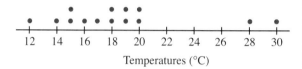

Dot Plot for Midnight Temperatures

Temperatures (°C)

(b) From the dot plot, we observe that
  – the data vary from 12 °C to 30 °C,
  – the data cluster between 14 °C and 20 °C,
  – the extreme temperatures 28 °C and 30 °C deviate considerably from other temperatures observed.

(c) The average noon temperature is higher than the average midnight temperature.

Section 15.3

2. The masses of five girls are 42 kg, 39 kg, 45 kg, 40 kg, and 44 kg. Find their mean mass.

Solution

Sum of the masses = 42 + 39 + 45 + 40 + 44
$$= 210 \text{ kg}$$
Mean mass $= \dfrac{210}{5}$
$$= 42 \text{ kg}$$

3. The mean of four numbers 17, t, 23, and 29 is 20.5. Find the value of t.

Solution

Mean of four numbers = 20.5
$$\frac{17 + t + 23 + 29}{4} = 20.5$$
$$t + 69 = 82$$
$$t = 13$$

4. The mean mass of four mathematics books is 1.4 kg. The mean mass of six English books is 0.9 kg. Find the mean mass of all the books, to the nearest tenth of a kg.

Solution

Total mass of the four mathematics books $= 1.4 \times 4$
$$= 5.6 \text{ kg}$$
Total mass of the six English books $= 0.9 \times 6$
$$= 5.4 \text{ kg}$$
Mean mass of the books $= \dfrac{5.6 + 5.4}{4 + 6}$
$$= 1.1 \text{ kg}$$

5. The dot plots below show the heights in inches of 10 basketball players and 10 soccer players chosen at random.

Dot Plots for the Heights of Players

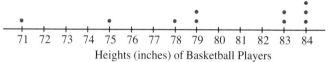

Heights (inches) of Basketball Players

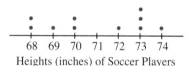

Heights (inches) of Soccer Players

(a) Analyze and compare the two distributions. What conclusions can you draw?
(b) Find the mean height of each set of players. What can you infer?

Solution

(a) The data values for the heights of basketball players vary from 71 inches to 84 inches.

The data values for the heights of soccer players vary from 68 inches to 74 inches.

That is, the range of the heights of the basketball players is greater than that of the soccer players.

(b) Mean height of the basketball players
$$= \frac{71 + 75 + 78 + 2 \times 79 + 2 \times 83 + 3 \times 84}{10}$$
$$= \frac{800}{10}$$
$$= 80 \text{ in.}$$

Mean height of the soccer players
$$= \frac{2 \times 68 + 69 + 2 \times 70 + 72 + 3 \times 73 + 74}{10}$$
$$= \frac{710}{10}$$
$$= 71 \text{ in.}$$

The mean height of the basketball players is higher than that of the soccer players. Hence, the basketball players are taller than the soccer players in general.

6. Jamie and Brenda each surveyed eight friends about the number of books they read in a week. Both surveys found a mean of five books read per week. The data values are presented in the dot plots below.

Jamie's Dot Plot for the Number of Books
Read per Week

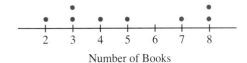

Number of Books

Brenda's Dot Plot for the Number of Books
Read per Week

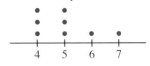

Number of Books

(a) Visually compare the two data distributions. What conclusions can you draw?

(b) Create a table showing the Data Value, Deviation from Mean, and Absolute Deviation for each set of data.

(c) Find the mean absolute deviation (MAD) for each set of data.

(d) Compare the MADs. What can you infer?

Solution

(a) The data values in Jamie's survey are more spread out while the data values in Brenda's survey are closer to the mean.

(b) Since both surveys found a mean of 5 books read per week, we can construct the following table:

Jamie's survey

Number of books read per week		
Data value	**Deviation from Mean**	**Absolute Deviation**
2	−3	3
3	−2	2
3	−2	2
4	−1	1
5	0	0
7	2	2
8	3	3
8	3	3
	Sum = 0	Sum = 16

Brenda's survey

Number of books read per week		
Data value	**Deviation from Mean**	**Absolute Deviation**
4	−1	1
4	−1	1
4	−1	1
5	0	0
5	0	0
5	0	0
6	1	1
7	2	2
	Sum = 0	Sum = 6

(c) MAD for Jamie's survey $= \dfrac{16}{8} = 2$

MAD for Brenda's survey $= \dfrac{6}{8} = 0.75$

(d) On average, the data values in Jamie's survey differ from the mean by 2 books while the data values in Brenda's survey differ from the mean by 0.75 books.

Sectin 15.4

7. The lengths (in centimeters) of eight fish caught by Billy are

28, 31, 20, 33, 17, 27, 25, and 30.

Find the median length of the fish.

Solution
Arrange the lengths of the fish in ascending order as follows:

17   20   25   27   28   30   31   33

middle position

Median length of the fish $= \dfrac{1}{2}(27 + 28)$

$= 27.5$ cm

8. The floor areas (in square meters) of six apartments in building *A* are as follows:

63, 94, 78, 80, 71, 62

The floor areas (in square meters) of five apartments in building *B* are as follows:

93, 104, 75, 88, 83

Find the median floor area of

(a) the apartments in building *A*,

(b) the apartments in building *B*,

(c) all the apartments.

Solution

(a) Arrange the floor areas of the apartments in building *A* in ascending order as follows:

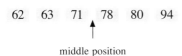

middle position

Median floor area of apartments in building *A*

$$= \frac{1}{2}(71 + 78)$$

$$= 74.5 \text{ m}^2$$

(b) Arrange the floor areas of the apartments in building *B* in ascending order as follows:

75   83 $\boxed{88}$ 93   104

middle position

Median floor area of apartments in building *B*
$$= 88 \text{ m}^2$$

(c) Arrange the floor areas of all the apartments in ascending order as follows:

62   63   71   75   78 $\boxed{80}$ 83   88   93   94   104

middle position

Median floor area of all the apartments $= 80 \text{ m}^2$

Section 15.5

9. The pulse rates (beats per minute) of three groups of people are as follows:

$$A = \{75, 72, 76, 72, 72, 80, 71\}$$
$$B = \{83, 56, 70, 73, 76\}$$
$$C = \{78, 71, 82, 69, 71, 70, 78, 65\}$$

Find the modal pulse rate of each group of people.

Solution

For group *A*, the modal pulse rate is 72 beats per minute.
For group *B*, there is no mode.
For group *C*, the modal pulse rates are 71 and 78 beats per minute.

Exercise 15.1
Basic Practice

1. Suggest a way (taking measurements, observing outcomes, conducting surveys, reading publications) to collect a random sample of each set of data below.
   - (a) Favorite sports of seventh grade students in your school
   - (b) Total number of seventh grade students in the United States in a given year
   - (c) Actual volume of each carton of orange juice in a sample of 20 cartons
   - (d) Body temperatures of patients in a hospital
   - (e) Popularity of a pop singer
   - (f) Customers' opinions about a bank's services
   - (g) Number of incoming calls in a doctor's office from 9:00 A.M. to 10:00 A.M.
   - (h) Birth weight of babies in a hospital
   - (i) Effectiveness of a new medicine
   - (j) Population of the United States, Canada, and Mexico

   Solution
   - (a) Conducting surveys
   - (b) Reading publications
   - (c) Taking measurements
   - (d) Taking measurements
   - (e) Conducting surveys
   - (f) Conducting surveys
   - (g) Observing outcomes
   - (h) Observing outcomes
   - (i) Taking measurements
   - (j) Reading publications

Further Practice

2. Professor Smith wanted to test the air quality in a certain city. He collected samples from some areas of the city with the busiest traffic during rush hour.
   - (a) What kind of data-collection method did he use?
   - (b) Do you think his results are representative of the general air quality of the city? Explain your answer.

   Solution
   - (a) The method used is observing outcomes
   - (b) No, because the emissions produced by vehicles during rush hour will affect the results greatly.

Further Practice

3. The principal wants to find out the favorite sports of students in the middle school. He collects the data in the following ways.
   - (i) Checking the school database of students who play sports in the school and tabulating how many play each sport
   - (ii) Asking five students from each class to fill out a survey about their favorite sports
   - (iii) Designing a form for students to fill in their favorite sports and return the forms to him
   - (a) Name the data-collection method used in each case.
   - (b) Which method(s) do you think will produce the most accurate results? Why?

   Solution
   - (a) Method (i): Reading publications
     Method (ii): Conducting surveys
     Method (iii): Conducting surveys
   - (b) Method (iii) will produce the most accurate results. This is because the results are provided by all students directly.

Math@Work

4. A restaurant manager requests a random sample of 100 customers to fill in the following questionnaire.

   ```
   ABC Restaurant
   Customer Satisfaction Survey
   1. How would you rate our food?
      [ ] very good   [ ] good   [ ] OK
      [ ] poor   [ ] very poor
   2. Is the service of our staff up to
      your expectation? _____
   ```

   - (a) What kind of data-collection method does the manager use?
   - (b) Which question in the survey is better? Why?
   - (c) Is it a good idea to ask customers to fill in the date of visit in the form? Why?

   Solution
   - (a) The method used is conducting surveys.
   - (b) Question 1 is better. It is simple and clear, easy to complete, and can convey useful information to the manager.
   - (c) It is good to fill in the date of visit. This is because the restaurant may have different teams of staff on different dates. The quality of service of each team may be different.

Brainwork

5. Design a questionnaire and collect data by using random sampling. Then, answer the following questions based on it.

    (a) What is the objective of the survey?

    (b) What types of questions will you use?

    (c) What are some of the good features of your survey?

    (d) How can you make sure that the people who participate in the survey are representative of the entire population?

    (e) Suggest some ways to improve your survey.

Solution
Answers may vary.

Exercise 15.2
Basic Practice

1. The following dot plot shows the number of text messages sent by a random sample of adults on a particular day.

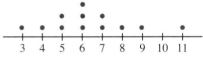

Dot Plot for the Number of Text Messages
Sent by Adults

Number of Text Messages

    (a) How many adult responses were collected?

    (b) What is the range of the number of text messages that were sent by the adults?

    (c) Briefly describe the distribution of the number of text messages sent by the adults.

Solution
    (a) 12 adult responses were collected.

    (b) The number of text messages that were sent by the adults varies from 3 to 11.

    (c) The data cluster around 6. There is an outlier at 11.

2. The following dot plot shows the number of text messages sent by a random sample of seventh grade students on the same day.

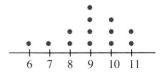

Dot Plot for the Number of Text Messages
Sent by Students

Number of Text Messages

    (a) How many student responses were collected?

    (b) What is the range of the number of text messages that were sent by the students?

    (c) Compare the distributions of the data collected from the adults in Question 1 and the students in this question. What conclusions can you draw?

Solution
    (a) 13 student responses were collected.

    (b) The number of text messages that were sent by the students varies from 6 to 11.

    (c) The data in Question 2 cluster around 9. Hence, the number of text messages sent by an adult is less than that sent by a student in general.

Further Practice

3. The masses (in grams) of 12 randomly selected eggs each in Carton *A* and Carton *B* are presented in the following dot plots.

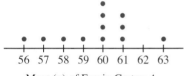

Dot Plot for the Masses of Eggs in Carton *A*

Mass (g) of Egg in Carton *A*

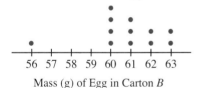

Dot Plot for the Masses of Eggs in Carton *B*

Mass (g) of Egg in Carton *B*

    (a) Find the range of the masses of eggs in each carton.

    (b) Briefly describe the distribution of the masses of eggs in each carton.

    (c) Analyze and compare the two distributions. What conclusions can you draw?

Solution
    (a) The ranges of the masses of eggs in Cartons *A* and *B* are both from 56 g to 63 g.

    (b) Carton *A*: The data values cluster around 60 g and 61 g. The distribution has a long tail on the left.

            Carton *B*: The data values cluster between 60 g and 63 g. The lowest point is an outlier.

    (c) The mass of an egg in Carton *B* is heavier than that in Carton *A* in general.

MathWork

4. Ronald made a six-faced die numbered 1 to 6. He rolled it 20 times and presented the scores in the dot plot below.

Dot Plot for the Scores Obtained in Rolling a Die

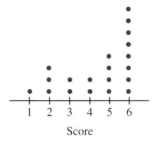

Score

(a) Find the percentage of times that the score is 6.
(b) Discuss the distribution of the scores obtained.

Solution

(a) The score 6 occurred 8 times.

The required percentage = $\dfrac{8}{20} \times 100\%$

$= 40\%$

(b) The score 6 occurred most frequently. The score 1 occurred only once. The distribution of the other scores obtained is more even.

Brainwork

5. The hourly wages (in dollars) of 12 workers in a company are presented in two different dot plots below.

Dot Plot *A* for Hourly Wages of Workers

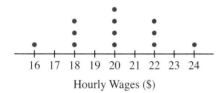

Hourly Wages ($)

Dot Plot *B* for Hourly Wages of Workers

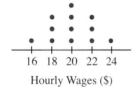

Hourly Wages ($)

(a) Do both dot plots give the same information?
(b) Compare the visual impressions between these two dot plots.
(c) What causes the difference between the visual impressions of these two dot plots?

Solution

(a) Yes, both dot plots give the same information.

(b) Dot plot *B* looks more clustered together. It gives an impression that the variation of hourly wages of workers is less than that in dot plot *A*.

(c) The scales of the number lines in the two dot plots are different.

Exercise 15.3
Basic Practice

1. Find the mean of each of the following data sets.
   (a) 13, 16, 23
   (b) 3, 7, 15, 20
   (c) 2, 5, 8, 13, 24
   (d) 6, 8, 9, 11, 37, 40

Solution

(a) Mean $= \dfrac{1}{3} \times (13 + 16 + 23)$

$= 17\dfrac{1}{3}$

(b) Mean $= \dfrac{1}{4} \times (3 + 7 + 15 + 20)$

$= 11.25$

(c) Mean $= \dfrac{1}{5} \times (2 + 5 + 8 + 13 + 24)$

$= 10.4$

(d) Mean $= \dfrac{1}{6} \times (6 + 8 + 9 + 11 + 37 + 40)$

$= 18.5$

2. The mean of five numbers is 29. Find the sum of these five numbers.

Solution

Sum of the five numbers $= 29 \times 5$

$= 145$

3. The mean of the numbers 52, *t*, and 68 is 61. What is the value of *t*?

Solution

$\dfrac{52 + t + 68}{3} = 61$

$t + 120 = 183$

$t = 63$

4. Find the mean of each of the following data sets.

(a)

34	31	40	28	33	29
30	37	28	35	32	36

(b)

12	18	9	10	14	20	18	11	16	17
14	22	13	15	21	16	10	19	19	12

Solution

(a) Mean $= \dfrac{1}{12} \times (34 + 31 + 40 + 28 + 33 + 29 + 30 + 37$
$\qquad\qquad + 28 + 35 + 32 + 36)$

$\qquad\quad = \dfrac{1}{12} \times 393$

$\qquad\quad = 32.75$

(b) Mean $= \dfrac{1}{20} \times (12 + 18 + 9 + 10 + 14 + 20 + 18 + 11$
$\qquad\qquad + 16 + 17 + 14 + 22 + 13 + 15 + 21$
$\qquad\qquad + 16 + 10 + 19 + 19 + 12)$

$\qquad\quad = \dfrac{1}{20} \times 306$

$\qquad\quad = 15.3$

5. Plot the following sets of data on separate dot plots.

Set A: 8, 2, 6, 3, 4, 6, 5, 8, 3
Set B: 6, 5, 4, 5, 5, 4, 5, 5, 6
Set C: 9, 1, 10, 1, 2, 10, 2, 1, 9

(a) Visually compare the three data distributions. Which set of data has the greatest variation?

(b) Duplicate the following table, one each for Sets A, B, and C, and hence, find the mean absolute deviation of each set of data.

Set _____		
Data Value	**Deviation from Mean**	**Absolute Deviation**
	Sum =	Sum =

(c) What can you say about the variation of the three sets of data?

Solution

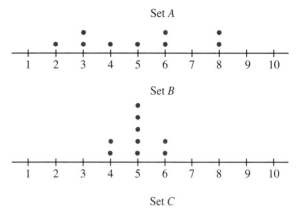

Set A

Set B

Set C

(a) By comparing the dot plots above visually, Set C has the greatest variation.

(b) Mean for Set $A = \dfrac{1}{9} \times (2 + 3 + 3 + 4 + 5 + 6 + 6$
$\qquad\qquad\qquad\qquad\qquad + 8 + 8)$
$\qquad\qquad\qquad = 5$

Mean for Set $B = \dfrac{1}{9} \times (4 + 4 + 5 + 5 + 5 + 5 + 5$
$\qquad\qquad\qquad\qquad\qquad + 6 + 6)$
$\qquad\qquad\qquad = 5$

Mean for Set $C = \dfrac{1}{9} \times (1 + 1 + 1 + 2 + 2 + 9 + 9$
$\qquad\qquad\qquad\qquad\qquad + 10 + 10)$
$\qquad\qquad\qquad = 5$

Set A		
Data value	**Deviation from Mean**	**Absolute Deviation**
2	−3	3
3	−2	2
3	−2	2
4	−1	1
5	0	0
6	1	1
6	1	1
8	3	3
8	3	3
	Sum = −2	Sum = 16

Set *B*		
Data value	Deviation from Mean	Absolute Deviation
4	–1	1
4	–1	1
5	0	0
5	0	0
5	0	0
5	0	0
5	0	0
6	1	1
6	1	1
	Sum = 0	Sum = 4

Set *C*		
Data value	Deviation from Mean	Absolute Deviation
1	–4	4
1	–4	4
1	–4	4
2	–3	3
2	–3	3
9	4	4
9	4	4
10	5	5
10	5	5
	Sum = 0	Sum = 36

MAD for Set *A* = $\frac{16}{9}$ = 1.78 (correct to 2 d.p.)

MAD for Set *B* = $\frac{4}{9}$ = 0.44 (correct to 2 d.p.)

MAD for Set *C* = $\frac{36}{9}$ = 4

(c) On average, the data values in Set *A*, *B*, and *C* differ from the mean by 1.78, 0.44, and 4 respectively. Hence, the data in Set *C* have the greatest variation.

Further Practice

6. The hourly wages of five workers are $15, $18, $20, $23, and $36. Find their mean hourly wage.

Solution
Mean hourly wage = $\frac{1}{5} \times (\$15 + \$18 + \$20 + \$23 + \$36)$

= $22.40

7. The daily minimum temperature was 20 °C, 26 °C, 21 °C, 25 °C, 26 °C, 23 °C, and 20 °C during a certain week. Find the mean daily minimum temperature.

Solution
Mean daily minimum temperature

= $\frac{1}{7} \times (20 + 26 + 21 + 25 + 26 + 23 + 20)$

= 23 °C

8. The mean mass of four apples is 250 g. If two apples of mass 280 g each are added to the group, what is the mean mass of the six apples?

Solution
Total mass of the four apples = 250 × 4

= 1,000 g

Mean mass of the six apples = $\frac{1,000 + 280 \times 2}{6}$

= 260 g

9. The mean age of 10 members in a committee is 42.5 years. If a member of age 74 years old retires, what is the mean age of the remaining nine members?

Solution
Total age of the 10 members = 42.5 × 10

= 425 years

Total age of the remaining nine members = 425 – 74

= 351 years

Mean age of the remaining nine members = $\frac{351}{9}$

= 39 years

10. The mean of *a*, *b*, and *c* is 16. Find the mean of
(a) *a* + 5, *b* + 5, and *c* + 5,
(b) *a* – 7, *b* + 11, and *c* + 17,
(c) 3*a* – 1, 3*b* – 1, and 3*c* – 1.

Solution
(a) $\frac{a + b + c}{3}$ = 16

∴ *a* + *b* + *c* = 48

The required mean = $\frac{(a + 5) + (b + 5) + (c + 5)}{3}$

= $\frac{(a + b + c) + 15}{3}$

= $\frac{48 + 15}{3}$

= 21

(b) The required mean $= \dfrac{(a - 7) + (b + 11) + (c + 17)}{3}$

$= \dfrac{(a + b + c) + 21}{3}$

$= \dfrac{48 + 21}{3}$

$= 23$

(c) The required mean $= \dfrac{(3a - 1) + (3b - 1) + (3c - 1)}{3}$

$= \dfrac{3a + 3b + 3c - 3}{3}$

$= \dfrac{3(a + b + c) - 3}{3}$

$= \dfrac{3 \times 48 - 3}{3}$

$= 47$

11. The number of children per family in a survey is as follows:

Number of children	0	1	2	3	4
Number of families	5	10	12	6	7

Find the mean number of children per family.

Solution

Total number of families
$= 5 + 10 + 12 + 6 + 7$
$= 40$

Total number of children
$= 0 \times 5 + 1 \times 10 + 2 \times 12 + 3 \times 6 + 4 \times 7$
$= 0 + 10 + 24 + 18 + 28$
$= 80$

Mean number of children per family
$= \dfrac{80}{40}$
$= 2$

12. The dot plots below show the masses in kilograms of 10 boys from a sixth grade class and 10 boys from a seventh grade class.

Dot Plot for the Masses of Boys
from a Sixth Grade Class

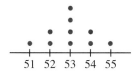

Mass (kilograms) of boys

Dot Plot for the Masses of Boys
from a Seventh Grade Class

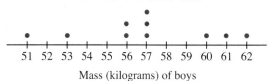

Mass (kilograms) of boys

(a) Analyze and compare the two distributions. What conclusions can you draw?

(b) Find the mean mass of each group of boy.

(c) Compare the means. What can you infer?

(d) Create a table showing the Data Value, Deviation from Mean, and Absolute Deviation for each set of data. Find their respective mean absolute deviations (MAD).

(e) Compare the MADs. What conclusions can you draw?

Solution

(a) The data values for the sixth grade class are more clustered together while the data values for the seventh grade class are more spread out.

(b) Mean mass of the boys from the sixth grade class
$= \dfrac{1}{10} \times (51 + 52 \times 2 + 53 \times 4 + 54 \times 2 + 55)$
$= 53$ kg

Mean mass of the boys from the seventh grade class
$= \dfrac{1}{10} \times (51 + 53 + 56 \times 2 + 57 \times 3 + 60 + 61 + 62)$
$= 57$ kg

(c) In general, the boys from the seventh grade class are heavier than the boys from the sixth grade class.

(d)

Sixth Grade Class

Mass of a boy		
Data value	Deviation from Mean	Absolute Deviation
51	−2	2
52	−1	1
52	−1	1
53	0	0
53	0	0
53	0	0
53	0	0
54	1	1
54	1	1
55	2	2
	Sum = 0	Sum = 8

Seventh Grade Class

Mass of a boy		
Data value	**Deviation from Mean**	**Absolute Deviation**
51	−6	6
53	−4	4
56	−1	1
56	−1	1
57	0	0
57	0	0
57	0	0
60	3	3
61	4	4
62	5	5
	Sum = 0	Sum = 24

MAD for the masses of boys from the sixth grade class

$= \dfrac{8}{10}$

$= 0.8$

MAD for the masses of boys from the seventh grade class

$= \dfrac{24}{10}$

$= 2.4$

(e) On average, the data values from the sixth grade class differ from the mean by 0.8 kg while the data values from the seventh grade class differ from the mean by 2.4 kg.

Math@Work

13. The mean score of Jason in three tests is 46 points. How many points must he score in the fourth test so that the mean score of the four tests is 50 points?

Solution
Let x points be the score in the fourth test.
Sum of the scores in the first three tests $= 46 \times 3$
$= 138$

$\therefore \dfrac{138 + x}{4} = 50$

$138 + x = 200$

$x = 62$

He should score 62 points in the fourth test.

14. The mean mass of 24 boys is 52 kg and the mean mass of 16 girls is 47 kg. Find the mean mass of all the boys and girls.

Solution
Total mass of the 24 boys $= 52 \times 24$
$= 1{,}248$ kg
Total mass of the 16 girls $= 47 \times 16$
$= 752$ kg

Mean mass of all the boys and girls $= \dfrac{1{,}248 + 752}{24 + 16}$

$= 50$ kg

15. The scores that two gymnasts, Bryan and Josh, obtained in six events of parallel bars were as follows:

Bryan	8.1	9.6	9.2	7.5	9.4	9.0
Josh	9.3	9.5	8.0	9.1	7.8	8.5

(a) Find the mean score of Bryan.
(b) Find the mean score of Josh.
(c) Whose performance was better?
(d) Find the mean absolute deviation for each set of data, correct your answers to one decimal place.

Solution
(a) Mean score of Bryan
$= \dfrac{1}{6} \times (8.1 + 9.6 + 9.2 + 7.5 + 9.4 + 9.0)$
$= 8.8$

(b) Mean score of Josh
$= \dfrac{1}{6} \times (9.3 + 9.5 + 8.0 + 9.1 + 7.8 + 8.5)$
$= 8.7$

(c) Since Bryan's mean score was better than Josh's mean score, Bryan's performance was better.

(d)

Bryan's score		
Data value	**Deviation from Mean**	**Absolute Deviation**
8.1	−0.7	0.7
9.6	0.8	0.8
9.2	0.4	0.4
7.5	−1.3	1.3
9.4	0.6	0.6
9.0	0.2	0.2
	Sum = 0	Sum = 4

Josh's score		
Data value	Deviation from Mean	Absolute Deviation
9.3	0.6	0.6
9.5	0.8	0.8
8.0	−0.7	0.7
9.1	0.4	0.4
7.8	−0.9	0.9
8.5	−0.2	0.2
	Sum = 0	Sum = 3.6

MAD for Bryan's scores

$= \dfrac{4}{6}$

$= 0.7$ (correct to 1 d.p.)

MAD for Josh's scores

$= \dfrac{3.6}{6}$

$= 0.6$

16. The Lawrence family must drive an average of 250 mi per day to complete their seven-day vacation on time. During the first six days, they travel 220 mi, 300 mi, 210 mi, 255 mi, 240 mi, and 250 mi. How many miles must they travel on the seventh day in order to finish their vacation on time?

Solution

Assume that they must travel x miles on the seventh day in order to finish their vacation on time.

$\therefore \quad \dfrac{220 + 300 + 210 + 255 + 240 + 250 + x}{7} = 250$

$220 + 300 + 210 + 255 + 240 + 250 + x = 1{,}750$

$x = 275$

Hence, they must travel 275 miles on the seventh day.

Brainwork

17. Measure the length of a room five times in centimeters with two different measuring devices, a ruler and a meter-stick.

(a) Record the results and find the mean absolute deviation of each set of data.

(b) Briefly explain any difference in variation from its mean.

(c) Suggest a measuring device which will give less variation. Measure the length of the room again with the suggested device and verify if the mean absolute deviation has been reduced.

Solution

Answers may vary.

Exercise 15.4
Basic Practice

1. Find the median of each of the following data sets.

(a)   9, 12, 17, 18, 25

(b)   25, 36, 38, 41, 50, 52, 58

(c)   137, 151, 167, 180

(d)   9, 12, 24, 33, 47, 59

Solution

(a)   9   12   17   18   25

middle position

Median = 17

(b)   25   36   38   41   50   52   58

middle position

Median = 41

(c)   137   151   167   180

middle position

Median $= \dfrac{1}{2}(151 + 167)$

$= 159$

(d)   9   12   24   33   47   59

middle position

Median $= \dfrac{1}{2}(24 + 33)$

$= 28.5$

2. Find the median of each of the following data sets.

(a)   24 s, 17 s, 32 s, 19 s

(b)   36 °C, 21 °C, 17 °C, 28 °C, 24 °C

(c)   9 m, 12 m, 11 m, 35 m, 42 m, 77 m, 29 m, 13 m

(d)   2.7 g, 3.0 g, 5.8 g, 4.7 g, 1.6 g, 5.2 g, 4.5 g, 8.1 g, 3.9 g

Solution

(a)   17   19   24   32

middle position

Median $= \dfrac{1}{2}(19 + 24)$

$= 21.5$ s

(b)   17   21 $\boxed{24}$ 28   36

↑
middle position

Median = 24 °C

(c)   9   11   12   13   29   35   42   77

↑
middle position

Median = $\frac{1}{2}$(13 + 29)

= 21 m

(d)   1.6   2.7   3.0   3.9 $\boxed{4.5}$ 4.7   5.2   5.8   8.1

↑
middle position

Median = 4.5 g

Further Practice

3. The areas of the four bedrooms in a house are 12 m^2, 9 m^2, 17 m^2, and 10 m^2 respectively. Find
  (a) the mean area,
  (b) the median area
of these rooms.

Solution

(a)   Mean area = $\frac{1}{4}$ (12 + 9 + 17 + 10)

= 12 m^2

(b)   Arrange the areas of the bedrooms in ascending order as follows:

9   10   12   17

↑
middle position

Median area = $\frac{1}{2}$ (10 + 12)

= 11 m^2

4. The grade point averages (GPA) of 10 seventh grade students are

3.62,   3.31,   3.14,   2.17,   3.75,   2.63,   3.97,
3.58,   2.50,   and   3.23.

Find
(a) the median grade point average,
(b) the mean grade point average
of these students.

Solution

(a) Arrange the GPAs of the students in ascending order as follows:

2.17   2.50   2.63   3.14   3.23   3.31   3.58   3.62   3.75   3.97

↑
middle position

Median GPA = $\frac{1}{2}$(3.23 + 3.31)

= 3.27

Mean GPA = $\frac{1}{10}$(3.62 + 3.31 + 3.14 + 2.17 + 3.75
+ 2.63 + 3.97 + 3.58 + 2.50 + 3.23)

= 3.19

5. (a) The median of the data set

16, 5, 11, 19, x, 4

is 9. Find the value of x.
(b) Find the median of the data set

23, 17, 14, 8, 6, 2, 25.

(c) The data sets in **(a)** and **(b)** are pooled together. Find the median of the combined data set.
(d) Can you derive the result in **(c)** using the results in **(a)** and **(b)**?

Solution

(a) When the data are arranged in ascending order, they can be as follows:

4   5 x 11   16   19

↑
middle position

Median = 9

$\frac{1}{2}$(x + 11) = 9

x + 11 = 18

x = 7

(b) Arrange the data in ascending order as follows:

2   6   8   14   17   23   25

↑
middle position

Median = 14

(c) Arrange the data of the two sets in ascending order as follows:

2   4   5   6   7   8 $\boxed{11}$ 14   16   17   19   23   25

↑
middle position

Median = 11

(d) No, we cannot derive the median of the combined data set from the medians of the two individual data sets.

6. The dot plot below shows the heights (in centimeters) of some plants.

Dot Plot for the Heights of Plants

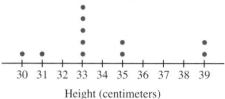

Height (centimeters)

(a) Find the mean height of the plants.
(b) Find the median height of the plants.
(c) Which of the above two measures is a better representation of the center of the distribution?

Solution
(a) Total height of the plants
$= 30 + 31 + 5 \times 33 + 2 \times 35 + 2 \times 39$
$= 374$ cm
Mean height of the plants
$= \frac{374}{11}$
$= 34$ cm

(b) Median height = 33 cm

(c) The median is a better representation of the center of the distribution since the mean is affected more by the extreme value, 39.

Math@Work

7. The population growth rates in the United States from 2005 to 2011 are as follows:

Year	Population Growth Rate (%)
2005	0.92
2006	0.91
2007	0.89
2008	0.88
2009	0.98
2010	0.97
2011	0.96

Source: www.indexmundi.com

(a) Find the mean population growth rate from 2005 to 2011.
(b) Find the median of these population growth rate figures.

Solution
(a) Mean population growth rate from 2005 to 2011
$= \frac{1}{7} (0.92\% + 0.91\% + 0.89\% + 0.88\% + 0.98\% + 0.97\% + 0.96\%)$
$= 0.93\%$

(b) Arrange the population growth rates in ascending order as follows:

0.88 0.89 0.91 0.92 0.96 0.97 0.98

middle position

Median of the population growth rate from 2005 to 2011
$= 0.92\%$

8. The monthly household incomes of 15 families in a survey are as follows:

$6,380	$3,150	$5,890	$4,136	$4,259
$5,420	$4,780	$2,830	$3,459	$8,125
$3,630	$7,365	$4,630	$2,396	$4,950

(a) Find the median income.
(b) Find the mean income.
(c) Determine whether the mean or median is a better representation of the measure of center in this survey.

Solution
(a) Arrange the monthly household incomes in ascending order as follows:

2,396 2,830 3,150 3,459 3,630 4,136 4,259 4,630

4,780 4,950 5,420 5,890 6,380 7,365 8,125

middle position

Median = $4,630

(b) Mean $= \frac{1}{15} (\$2,396 + \$2,830 + \$3,150 + \$3,459$
$+ \$3,630 + \$4,136 + \$4,259 + \$4,630$
$+ \$4,780 + \$4,950 + \$5,420 + \$5,890$
$+ \$6,380 + \$7,365 + \$8,125)$
$= \frac{\$71,400}{15}$
$= \$4,760$

(c) The mean is affected more by the top three incomes, $6,380, $7,365, and $8,125.
The median is a better representation of center in this survey.

Brainworks

9. Construct a data set with five different items so that the median is 37.

   ### Solution
   One possible data set with median = 37 is
   {10, 30, 37, 40, 42}.

10. Construct a data set with six different items so that the mean is 13 and the median is 10.

    ### Solution
    If $x > 13$, the data set {7, 8, 9, 11, 13, x} will have median = 10.
    If the mean = 13,
    $$7 + 8 + 9 + 11 + 13 + x = 13 \times 6$$
    $$x = 30$$
    ∴ one possible data set is {7, 8, 9, 11, 13, 30}.

Exercise 15.5

Basic Practice

1. Find the mode of each of the following data sets.
   (a) 4, 3, 5, 11, 4, 7, 5, 4
   (b) 9, 8, 2, 11, 8, 3, 2
   (c) 13, 16, 17, 9, 7, 6, 11, 5
   (d) 8.4, 3.6, 2.0, 7.5, 3.6, 5.7, 7.5, 3.6, 6.9

   ### Solution
   (a) The data value 4 occurs most often, i.e., 3 times.
       ∴ mode = 4
   (b) The data values 2 and 8 occur most often, i.e., 2 times.
       ∴ mode = 2 and 8
   (c) There is no mode.
   (d) The data value 3.6 occurs most often, i.e., 3 times.
       ∴ mode = 3.6

2. Find the mode of each of the following data sets.
   (a)

0	4	3	2	2	1
0	2	1	0	1	3
2	0	2	0	1	5

   (b)

20	30	20	25	35	15
35	20	15	30	25	20
25	20	25	15	20	30
20	15	25	20	25	25

Solution
(a) The data values 0 and 2 occur most often, i.e., 5 times.
    ∴ mode = 0 and 2
(b) The data value 20 occurs most often, i.e., 8 times.
    ∴ mode = 20

Further Practice

3. The typing speeds, in words per minute, of 12 secretaries are

   37, 46, 43, 39, 46, 51, 38, 47, 46,
   40, 49, 43.
   What is the modal typing speed?

   ### Solution
   The data value 46 occurs most often, i.e., 3 times.
   ∴ mode = 46

4. The sizes of eight pairs of shoes sold are as follows:
   $$7\tfrac{1}{2}, \quad 6, \quad 5, \quad 5\tfrac{1}{2}, \quad 7, \quad 7\tfrac{1}{2}, \quad 6\tfrac{1}{2}, \quad 7\tfrac{1}{2}$$

   (a) Find the modal size.
   (b) Find the median size.
   (c) Is the median size one of the available sizes?

   ### Solution
   (a) The data value $7\tfrac{1}{2}$ occurs most of them, i.e., 3 times.
       ∴ modal size = $7\tfrac{1}{2}$

   (b) Arrange the sizes of the shoes in ascending order as follows:

5	$5\tfrac{1}{2}$	6	$6\tfrac{1}{2}$	7	$7\tfrac{1}{2}$	$7\tfrac{1}{2}$	$7\tfrac{1}{2}$

   ↑
   middle position

   $$\text{Median size} = \tfrac{1}{2}\left(6\tfrac{1}{2} + 7\right)$$
   $$= 6\tfrac{3}{4}$$

   (c) Shoe sizes available are 5, $5\tfrac{1}{2}$, 6, $6\tfrac{1}{2}$, 7, and $7\tfrac{1}{2}$.
       The median size $6\tfrac{3}{4}$ is not one of the available sizes.

5. The daily temperatures, in degrees Celsius, for eleven days in Juneau, Alaska, are shown below.

–2.5, –1.0, 1.2, 0, –3.8, 1.0, –2.5,
–1.2, –1.0, –2.5, –3.1

Find

(a) the mode of these temperatures,

(b) the median temperature,

(c) the mean temperature.

Solution

(a) The data value –2.5 occurs most often, i.e., 3 times.

∴ mode = –2.5 °C

(b) Arrange the daily temperatures in ascending order as follows:

–3.8 –3.1 –2.5 –2.5 –2.5 –1.2 –1.0 –1.0 0 1.0 1.2

↑
middle position

Median = –1.2 °C

(c) Mean = $\frac{1}{11}$[(–2.5) + (–1.0) + 1.2 + 0 + (–3.8) + 1.0 +(–2.5)+(–1.2)+(–1.0)+(–2.5)+(–3.1)]

= –1.4 °C

6. The dot plot below shows the number of spelling mistakes in an essay made by each student in a class.

Dot Plot for the Number of Spelling Mistakes

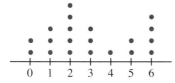

Number of Spelling Mistakes Made
by Each Student

(a) How many students are there in the class?

(b) What is the modal number of spelling mistakes made by the students?

(c) Find the median number of spelling mistakes made by the students.

(d) Find the mean number of spelling mistakes made by the students.

Solution

(a) Number of students = 2 + 3 + 5 + 3 + 1 + 2 + 4
= 20

(b) Mode = 2

(c) Median = $\frac{1}{2}$(2 + 3)
= 2.5

(d) Mean = $\frac{1}{20}$(0 + 3 × 1 + 5 × 2 + 3 × 3 + 4 × 1 + 5 × 2 + 4 × 6)

= $\frac{60}{20}$

= 3

Math@Work

7. The following table shows the number of traffic accidents on a road during each month in a particular year.

Month	Number of traffic accidents
January	19
February	17
March	15
April	13
May	11
June	10
July	18
August	17
September	12
October	17
November	15
December	28

(a) What is the total number of traffic accidents on the road in that year?

(b) Find the mean, median, and mode for the number of traffic accidents in that year.

(c) Which measure is the most appropriate as an average figure for public information?

Solution

(a) Total number of traffic accidents
= 19 + 17 + 15 + 13 + 11 + 10 + 18 + 17 + 12 + 17 + 15 + 28
= 192

(b) Mean = $\frac{192}{12}$

= 16 traffic accidents

Arrange the data in ascending order as follows:

10 11 12 13 15 15 17 17 17 18 19 28

↑
middle position

Median = $\frac{1}{2}$(15 + 17)

= 16 traffic accidents
Mode = 17 traffic accidents

(c) The mode, 17, is a bit higher than the average. Thus, in this case, both the mean and median are the most appropriate as an average figure for public information.

8. The following table shows the number of pets of some households.

Number of pets in each household	Number of households
0	5
1	5
2	7
3	1
4	2

(a) What is the total number of pets in this sample?
(b) Find the median and mode of the data.
(c) Find the mean number of pets per household.
(d) Which one is the most appropriate as a measure of center in this case?

Solution
(a) Total number of plots
$$= 5 \times 0 + 5 \times 1 + 7 \times 2 + 1 \times 3 + 2 \times 4$$
$$= 30$$

(b) Median $= \frac{1}{2}(1 + 2)$

$\qquad\qquad = 1.5$ pets
$\qquad$ Mode $= 2$ pets

(c) Mean $= \frac{30}{20}$

$\qquad\qquad = 1.5$ pets

(d) The mean is the most appropriate measure of center in this case.

9. The numbers of working hours of 15 workers in a week are as follows:

41	36	43	58	8	40	45	50
51	45	40	49	35	45	44	

(a) Find the mean, median, and mode of the data.
(b) Would you use the mean or the median as a measure of center of the data? Why?

Solution
(a) Mean $= \frac{1}{15}(41 + 36 + 43 + 58 + 8 + 40 + 45 + 50$
$\qquad\qquad\qquad + 51 + 45 + 40 + 49 + 35 + 45 + 44)$

$\qquad\quad = \frac{630}{15}$

$\qquad\quad = 42$ hours

Arrange the data in ascending order as follows:

8 35 36 40 40 41 43 |44| 45 45 45 49 50 51 58

↑ middle position

$\qquad$ Median $= 44$ hours
$\qquad$ Mode $= 45$ hours

(b) The extreme value, 8, affects the mean. Hence, it is better to use the median as a measure of center of the data.

Brainworks

10. Construct a data set with seven items so that the mean, median, and mode are all equal to 8.

Solution
Each of the following data sets have seven items such that the mean = median = mode = 8.
(i) 8, 8, 8, 8, 8, 8, 8
(ii) 4, 6, 8, 8, 8, 10, 12

11. Construct a data set with eight items so that the mean is 4, the median is 3, and the mode is 2.

Solution
If $x \geqslant 6$, the data set
$$2, 2, 2, 3, 3, 5, 6, x$$
has median = 3 and mode = 2.
If the mean = 4,
$$2 + 2 + 2 + 3 + 3 + 5 + 6 + x = 4 \times 8$$
$$x = 9$$
One possible data set with eight items so that the mean is 4, the median is 3, and the mode is 2 is
$$2, 2, 2, 3, 3, 5, 6, 9.$$

Review Exercise 15

1. Parade organizers in a town conducted an online poll on its website about the complimentary items that were distributed during the parade. There were 7,200 votes. The poll and its results are shown below.

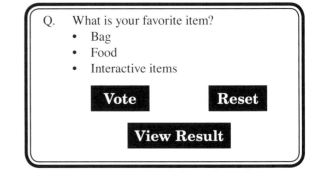

Results

Item	Percentage
Bag	25%
Food	9%
Interactive items	66%

(a) What kind of data-collection method was used?
(b) What problems might be inherent when using the Internet to collect data or perform polls?
(c) How can the problems in **(b)** be mitigated?

Solution
(a) Conducting survey
(b) Each person who participates in the online poll might vote more than once.
(c) The participants are required to fill in their names and email addresses.

2. The following list shows the volume, in fluid ounces, of 25 cups of soda which are filled by a vending machine.

11.8	12.0	11.9	12.1	11.8
12.0	11.6	12.2	12.0	11.9
12.0	12.0	11.8	11.9	11.5
11.9	11.8	12.0	11.6	12.1
12.0	11.9	11.9	11.8	12.0

(a) Represent the data on a dot plot.
(b) Briefly describe the distribution of the volumes of soda.
(c) The cups of soda whose volumes are less than 11.8 fl oz are considered "below expectation". What is the percentage of the total number of cups which are below expectation?
(d) What are the modal and median volumes?
(e) Find the mean volume.

Solution
(a)

Dot plot for the volume of 25 cups of soda

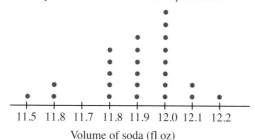

Volume of soda (fl oz)

(b) The data values cluster between 11.8 fl oz and 12.0 fl oz. There is an outlier at 11.5.

(c) There are 3 cups of soda whose volumes are less than 11.8 fl oz.

$$\text{Required percentage} = \frac{3}{25} \times 100\%$$
$$= 12\%$$

(d) Mode = 12.0 fl oz
Median = 11.9 fl oz

(e) Mean = $\frac{1}{25}$ (11.5 + 2 × 11.6 + 5 × 11.8 + 6 × 11.9 + 8 × 12.0 + 2 × 12.1 + 12.2)
= 11.9 fl oz

3. In a survey, the number of people in each of the 10 cars passing a certain traffic junction was tracked. The results are represented by the dot plot below.

Dot Plot for the Number
of People in a Car

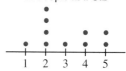

Number of People in a Car

(a) Find the mean, median, and mode of the data.
(b) Find the mean absolute deviation of the data.

Solution
(a) Mean = $\frac{1}{10}$ (1 + 4 × 2 + 3 + 2 × 4 + 2 × 5)
= 3 cars

Median = $\frac{1}{2}$ (2 + 3)
= 2.5 cars

Mode = 2 cars

(b)

Data value	Deviation from Mean	Absolute Deviation
1	–2	2
2	–1	1
2	–1	1
2	–1	1
2	–1	1
3	0	0
4	1	1
4	1	1
5	2	2
5	2	2
	Sum = 0	Sum = 12

MAD = $\frac{12}{10}$
= 1.2

4. The masses of six women are as follows:

46 kg, 43 kg, 72 kg, 50 kg, 43 kg, 58 kg

(a) Find the mean, median, and mode of their masses.
(b) Which measure would give a fair gauge of the average mass of these women?

Solution

(a) Mean mass $= \frac{1}{6}(46 + 43 + 72 + 50 + 43 + 58)$

$= \frac{312}{6}$

$= 52$ kg

Arrange the masses of the women in ascending order as follows:

43 43 46 50 58 72

↑

middle position

Median mass $= \frac{1}{2}(46 + 50)$

$= 48$ kg

Modal mass $= 43$ kg

(b) The mean is affected by the extreme value, 72 kg.
The mode is the lowest value in the data.
The median would give a fair gauge of the average mass of these women.

5. The mean age of five basketball players is 24 years.
(a) If the mean age of four of them is 23 years, find the age of the fifth player.
(b) Find the mean age of these players after three years.

Solution

(a) Let the age of the fifth player be x years.

$\frac{23 \times 4 + x}{5} = 24$

$92 + x = 120$

$x = 28$

The age of the fifth player is 28 years.

(b) The mean age of the players after three years
$= 24 + 3$
$= 27$ years

6. Five boys participated in a fishing competition. None of them caught more than nine fish. The mean, median, and mode of the numbers of fish caught by them are 6, 5, and 4 respectively. Find the number of fish caught by each boy.

Solution

Let $x_1, x_2, x_3, x_4,$ and x_5 be the number of fish caught in ascending order by the boys.

Median $= x_3 = 5$

Mode $= x_1 = x_2 = 4$

Mean $= 6$

$\therefore \quad \frac{x_1 + x_2 + x_3 + x_4 + x_5}{5} = 6$

$x_1 + x_2 + x_3 + x_4 + x_5 = 30$

$4 + 4 + 5 + x_4 + x_5 = 30$

$x_4 + x_5 = 17$

As x_4 and x_5 are integers less than or equal to 9, $x_4 = 8$ and $x_5 = 9$.

The number of fish caught by each boy are 4, 4, 5, 8, and 9 respectively.

7. The table below shows the salaries of 25 employees of a company.

Salary ($)	2,000	2,500	3,000	3,500
Number of employees	3	9	x	5

Find
(a) the value of x,
(b) the modal salary,
(c) the median salary,
(d) the mean salary.

Solution

(a) $3 + 9 + x + 5 = 25$

$\therefore \quad x = 8$

(b) Modal salary $= \$2,500$

(c) Since there are 25 employees, the middle term is 13th term.

(d) Median salary $= \$3,000$

Mean salary $= \frac{1}{25}(\$2,000 \times 3 + \$2,500 \times 9 + \$3,000 \times 8 + \$3,500 \times 5)$

$= \$2,800$

8. The weights (in pounds) of 10 randomly selected bags of apples from Supermarket A and Supermarket B are presented in the following dot plots.

Dot Plot for the Weights of Bags of Apples from Supermarket A

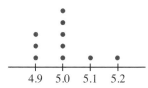

Weight (pounds) of Each Bag of Apples

Dot Plot for the Weights of Bags of Apples from Supermarket B

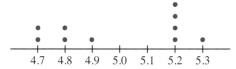

Weight (pounds) of Each Bag of Apples

(a) Briefly describe the two distributions.
(b) Find the median weight of a bag of apples from each of the supermarkets.
(c) Find the mean weight of a bag of apples from each of the supermarkets.
(d) Find the mean absolute deviation (MAD) for each set of data.
(e) Compare the MADs. What conclusions can you draw?

Solution

(a) Supermarket A:
The weights of bags of apples vary from 4.9 pounds to 5.2 pounds. The distribution has its peak at weight = 5.0 pounds and a short tail on the right.

Supermarket B:
The weights of bags of apples vary from 4.7 pounds to 5.3 pounds. The distribution has its peak at weight = 5.2 pounds.

(b) Median weight of a bag of apples from Supermarket A
= 5.0 pounds
Median weight of a bag of apples from Supermarket B
$= \frac{1}{2}(4.9 + 5.2)$
= 5.05 pounds

(c) Mean weight of a bag of apples from Supermarket A
$= \frac{1}{10}(3 \times 4.9 + 5 \times 5.0 + 5.1 + 5.2)$
= 5.0 pounds
Mean weight of a bag of apples from Supermarket B
$= \frac{1}{10}(2 \times 4.7 + 2 \times 4.8 + 4.9 + 4 \times 5.2 + 5.3)$
= 5.0 pounds

(d)

Supermarket A

Weight of a bag of apples		
Data value	Deviation from Mean	Absolute Deviation
4.9	−0.1	0.1
4.9	−0.1	0.1
4.9	−0.1	0.1
5.0	0	0
5.0	0	0
5.0	0	0
5.0	0	0
5.0	0	0
5.1	0.1	0.1
5.1	0.2	0.2
	Sum = 0	Sum = 0.6

Supermarket B

Weight of a bag of apples		
Data value	Deviation from Mean	Absolute Deviation
4.7	−0.3	0.3
4.7	−0.3	0.3
4.8	−0.2	0.2
4.8	−0.2	0.2
4.9	−0.1	0.1
5.2	0.2	0.2
5.2	0.2	0.2
5.2	0.2	0.2
5.2	0.2	0.2
5.3	0.3	0.3
	Sum = 0	Sum = 2.2

MAD for the weights of bags of apples from Supermarket A
$= \frac{0.6}{10}$
= 0.06 pounds

MAD for the weights of bags of apples from Supermarket B
$= \frac{2.2}{10}$
= 0.22 pounds

(e) On average, the data values from Supermarket A differ from the mean by 0.06 pounds while the data values from Supermarket B differ from the mean by 0.22 pounds.

9. A class of 32 students was randomly divided into two equal groups, A and B. Each group was taught a new mathematics topic using different methods. Their scores in a common test on that topic are as follows:

Group A	74	74	30	42	68	53	42	66
	29	64	96	70	68	85	53	30
Group B	69	80	72	27	60	60	55	80
	72	32	45	61	45	32	72	66

(a) Find the mean and median scores of Group A.
(b) Find the mean and median scores of Group B.
(c) Which group's performance is better? Why?
(d) Create a table showing the Data Value, Deviation from Mean, and Absolute Deviation for each set of data. Hence, find their respective mean absolute deviations (MAD).
(e) Compare the MADs. What conclusions can you draw?

Solution
(a) For Group A,

$$\text{mean score} = \frac{1}{16}(74 + 74 + 30 + 42 + 68 + 53$$
$$+ 42 + 66 + 29 + 64 + 96 + 70$$
$$+ 68 + 85 + 53 + 30)$$
$$= \frac{944}{16}$$
$$= 59$$

Arrange the scores for Group A's students in ascending order as follows:

29 30 30 42 42 53 53 64 66 68 68 74 74 74 85 96

↑
middle position

$$\text{Median score} = \frac{1}{2}(64 + 66)$$
$$= 65$$

(b) For Group B,

$$\text{mean score} = \frac{1}{16}(69 + 80 + 72 + 27 + 60 + 60$$
$$+ 55 + 80 + 72 + 32 + 45 + 61$$
$$+ 45 + 32 + 72 + 66)$$
$$= \frac{928}{16}$$
$$= 58$$

Arrange the scores for Group B's students in ascending order as follows:

27 32 32 45 45 55 60 60 61 66 69 72 72 72 80 80

↑
middle position

$$\text{Median score} = \frac{1}{2}(60 + 61)$$
$$= 60.5$$

(c) Both the mean and median scores of Group A are higher than those of Group B. Therefore, Group A's performance is better.

(d)

Group A

Score		
Data value	Deviation from Mean	Absolute Deviation
29	−30	30
30	−29	29
30	−29	29
42	−17	17
42	−17	17
53	−6	6
53	−6	6
64	5	5
66	7	7
68	9	9
68	9	9
74	15	15
74	15	15
74	15	15
85	26	26
96	37	37
	Sum = 4	Sum = 272

Group B

Score		
Data value	Deviation from Mean	Absolute Deviation
27	−31	31
32	−26	26
32	−26	26
45	−13	13
45	−13	13
55	−3	3
60	2	2
60	2	2
61	3	3
66	8	8
69	11	11
72	14	14
72	14	14
72	14	14
80	22	22
80	22	22
	Sum = 0	Sum = 224

MAD for Group $A = \dfrac{272}{16} = 17$

MAD for Group $B = \dfrac{224}{16} = 14$

(e) On average, the data values from Group A differ from the mean (59 points) by 17 points while the data values from Group B differ from the mean (58 points) by 14 points.

10. The number of goals scored by soccer teams in the soccer league is shown in the following table.

Number of goals	0	1	2	3
Number of teams	5	6	3	y

(a) State the largest possible value of y if the mode is 1 goal.

(b) If the median is 1 goal, find the largest possible value of y.

(c) Find the value of y given that the mean is 1 goal.

Solution

(a) If the mode is 1 goal, y must be smaller than 6. Hence, the largest possible value of y is 5.

(b) When the middle position is at the last 1 as shown below, y has the largest value.

$$\overbrace{0, 0, 0, 0, 0, 1, 1, 1, 1, 1, 1}^{10 \text{ terms}}, 2, 2, 2, 3, 3, \overbrace{\ldots, 3}^{y \text{ terms}}$$

middle position

$\therefore$ the largest possible value of $y = 10 - 3 = 7$.

(c)
$$\text{Mean} = 1 \text{ goal}$$
$$\frac{5 \times 0 + 6 \times 1 + 3 \times 2 + y \times 3}{5 + 6 + 3 + y} = 1$$
$$\frac{12 + 3y}{14 + y} = 1$$
$$12 + 3y = 14 + y$$
$$2y = 2$$
$$\therefore \quad y = 1$$

Chapter 16   Probability Of Simple Events

Class Activity 1

Objective: To understand the probability of a chance event by collecting data and observing the frequency of its happening.

Tasks

(a)   Conduct a random experiment of tossing a coin 20 times.

Head   Tail

In tossing a coin, the results of getting a *head* or a *tail* are the two possible outcomes.

(b)   Copy the following table. Record the result of each toss in it. Use the notation 'H' for *head* and 'T' for *tail*.

Trial	1st	2nd	3rd	4th	5th	6th	7th	8th	9th	10th
Outcome										

Trial	11th	12th	13th	14th	15th	16th	17th	18th	19th	20th
Outcome										

Note: The results depend on the outcomes obtained by each student.

Questions

1.   Before a coin is tossed, will you be able to predict with certainty the outcome of the toss?

No, the outcome cannot be predicted with certainty before a coin is tossed.

2.   In your result table, is there any trend in the outcomes?

No, there is no trend in the outcomes.

3.   Find the percentage of getting a *head* in your 20 tosses.

The answer depends on the actual outcomes. For example, if there are *h heads*, the answer is $\frac{h}{20} \times 100\%$.

4.   Compare and discuss your results with your classmates. What can you say about the nature of the results of tossing a coin?

The results of each classmate are likely to be different. However, the percentage of *heads* obtained by most students would be close to 50%.

The results obtained are those of a random experiment.

5.   In tossing a coin, what would you say about the chance of getting a *head*?

The chance of getting a *head* is $\frac{1}{2}$.

Class Activity 2

Objective: To collect data from another chance process and to predict the probability of a chance event from its relative frequency of occurrence.

Tasks

(a) Conduct a random experiment of rolling a die with six faces for 30 times. Each face denotes the numbers 1, 2, 3, 4, 5, and 6 respectively as shown below.

(b) Copy and complete the following table with the results obtained from rolling the die.

Trial	1st	2nd	3rd	4th	5th	6th	7th	8th	9th	10th
Outcome										

Trial	11th	12th	13th	14th	15th	16th	17th	18th	19th	20th
Outcome										

Trial	21st	22nd	23rd	24th	25th	26th	27th	28th	29th	30th
Outcome										

Note: The results depend on the outcomes obtained by each student.

Questions

1. What are the possible outcomes?

   The possible outcomes are 1, 2, 3, 4, 5, and 6.

2. Before a die is rolled, will you be able to predict with certainty the outcome of the throw?

   No, the outcome cannot be predicted with certainty before a die is rolled.

3. In your result table, is there any trend in the outcomes?

   No, there is no trend in the outcomes.

4. Find the percentage of getting a '2' in your 30 throws.

   The answer depends on the actual outcomes of each student.

5. Compare and discuss your results with your classmates. What can you say about the nature of the results of rolling a die?

   The results of each classmate are likely to be different. The results obtained are those of a random experiment.

6. In rolling a die, what can you say about the chance of getting a '2'?

   The chance of getting a '2' is $\frac{1}{6}$.

Class Activity 3

Objective: To further study relative frequency of occurrence of a chance event and its probability of occurrence using random numbers generated from a spreadsheet program.

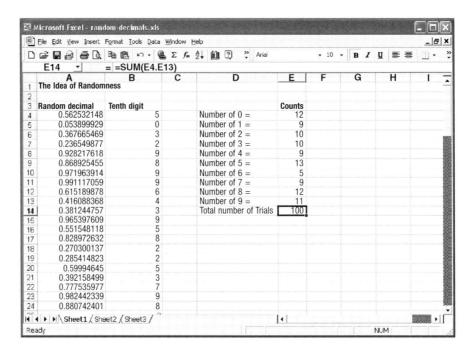

The random number function RAND() of Excel generates an evenly distributed random number greater than or equal to 0 and less than 1 each time. You may imagine it as picking up a number x randomly between 0 and 1 on the number line, such that $0 \leq x < 1$.

Tasks

(a) Create the headers in the first three rows and the text at cells D4 to D14 on a spreadsheet as shown above.

(b) At the cell A4, enter the formula =RAND(). A random decimal between 0 and 1 will appear.

(c) At the cell B4, enter the formula =INT(A4*10). The tenth digit of the random decimal at the cell A4 will appear. It can be regarded as a random digit which may be 0, 1, 2, ..., or 9.

(d) Copy the cells A4 and B4 to the cells from A5 to B103. Then we will have generated 100 random digits in column B from cells B4 to B103.

(e) At the cell E4, enter the formula =COUNTIF(B4:B103, 0). This gives the number of 0's in column B.

(f) At the cell E5, enter the formula =COUNTIF(B4:B103, 1). This gives the number of 1's in column B.

(g) Similarly, complete the counts for the number of each random digit in column B.

(h) At the cell E14, enter the formula =SUM(E4:E13). This gives the total number of random digits generated. This should be 100.

(i) Enter a number at any empty cell, say E18. The random numbers will be regenerated.

Questions

1. Describe in your own words the random number generated from the spreadsheet program.

   The random number generated by the spreadsheet program is a decimal between 0 and 1. Each decimal has an equal chance of occurring.

2. Can you observe any patterns of the random digits in column B?

   No, there is no pattern observed.

3. What can you say about the count of each random digit in column B?

   The count of each random digit may not be equal.

4. When you regenerate the random numbers, will the counts of individual random digits be unchanged?

   Every time when the random digits are regenerated, the counts of individual random digits may differ from previous ones.

5. If you generate 1,000 random digits in column B in the same way, how many 8's do you expect to get in these 1,000 random digits?

   I expect to get close to 100 of them.

Class Activity 4

Objective: To compare observed frequencies from a random experiment to the probabilities obtained from the definition of probability.

Tasks

1. A coin is tossed.

   (a) How many likely outcomes are there?

   There are 2 likely outcomes, which are *head* and *tail*.

   (b) Use the definition of probability to determine the probability of getting a *head*.

   By using the definition of probability, the probability of getting a *head* = $\frac{1}{2}$.

   (c) Refer to your results of Class Activity 1. What fraction of your tosses resulted in *head*s?

   The results of each classmate are likely to be different. However, the fraction of the tosses resulted in *head*s should be close to $\frac{1}{2}$.

   (d) How does the answer in **(c)** compare to that in **(b)**? Are they exactly the same?

   The answers in (b) and (c) should be same or close to each other.

   (e) If the results are different, why do you think they are different?

   The answer in (c) depends greatly on the number of trials, i.e., the more trials that are conducted in the experiment, the closer the calculations will be for the answers in (b) and (c).

2. Collect the results for Class Activity 1 from the entire class.

(a) Calculate the fraction of tosses that result in getting a *head*.

The fraction of tosses that result in getting a *head* should be close to $\frac{1}{2}$.

(b) Compare the result in **2(a)** to your answers for **1(b)** and **(c)**. Explain any differences.

The answers for 2(a), 1(b), and 1(c) should be same or close to each other. However, the result in 2(a) might be closer to $\frac{1}{2}$ if compared to the answer for 1(c) due to the increase of number of trials.

3. Design a probability experiment involving drawing a card from a deck or partial deck of playing cards. Conduct the experiment and record the results of the chance process.

(a) Using the definition of probability stated earlier, find the probability of one random event of your experiment.

The results depend on the outcomes obtained by each student.

(b) Compare the answer in **3(a)** to the probabilities obtained from your experimental results as well as from the entire class result. Explain any possible sources of discrepancy.

The results depend on the outcomes obtained by each student.

Discuss

Page 177
Consider the two sets below:
A = {teachers below 30 years of age in *XYZ* School}
B = {young teachers in *XYZ* School}.
Which set is well-defined? Why?

Set *A* is well-defined but set *B* is not because "below 30 years of age" gives us a specified boundary whereas "young" does not.

Page 179
Is there only one way to express the set S in Example 3 in set-builder notation?

No. One of the possible ways could be: "$\{x^2 : x = 1, 2, 3, 4, \text{ or } 5\}$".

Page 181
Is the statement "*If $F \subseteq G$ and $G \subseteq F$, then $F = G$*" correct? Why?

Yes.
Every element in *F* is also in *G*, and every element in *G* is also in *F*. This means that *F* and *G* contain exactly the same elements. Hence, they are equal.

Page 182
Do you think the set A = {x : x is an integer and 2x + 3 = 0} is an empty set? Why?

Yes. Since the only solution of $2x + 3 = 0$ is $x = -\frac{3}{2} = -1\frac{1}{2}$, which is not an integer, an integer *x* that satisfies $2x + 3 = 0$ does not exist.

Page 194
1. Refer to Example 11. Are the event of drawing a yellow ball and the event of drawing a green ball equally likely?
No

2. What is the range of the value of P(*E*) for any event *E*?
0 to 1

3. Can we have an event *E* such that P(*E*) = 1?
Yes.

Extend Your Learning Curve

Probability Involving Geometry

(a) In the figure, P is a random point on the line segment AB.

Find the probability that $AP : PB$ is less than $1 : 2$.

(b) The figure shows a circular target of radius 15 cm. The bull's eye is of radius 5 cm. Considering one of your throws which has hit the target, what is the probability that it will hit the bull's eye?

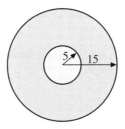

(c) What are the sample spaces in **(a)** and **(b)**? Are they finite?

Suggested Answer:

(a)

As shown in the figure, let $AB = k$, $AP_0 = h$, and $AP = x$, where P_0 is a point on AB such that $AP_0 : P_0B = 1 : 2$.

Then $\qquad P_0B = k - h$.

$$h : (k - h) = 1 : 2$$
$$2h = k - h$$
$$3h = k$$
$$h = \frac{k}{3}$$

If P is a point on the line segment AP_0,

then $\qquad AP : PB = x : (k - x)$

$\qquad\qquad\qquad < h : (k - h) \qquad$ Since $x < h$, $\frac{x}{k-x} < \frac{h}{k-h}$.

$\qquad\qquad\qquad = AP_0 : P_0B$

$\qquad\qquad\qquad = 1 : 2$

Since the point P is equally likely to be any point on the line segment AB,

probability that $AP : PB$ will be less than $1 : 2 = \dfrac{AP_0}{AB}$

$$= \frac{1}{3}$$

(b) Probability of hitting the bull's eye $= \dfrac{\text{Area of the bull's eye}}{\text{Area of the target}}$

$$= \frac{\pi \times 5^2}{\pi \times 15^2}$$

$$= \frac{25}{225}$$

$$= \frac{1}{9}$$

(c) The sample space in **(a)** consists of all the points on the line segment AB.
The sample space in **(b)** consists of all the points on the target.
Both of them are infinite.

> **Note:** The definition of probability stated in Section 16.2 is for **finite** sample space only. We have to extend this definition to cater for the probability involving geometry.

Try It!

Section 16.1

1. Given the set C = {letters of the word '*STUDENT*'},
   (a) list the elements of the set C,
   (b) find $n(C)$.

   ### Solution
   (a) $C = \{S, T, U, D, E, N\}$
   (b) $n(C) = 6$

2. Give the set B = {colors of the American flag},
   (a) list the elements of the set B,
   (b) state $n(B)$,
   (c) is '*red*' an element of B?

   ### Solution
   (a) $B = \{blue, red, white\}$
   (b) $n(B) = 3$
   (c) Yes, $red \in B$.

3. Let $T = \{3, 4, 5, 6\}$.
   (a) Is $\frac{1}{3}$ an element of T?
   (b) Express T in set-builder notation.

   ### Solution
   (a) No, $\frac{1}{3} \notin T$.
   (b) $T = \{x : x$ is an integer and $2 < x < 7\}$

4. Let $C = \{x : x$ is a digit from the phone number '92883388'}
   and $D = \{x : x$ is a digit from the phone number '92382238'}.
   Is $C = D$?

   ### Solution
   $C = \{9, 2, 8, 3\}$
   $D = \{9, 2, 3, 8\}$
   Since both sets C and D have the same elements,
   $C = D$.

5. Let $P = \{1, 3\}$, $Q = \{1, 2, 3, 4\}$, $R = \{4, 3, 2, 1\}$, and
   $S = \{1, 3, 5\}$. Using '⊂' '⊄', '⊈', and '=', describe the
   relationship between the following sets.
   (a) P and Q (b) Q and R
   (c) P and S (d) Q and S

   ### Solution
   $P = \{1, 3\}$
   $Q = \{1, 2, 3, 4\}$
   $R = \{4, 3, 2, 1\}$
   $S = \{1, 3, 5\}$

   (a) $1 \in P$ and $1 \in Q$,
       $3 \in P$ and $3 \in Q$,
       $2 \in Q$ but $2 \notin P$.
       $\therefore P \subset Q$.

   (b) Since $Q \subseteq R$ and $R \subseteq Q$, $Q = R$.

   (c) $1 \in P$ and $1 \in S$,
       $3 \in P$ and $3 \in S$,
       $5 \in S$ but $5 \notin P$.
       $\therefore P \subset S$.

   (d) $2 \in Q$ but $2 \notin S$,
       $5 \in S$ but $5 \notin Q$.
       Hence, $Q \nsubseteq S$ and $S \nsubseteq Q$.

6. Suggest a universal set ξ for each of the following sets.
   (a) $Q = \{drill, screwdriver, hammer, saw\}$
   (b) $R = \{1, 3, 5\}$

   ### Solution
   (a) $\xi = \{carpentry\ tools\}$
   (b) $\xi = \{x : x$ is an odd number$\}$

7. Let $B = \{1, 2, 3, 4\}$. List all the subsets of B.

   ### Solution
   $B = \{1, 2, 3, 4\}$
   The subsets of B are as follows:
   $\phi, \{1\}, \{2\}, \{3\}, \{4\},$
   $\{1, 2\}, \{1, 3\}, \{1, 4\}, \{2, 3\}, \{2, 4\}, \{3, 4\},$
   $\{1, 2, 3\}, \{1, 2, 4\}, \{1, 3, 4\}, \{2, 3, 4\},$
   $\{1, 2, 3, 4\}.$

8. Let $\xi = \{a, b, c, x, y, z\}$,
   $P = \{b, y, z\}$,
   and $Q = \{x, y, z, c, b, a\}$.
   (a) List the elements of
       (i) P',
       (ii) Q'.
   (b) Describe the relationship between Q and ξ.
   (c) What can you say about the complement of ξ?

   ### Solution
   (a) (i) $P' = \{a, c, x\}$
       (ii) $Q' = \phi$
   (b) Since Q and ξ have exactly the same elements,
       $Q = \xi$.
   (c) The complement of ξ is an empty set.

Section 16.2

9. A fair die is rolled. Find the probability of getting
  (a) a 5,
  (b) a multiple of 3.

Solution
  (a) The possible outcomes are 1, 2, 3, 4, 5, and 6.
  $$P(\text{getting a 5}) = \frac{1}{6}$$
  (b) The outcomes which are multiples of 3 are 3 and 6.
  $$P(\text{getting a multiple of 3}) = \frac{2}{6}$$
  $$= \frac{1}{3}$$

10. A card is drawn randomly from a deck of 52 playing cards. Find the probability that the card is
  (a) black, (b) an ace,
  (c) a red queen.

Solution
  (a) There are 13 black spades and 13 black clubs.
  $$P(\text{a black card}) = \frac{26}{52}$$
  $$= \frac{1}{2}$$
  (b) There are 4 aces.
  $$P(\text{an ace card}) = \frac{4}{52}$$
  $$= \frac{1}{13}$$
  (c) There are 2 red queens (heart queen and diamond queen).
  $$\therefore P(\text{a red queen card}) = \frac{2}{52}$$
  $$= \frac{1}{26}$$

11. There are 40 students in a class. Six of them wear glasses, four of them wear contact lenses, and the rest can see without vision correction. A student is selected at random. Find the probability that the student selected
  (a) does not have to correct his vision,
  (b) is blind.

Solution
  (a) $40 - 6 - 4 = 30$ students can see without vision correction.
  P(selecting a student who does not have to correct his vision)
  $$= \frac{30}{40}$$
  $$= \frac{3}{4}$$
  (b) There are no students who are blind in the class.
  P(selecting a student who is blind)
  $$= \frac{0}{40}$$
  $$= 0$$

Section 16.3

12. A multiple-choice question has five options, namely A, B, C, D, and E. A student marks an option at random.
  (a) What is the sample space S of the experiment?
  (b) Option B is the only correct answer for this question. Let F be the event that the option marked by the student is incorrect. List all the possible outcomes of this event.
  (c) State the values of $n(S)$ and $n(F)$.
  (d) Find P(F).

Solution
  (a) Sample space $S = \{A, B, C, D, E\}$
  (b) $F = \{A, C, D, E\}$
  (c) $n(S) = 5$, $n(F) = 4$
  (d) $P(F) = \frac{4}{5}$

13. The reading in seconds of a digital clock is observed at random.
  (a) List the sample space S.
  (b) Let G be the event that at least one of the digits in the reading is '5'. List the event G.
  (c) State the values of $n(S)$ and $n(G)$.
  (d) Find P(G).
  (e) Find P(G').

Solution
  (a) Sample space $= \{00, 01, 02, \ldots, 59\}$
  (b) $G = \{05, 15, 25, 35, 45, 55, 50, 51, 52, 53, 54, 56, 57, 58, 59\}$.
  (c) $n(S) = 60$, $n(G) = 15$
  (d) $P(G) = \frac{n(G)}{n(S)}$
  $$= \frac{15}{60}$$
  $$= \frac{1}{4}$$
  (e) $P(G') = 1 - P(G)$
  $$= 1 - \frac{1}{4}$$
  $$= \frac{3}{4}$$

14. There are 15 cats, 18 dogs, and 3 rabbits in a pet store. An animal is selected at random. Find the probability that the animal

(a) has four legs,

(b) is an insect,

(c) is not a rabbit.

Solution

(a) Total number of animals = 15 + 18 + 3

$$= 36$$

The cat, dog, and rabbit have 4 legs each.

$$\therefore \ \text{P(an animal has 4 legs)} = \frac{36}{36}$$

$$= 1$$

(b) All the animals are not insects.

$$\text{P(an insect)} = \frac{0}{36}$$

$$= 0$$

(c) $\text{P(not a rabbit)} = \dfrac{15 + 18}{36}$

$$= \frac{33}{36}$$

$$= \frac{11}{12}$$

Exercise 16.1

Basic Practice

1. Represent each of the following sets by listing its elements.
   (a) A = {letters in the word '*mathematics*'}
   (b) B = {consonants in the word '*WASHINGTON*'}
   (c) C = {the seasons in a year}
   (d) D = {days of a week}

   Solution
   (a) A = {*m, a, t, h, e, i, c, s*}
   (b) B = {*W, S, H, N, G, T*}
   (c) C = {*spring, summer, autumn, winter*}
   (d) D = {*Monday, Tuesday, Wednesday, Thursday, Friday, Saturday, Sunday*}

2. List the elements in each of the following sets.
   (a) P = {$x : x$ is a digit in the password '501314'}
   (b) Q = {$x : x$ is an even prime number}
   (c) R = {$x : x$ is a multiple of 9 less than 50}
   (d) S = {$x : x$ is a non-negative integer}

   Solution
   (a) P = {5, 0, 1, 3, 4}
   (b) Q = {2}
   (c) R = {9, 18, 27, 36, 45}
   (d) S = {0, 1, 2, 3, 4, ...}

3. Express each of the following sets in set-builder notation.
   (a) The set of factors of 12.
   (b) {3, 6, 9, 12, ...}
   (c) {2, 3, 5, 7, 11, 13, ...}

   Solution
   (a) A = {factors of 12}
   $\quad$ = {$x : x$ is a factor of 12}
   (b) B = {3, 6, 9, 12, ...}
   $\quad$ = {$x : x$ is a multiple of 3}
   (c) C = {2, 3, 5, 7, 11, 13, ...}
   $\quad$ = {$x : x$ is a prime number}

4. Let A = {1, 4, 7, 12, 16}. Determine whether each of the following statements is true or false.
   (a) $10 \notin A$
   (b) $1 + 4 \in A$
   (c) {12, 16} $\in A$
   (d) {1} $\subset A$

   Solution
   (a) '$10 \notin A$' is true.
   (b) $1 + 4 = 5$ and $5 \notin A$.
   '$1 + 4 \in A$' is false.

(c) {12, 16} is a subset of A.
   '{12, 16} $\in A$' is false.
   (d) '{1} $\subset A$' is true.

5. Let X = {a, e, i, o, u}. Determine whether each of the following statements is true or false.
   (a) $\phi \subset X$
   (b) {u, o, i, e, a} = X
   (c) {a, i, u} $\subset X$
   (d) {a} $\in X$

   Solution
   (a) The empty set, ϕ, is a subset of every set.
   '$\phi \subset X$' is true.
   (b) '{u, o, i, e, a} = X' is true.
   (c) '{a, i, u} $\subset X$' is true.
   (d) {a} is a subset of X, not an element of X.
   '{a} $\in X$' is false.

6. (a) List all the subsets of the set S = {*on, off*}.
   (b) Write down the subset of S which is not a proper subset.

   Solution
   (a) The subsets of S = {*on, off*} are as follows:
   ϕ, {*on*}, {*off*}, {*on, off*}.
   (b) The required subset is {*on, off*}.

7. (a) List all the subsets of the set T = {3, 6, 9}.
   (b) Write down the number of proper subsets of T.

   Solution
   (a) The subsets of T = {3, 6, 9} are as follows:
   ϕ, {3}, {6}, {9}, {3, 6}, {3, 9}, {6, 9}, {3, 6, 9}.
   (b) The number of proper subsets of T is 7.

8. Let ξ = {*fog, snow, cloud, rain, dew, ice*},
   M = {*cloud, rain*},
   and N = {*snow*}.
   List the elements of the set
   (a) M',
   (b) N'.

   Solution
   (a) M' = {*fog, snow, dew, ice*}
   (b) N' = {*fog, cloud, rain, dew, ice*}

9. Let ξ = {letters in the word '*complement*'}
    and A = {letters in the word '*element*'}.
    (a) List the elements of ξ and A.
    (b) List the elements of A'.

    Solution
    (a) ξ = {*c, o, m, p, l, e, n, t*}
        A = {*e, l, m, n, t*}

    (b) A' = {*c, o, p*}

10. Let ξ = {*sodium, potassium, calcium, magnesium, zinc,*
        iron, lead}
    and A = {*calcium, zinc, lead*}. Find
    (a) $n(\xi)$,   (b) $n(A)$,
    (c) $n(A')$,   (d) $n(\phi)$.

    Solution
    (a) $n(\xi) = 7$
    (b) $n(A) = 3$
    (c) A' = {*sodium, potassium, magnesium, iron*}
        $n(A') = 4$
    (d) $n(\phi) = 0$

Further Practice

11. Let A = {$x : x$ is an integer greater than 0 but less than
        4},
    B = {$x : x$ is a root of $5x - 10 = 0$},
    C = {3, 2, 1},
    and D = {0, 1, 2}.
    (a) Describe the relationship for each of the following
        sets using '$\subset$', '$\subseteq$', '$\not\subseteq$', and '='.
        (i) A and B (ii) A and C
        (iii) B and D (iv) C and D
    (b) Find the number of elements in each of the following
        sets.
        (i) A (ii) B

    Solution
    (a) A = {1, 2, 3}
        B = {2}
        C = {3, 2, 1}
        D = {0, 1, 2}
        (i) $B \subset A$ (ii) $A = C$
        (iii) $B \subset D$ (iv) $C \not\subseteq D, D \not\subseteq C$
    (b) (i) $n(A) = 3$ (ii) $n(B) = 1$

12. Let A = {a, b, c}. Determine whether each of the following
    is true or false.
    (a) {a, b} $\in A$ (b) $A \in \xi$
    (c) $A \subseteq A$ (d) {ϕ} = ϕ

Solution
(a) {a, b} is a subset of A.
    '{a, b} $\in A$' is false.

(b) A is a subset of ξ, not an element of ξ.
    '$A \in \xi$' is false.

(c) $A \subseteq A$ is true.

(d) {ϕ} is a set with the element ϕ. Hence, it is non-empty.
    '{ϕ} = ϕ' is false.

13. A, B, and C are three sets such that $A \subset B$ and $B \subset C$.
    (a) If $x \in B$, is it necessary that
        (i) $x \in A$?
        (ii) $x \in C$?
    (b) What is the relationship between the sets, A and C?

Solution
(a) (i)   If A = {1, 6} and B = {1, 4, 6},
        then $A \subset B$, $4 \in B$ but $4 \notin A$.
        $\therefore$ it is NOT necessary that $x \in A$.
    (ii) By the definition of subset, $x \in C$.
(b) If $x \in A$, then $x \in B$.
    If $x \in B$, then $x \in C$.
    $\therefore$ if $x \in A$, then $x \in C$.
    i.e., $A \subset C$.

14. Suggest a universal set for each of the following sets.
    (a) {*birds, cats, dogs, fish*}
    (b) {*oxygen, hydrogen, nitrogen*}
    (c) {*Arizona, California, Oregon, Texas*}
    (d) {1, 2, 3, 4}

Solution
(a) The universal set may be {all animals}.
(b) The universal set may be {all chemical elements}.
(c) The universal set may be
    {all states in the United States}.
(d) The universal set may be {all whole numbers}.

15. Let ξ = {$x : x$ is a whole number},
    A = {$x : x$ is an odd integer},
    and B = {$x : x$ is a multiple of 4}.
    (a) Express ξ, A, and B by listing their elements.
    (b) Express A' by
        (i)   listing its elements,
        (ii) using set-builder notation.

Solution
(a) ξ = {$x : x$ is a whole number}
        = {0, 1, 2, 3, ...}
    A = {$x : x$ is an odd integer}
        = {1, 3, 5, 7, ...}
    B = {$x : x$ is a multiple of 4}
        = {4, 8, 12, 16, ...}

(b) **(i)** $A' = \{0, 2, 4, 6, ...\}$
    (ii) $A' = \{x : x$ is not an odd integer$\}$

Math@Work

16. Let $R = \{$the seven colors of a rainbow perceived by human color vision$\}$
and $P = \{black, cyan, magenta, yellow\}$,
which is the set of colors used for four-color printing.
(a) List the elements of the set R.
(b) Is white $\in R$?
(c) Is $P \subset R$?
(d) Suggest a universal set for the sets R and P.

Solution
(a) $R = \{$the seven colors of a rainbow perceived by human color vision$\}$
    $= \{red, orange, yellow, green, blue, indigo, violet\}$

(b) No, $white \notin R$.

(c) $black \in P$ but $black \notin R$.
    $\therefore P$ is NOT a proper subset of R.

(d) The universal set may be $\{$all colors$\}$.

17. On a lunch menu, the choices of main dishes are chicken and fish, and the choices of beverages are coffee, tea, and fruit juice.
(a) List the elements of
    (i) the set of choices of main dishes, M,
    (ii) the set of choices of beverages, B.
(b) Suggest a universal set for each of the following sets.
    (i) M,
    (ii) B.
(c) If $E = \{chicken, fish, lamb\}$, what is the relationship between E and M?

Solution
(a) **(i)** $M = \{chicken, fish\}$
    (ii) $B = \{coffee, tea, fruit juice\}$

(b) **(i)** A universal set for the set M may be $\{$all main dishes$\}$.
    (ii) A universal set for the set B may be $\{$all beverages$\}$.

(c) All the elements of M are elements of E,
    $lamb \in E$ but $lamb \notin M$,
    $\therefore M \subset E$.

18. Let ξ be the set of all students in SMART School.
Suppose $A = \{$all seventh grade students$\}$
and $B = \{$all seventh grade female students$\}$.
(a) Describe the sets A' and B'.
(b) Describe the relationship for each of the following sets.
    (i) A and B **(ii)** A' and B'

Solution
(a) $A' = \{$all non-seventh grade students$\}$
    $B' = \{$all students who are not seventh grade female students$\}$

(b) **(i)** $B \subset A$
    (ii) $A' \subset B'$

19. Let $A = \{1, 3, 8\}$ and $B = \{3, 6, 8\}$.
(a) Create a universal set ξ such that $A \subset \xi$ and $B \subset \xi$
(b) Create a set C such that $C \subset A$ and $C \subset B$.

Solution
(a) The universal set may be $\xi = \{1, 2, 3, 6, 7, 8\}$.
(b) The set C may be $C = \{8\}$.

Exercise 16.2
Basic Practice

1. An unbiased coin is tossed. What is the probability of getting
(a) a head,
(b) a tail?

Solution
(a) P(a head) $= \dfrac{1}{2}$

(b) P(a tail) $= \dfrac{1}{2}$

2. A fair die is rolled. Find the probability of getting
(a) a 3,
(b) an even number,
(c) a number greater than 4.

Solution
(a) P(getting a 3) $= \dfrac{1}{6}$

(b) The favorable outcomes of the event of getting an even number are 2, 4, and 6.
    P(getting an even number) $= \dfrac{3}{6}$
    $= \dfrac{1}{2}$

(c) The favorable outcomes of the event of getting a number greater than 4 are 5 and 6.
    P(getting a number greater than 4) $= \dfrac{2}{6}$
    $= \dfrac{1}{3}$

3. A card is drawn at random from a deck of 52 playing cards. Find the probability that the card drawn is
   (a) green,
   (b) a king,
   (c) a number card.

   Solution
   (a) There is no green card.
       P(a green card) = 0
   (b) P(a king card) = $\frac{4}{52}$
                      = $\frac{1}{13}$
   (c) The number cards in each suit are 2, 3, 4, 5, 6, 7, 8, 9, and 10.

       There are 9 × 4 = 36 number cards.

       P(a number card) = $\frac{36}{52}$
                        = $\frac{9}{13}$

4. A letter is chosen at random from the word '*PORTLAND*'. Find the probability that the chosen letter is
   (a) the letter '*P*',
   (b) a vowel.

   Solution
   (a) There are 8 letters in the word '*PORTLAND*'.

       P(choosing the letter '*P*') = $\frac{1}{8}$

   (b) The vowels in the word '*PORTLAND*' are *O* and *A*.

       P(choosing a vowel) = $\frac{2}{8}$
                           = $\frac{1}{4}$

5. There are 20 boys and 16 girls in a class. If one of the students is selected at random to present her solution of a mathematics question to the class, what is the probability that the student is
   (a) a boy?
   (b) a girl?

   Solution
   (a) Total number of students = 20 + 16
                                = 36

       P(a boy) = $\frac{20}{36}$
                = $\frac{5}{9}$
   (b) P(a girl) = $\frac{16}{36}$
                 = $\frac{4}{9}$

6. A bag contains 15 coins, of which 12 are silver coins and the rest are gold coins. A coin is drawn at random from the bag. Find the probability of drawing a
   (a) silver coin,
   (b) gold coin,
   (c) copper coin.

   Solution
   (a) P(a silver coin) = $\frac{12}{15}$
                        = $\frac{4}{5}$

   (b) Number of gold coins = 15 − 12
                           = 3

       P(a gold coin) = $\frac{3}{15}$
                      = $\frac{1}{5}$

   (c) There is no copper coin.
       P(a copper coin) = 0

Further Practice

7. A box contains ten chips that are numbered from 1 to 10. A chip is drawn at random from the box. Find the probability that the number on the chip is
   (a) greater than 7,   (b) a prime,
   (c) a multiple of 4.

   Solution
   (a) Outcomes that are greater than 7 are 8, 9, and 10.

       P(a number is greater than 7) = $\frac{3}{10}$

   (b) Outcomes that are primes are 2, 3, 5, and 7.

       P(a number is a prime) = $\frac{4}{10}$
                              = $\frac{2}{5}$

   (c) Outcomes that are multiples of 4 are 4 and 8.

       P(a number is a multiple of 4) = $\frac{2}{10}$
                                      = $\frac{1}{5}$

8. There are 12 eggs in a basket, of which two are rotten. If an egg is picked randomly from the basket, what is the probability of getting an egg that is not rotten?

   Solution
   P(an egg is not rotten) = $\frac{12-2}{12}$
                          = $\frac{10}{12}$
                          = $\frac{5}{6}$

9. There are three yellow roses, four white roses, and five red roses in a bouquet of flowers. If a rose is selected at random from the bouquet, find the probability that the rose is
(a) white,
(b) red,
(c) blue.

Solution
(a) Total number of roses = 3 + 4 + 5
$$= 12$$

P(a white rose) $= \dfrac{4}{12}$

$$= \dfrac{1}{3}$$

(b) P(a red rose) $= \dfrac{5}{12}$

(c) There is no black rose.
P(a black rose) = 0

10. A letter is chosen at random from the word 'MATHEMATICS'. Find the probability that the chosen letter is
(a) the letter 'M',
(b) a consonant,
(c) the letter 'K'.

Solution
(a) Total number of letters in 'MATHEMATICS'
$$= 11$$

P(choosing the letter 'M') $= \dfrac{2}{11}$

(b) The consonants in the word 'MATHEMATICS' are M, T, H, M, T, C, and S.

P(choosing a consonant) $= \dfrac{7}{11}$

(c) There is no letter 'K' in the word.
P(choosing the letter 'K') = 0

Math@Work

11. There are 12 mathematics books and 8 science books on a shelf. Three of the science books are biology books. A book is taken at random from the shelf. Find the probability that the book is
(a) a history book,
(b) a mathematics book,
(c) not a biology book,
(d) a science book which is not a biology book.

Solution
(a) Total number of books on the shelf = 12 + 8
$$= 20$$

There is no history book.
P(a history book) = 0

(b) P(a mathematics book) $= \dfrac{12}{20}$

$$= \dfrac{3}{5}$$

(c) P(not a biology book) $= \dfrac{20 - 3}{20}$

$$= \dfrac{17}{20}$$

(d) P(a science book which is not a biology book)
$$= \dfrac{8 - 3}{20}$$

$$= \dfrac{5}{20}$$

$$= \dfrac{1}{4}$$

12. A store has 15 LCD TV sets and n Smart TV sets on display. If a TV set is sold at random, the probability of selling a Smart TV set is $\dfrac{4}{9}$. Find the value of n.

Solution
P(a Smart TV set is sold) $= \dfrac{4}{9}$

$$\dfrac{n}{15 + n} = \dfrac{4}{9}$$

$\therefore\ 9n = 4(15 + n)$
$9n = 60 + 4n$
$5n = 60$
$n = 12$

13. In a batch of 20 vases, there are four defective ones. A quality control inspector checks the vases in the batch one by one without repetition.
(a) Find the probability that the first vase checked is defective.
(b) If the first vase checked is defective, find the probability that the second vase checked is also defective.

Solution
(a) P(1st vase is defective) $= \dfrac{4}{20}$

$$= \dfrac{1}{5}$$

(b) There are 3 defective vases among the 19 remaining vases.

∴ P(2nd vase is defective) = $\frac{3}{19}$

Brainworks

14. John and Navin will play a game of chess next week. There are three possible outcomes for John: win, draw, or lose. Is it true that the probability of John winning is $\frac{1}{3}$? Explain your answer.

Solution

No, the probability of John winning may not be $\frac{1}{3}$. This is because the probabilities that John will win, draw, and lose a game are usually not equally likely.

15. Many studies have shown that a high percentage of lung cancer cases are caused by smoking. If a lung cancer patient is selected at random, would the probability that the patient is a smoker be the same as the probability that the patient is a non-smoker?

Solution

Since a smoker is more likely to have lung cancer than a non-smoker, the probability that the patient selected is a smoker is higher than the probability that the patient is a non-smoker.

Exercise 16.3
Basic Practice

1. List the sample space for each of the following:
   (a) Tossing two coins
   (b) Choosing a letter at random from the word '*SQUARE*'
   (c) Choosing an odd number from 1 to 11 at random
   (d) Choosing a prime number less than 15 at random
   (e) Choosing a letter at random from the word '*DIVIDE*'
   (f) Choosing one jelly bean at random from a jar containing five red, seven blue, and two green jelly beans

Solution
   (a) Sample space S = {(*head*, *tail*), (*tail*, *head*), (*head*, *head*), (*tail*, *tail*)}
   (b) Sample space S = {*S, Q, U, A, R, E*}
   (c) Sample space S = {1, 3, 5, 7, 9, 11}
   (d) Sample space S = {2, 3, 5, 7, 11, 13}
   (e) Sample space S = {*D, I, V, E*}
   (f) Sample space S = {*red jelly bean, blue jelly bean, green jelly bean*}

2. A boy picks a day of a week at random to clean his room.
   (a) List the sample space S.
   (b) Let F be the event that the day he picks begins with the letter '*T*'. List all the possible outcomes of event F.
   (c) Find P(F).
   (d) Find the probability that the day he picks has the letter '*a*' in its spelling.

Solution
   (a) Sample space S
   = {*Sunday, Monday, Tuesday, Wednesday, Thursday, Friday, Saturday*}
   (b) F = {*Tuesday, Thursday*}
   (c) P(F) = $\frac{n(F)}{n(S)}$

   = $\frac{2}{7}$

   (d) Every day of a week has the letter '*a*' in its spelling.

   P(the day has the letter '*a*' in its spelling)
   = $\frac{7}{7}$
   = 1

3. Twenty cards are numbered 1 to 20. A card is selected at random and the number on it is noted.
   (a) List the sample space S.
   (b) Let M be the event that the number on the card selected is a multiple of 3. List all the possible outcomes of event M.
   (c) Find P(M).
   (d) Find P(M′).

Solution
   (a) Sample space S
   = {1, 2, 3, 4, 5, 6, 7, 8, 9, 10, 11, 12, 13, 14, 15, 16, 17, 18, 19, 20}
   (b) M = {3, 6, 9, 12, 15, 18}
   (c) P(M) = $\frac{n(M)}{n(S)}$

   = $\frac{6}{20}$

   = $\frac{3}{10}$

   (d) P(M′) = 1 − P(M)

   = 1 − $\frac{3}{10}$

   = $\frac{7}{10}$

4. A spinner has four equal quarters colored red, yellow, blue, and green respectively. When the pointer on it is spun, the color of the quarter where the pointer stopped is noted.

   (a) List the sample space S.
   (b) Find the probability that the color of the quarter where the pointer stopped is
      (i) red, (ii) white, (iii) not red.

Solution
(a) Sample space S = {*red, yellow, blue, green*}

(b) (i) P(color is red) = $\dfrac{1}{4}$

   (ii) P(color is white) = $\dfrac{0}{4}$
       $= 0$

   (iii) P(color is not red) = 1 – P(color is red)
       $= 1 - \dfrac{1}{4}$
       $= \dfrac{3}{4}$

5. A two-digit number is formed at random using the digits 1, 3, and 8 with repetition of digits allowed.
   (a) List the sample space S.
   (b) Let D be the event that the number formed is a double number (e.g., 33),
      (i) list all the possible outcomes of D,
      (ii) find P(D).
   (c) Let E be the event that the number formed is greater than 35,
      (i) list all the possible outcomes of E,
      (ii) find P(E),
      (iii) find P(E').

Solution
(a) Sample space S
   = {11, 13, 18, 31, 33, 38, 81, 83, 88}

(b) (i) D = {11, 33, 88}

   (ii) P(D) = $\dfrac{n(D)}{n(S)}$
       $= \dfrac{3}{9}$
       $= \dfrac{1}{3}$

(c) (i) E = {38, 81, 83, 88}

   (ii) P(E) = $\dfrac{n(E)}{n(S)}$
       $= \dfrac{4}{9}$

(iii) P(E') = 1 – P(E)
    $= 1 - \dfrac{4}{9}$
    $= \dfrac{5}{9}$

Further Practice
6. A quiz has 10 true/false questions and each question carries one point for a correct answer. A student's total score in the quiz is observed.
   (a) List the sample space S for the total score.
   (b) Let G be the event that the student's total score is above 7. List all the possible outcomes of
      (i) the event G,
      (ii) the event G'.
   (c) If a student attempts each question by guessing, are the events of getting a total score of 0 and a total score of 1 equally likely to occur?

Solution
(a) Sample space S = {0, 1, 2, 3, 4, 5, 6, 7, 8, 9, 10}

(b) (i) G = {8, 9, 10}
   (ii) G' = {0, 1, 2, 3, 4, 5, 6, 7}

(c) No, the two events are not equally likely to occur. For example, P(score is 10) < P(score is 4).

7. A three-digit number is formed at random using the digits 0, 2, 5, and 8 without repetition of the digits.
   (a) List the sample space.
   (b) Let T be the event that the number formed is less than 300. Find
      (i) P(T),
      (ii) P(T').

Solution
(a) Sample space S
   = {205, 208, 250, 258, 280, 285, 502, 508, 520, 528, 580, 582, 802, 805, 820, 825, 850, 852}

(b) T = {205, 208, 250, 258, 280, 285}

   (i) P(T) = $\dfrac{n(T)}{n(S)}$
       $= \dfrac{6}{18}$
       $= \dfrac{1}{3}$

   (ii) P(T') = 1 – P(T)
       $= 1 - \dfrac{1}{3}$
       $= \dfrac{2}{3}$

8. There are 7 red, 10 green, 9 blue, 8 yellow, and 6 brown jelly beans in a bag. A bean is removed at random from the bag.
   (a) **(i)** List the sample space of the possible colors of the bean removed from the bag.
   (ii) Are the outcomes equally likely? Why?
   (b) Find the probability that the bean removed is
   (i) orange,
   (ii) brown,
   (iii) not orange,
   (iv) not brown.

Solution
   (a) **(i)** Sample space S
      = {*red, green, blue, yellow, brown*}
   (ii) The outcomes are not equally likely. This is because the number of beans of each color is different.
   (b) Total number of jelly beans = 7 + 10 + 9 + 8 + 6
         = 40
   (i) There is no orange jelly bean.
      P(jelly bean is orange) = 0
   (ii) P(jelly bean is brown) = $\frac{6}{40}$
         = $\frac{3}{20}$
   (iii) P(jelly bean is not orange)
         = 1 – P(jelly bean is orange)
         = 1 – 0
         = 1
   (iv) P(jelly bean is not brown)
         = 1 – P(jelly bean is brown)
         = $1 - \frac{3}{20}$
         = $\frac{17}{20}$

9. A book consists of three volumes A, B, and C. These volumes are arranged on a shelf in a random order and the volume letters are read from left to right.
   (a) List the sample space S.
   (b) Let H be the event that the first volume arranged is volume B. List all the possible outcomes of H.
   (c) Find P(H).

Solution
   (a) Sample space S
      = {*ABC, ACB, BAC, BCA, CAB, CBA*}
   (b) H = {*BAC, BCA*}
   (c) P(H) = $\frac{2}{6}$
         = $\frac{1}{3}$

Math@Work
10. Richard randomly selects an ASEAN country to visit.
   (a) List all the ASEAN countries. Check your answers on the Internet.
   (b) Find the probability that the country Richard selects is
   (i) in Asia,
   (ii) Japan.
   (c) Find the probability that the name of the country he selects contains the letter '*p*'.

Solution
   (a) Sample S = {*Brunei, Cambodia, Indonesia, Laos, Malaysia, Myanmar, Philippines, Singapore, Thailand, Vietnam*}
   (b) **(i)** As each country in S is in Asia,
         P(country selected is in Asia) = $\frac{10}{10}$
         = 1
   (ii) *Japan* $\notin S$
         P(country selected is Japan) = 0
   (c) Names of countries that have the letter '*p*' are *Philippines* and *Singapore*.
      P(name of country selected has the letter '*p*')
      = $\frac{2}{10}$
      = $\frac{1}{5}$

11. A batch of computer chips comprises chips of grades A, B, and C. If a chip is selected at random from the batch, the probability that it is of grade A is $\frac{1}{4}$ and the probability that it is of grade B is $\frac{5}{12}$.
   (a) If a chip is selected at random from the batch, find the probability that it is of grade C.
   (b) If there are 72 grade C chips in the batch, find the total number of chips in the batch.

Solution
   (a) P(chip is of grade C)
      = 1 – P(chip is of grade A) – P(chip is of grade B)
      = $1 - \frac{1}{4} - \frac{5}{12}$
      = $\frac{12 - 3 - 5}{12}$
      = $\frac{4}{12}$
      = $\frac{1}{3}$

(b) Let N be the total number of chips in the batch.

$$\frac{72}{N} = \frac{1}{3}$$
$$N = 72 \times 3$$
$$= 216$$

The total number of chips in the batch is 216.

Brainworks

12. Describe a certain event in a sample space.

Solution

In rolling a die, the event that getting a whole number is a certain event.

13. Describe an impossible event in a sample space.

Solution

In drawing a card from a deck of 52 playing cards, the event that the card drawn is a joker is an impossible event.

14. Two fair dice are rolled. The sums of the scores obtained are recorded.
(a) What is the sample space?
(b) Are the outcomes in the sample space equally likely? Explain briefly.

Solution

(a) The sample space S
$= \{2, 3, 4, 5, 6, 7, 8, 9, 10, 11, 12\}$

(b) The outcomes in S are not equally likely.
For example,

$$P(\text{sum is 2}) = \frac{1}{36}$$

and $P(\text{sum is 3}) = \frac{2}{36} = \frac{1}{18}$.

Review Exercise 16

1. A multiple-choice question has five options and only one of them is the correct answer. If a boy picks an option at random, what is the probability that it is not the correct answer?

Solution

There are $5 - 1 = 4$ wrong answers.

$P(\text{option picked is not correct}) = \frac{4}{5}$

2. A day of the week is chosen at random. Find the probability that the day chosen is
(a) a Monday,
(b) a day that has the letter 'u' in its spelling.

Solution

(a) There are 7 days in a week.

$P(\text{choosing a Monday}) = \frac{1}{7}$

(b) The days that have the letter 'u' in its spelling are *Tuesday, Thursday, Saturday,* and *Sunday.*
P(choosing a day that has the letter 'u' in its spelling)
$= \frac{4}{7}$.

3. Let $A = \{ruler, pencil, compasses, marker\}$.
(a) Find $n(A)$.
(b) Is $pen \in A$?
(c) Is $\{marker\} \subset A$?
(d) Suggest a universal set for the set A.
(e) If $B \subset A$, $compasses \notin B$, and $n(B) = 3$, find the set B.

Solution

(a) $n(A) = 4$
(b) No, $pen \notin A$.
(c) Yes, $\{marker\} \subset A$.
(d) $\xi = \{\text{all stationery items}\}$
(e) $B = \{ruler, pencil, marker\}$

4. Let $A = \{\text{letters from the word '}later\text{'}\}$,
$B = \{\text{letters from the word '}latter\text{'}\}$,
and $C = \{\text{letters from the word '}letter\text{'}\}$.
(a) List the elements of the sets A, B, and C.
(b) Find $n(C)$.
(c) Describe the relationship between the following sets using '$\subset$', '$=$', or '$\in$'.
(i) A and B　　**(ii)** B and C

Solution

(a) $A = \{\text{letters from the word '}later\text{'}\}$
$= \{l, a, t, e, r\}$
$B = \{\text{letters from the word '}latter\text{'}\}$
$= \{l, a, t, e, r\}$
$C = \{\text{letters from the word '}letter\text{'}\}$
$= \{l, e, t, r\}$

(b) $n(C) = 4$
(c) **(i)** $A = B$
(ii) $C \subset B$

5. Let A = {quadrilaterals with four right angles},
$\qquad B$ = {quadrilaterals with four equal sides},
and C = {quadrilaterals with two pairs of parallel sides}.
  (a) List the elements of the sets A, B, and C.
  (b) Suggest a universal set for these sets.
  (c) Describe the relationship between B and C.
  (d) Are all trapezoids elements of C?

Solution
  (a) A = {quadrilaterals with four right angles}
      = {*rectangle, square*}
      B = {quadrilaterals with four equal sides}
      = {*rhombus, square*}
      C = {quadrilaterals with two pairs of parallel sides}
      = {*parallelogram, rectangle, rhombus, square*}
  (b) The universal set may be
      ξ = {all types of quadrilaterals}.
  (c) $B \subset C$
  (d) No, *trapezoid* $\notin C$.

6. Let ξ = {$x : x$ is an integer},
$\qquad P$ = {$x : x$ is a factor of 36},
and Q = {$x : x$ is a factor of 60}.
  (a) List the elements of the sets P and Q.
  (b) Is P a subset of Q?
  (c) Describe a set R such that $R \subset P$ and $R \subset Q$.

Solution
  (a) P = {1, 2, 3, 4, 6, 9, 12, 18, 36}
      Q = {1, 2, 3, 4, 5, 6, 10, 12, 15, 20, 30, 60}
  (b) Since $9 \in P$ but $9 \notin Q$,
      $\therefore$ P is not a subset of Q.
  (c) R = {1, 2, 3, 4, 6, 12}

7. A fair die has 12 faces, numbered 1 to 12. When it is rolled, find the probability of getting a prime number.

Solution
The outcomes of prime numbers are 2, 3, 5, 7, and 11.
P(a prime number) = $\dfrac{5}{12}$

8. A bag contains some red balls and some green balls. A ball is drawn at random from the bag. If the probability of drawing a red ball is 0.55, what is the probability of drawing a green ball?

Solution
$\qquad$ P(a red ball) = 0.55
P(a green ball) = 1 − P(a red ball)
$\qquad\qquad\qquad$ = 1 − 0.55
$\qquad\qquad\qquad$ = 0.45

9. There are three bottles of barbecue sauce, two bottles of steak sauce, and one bottle of hot sauce on a shelf. A bottle is selected at random. Find the probability that the bottle
  (a) contains barbecue sauce,
  (b) does not contain hot sauce.

Solution
  (a) Total number of bottles = 3 + 2 + 1
                    = 6
      P(bottle contains barbecue sauce) = $\dfrac{3}{6}$
                                = $\dfrac{1}{2}$
  (b) P(bottle does not contain hot sauce) = $\dfrac{3+2}{6}$
                                    = $\dfrac{5}{6}$

10. A box contains six red pens, nine blue pens, and three black pens. A pen is selected at random from the box. Find the probability that the pen is
  (a) green,
  (b) not green,
  (c) black,
  (d) not black.

Solution
  (a) Total number of pens = 6 + 9 + 3
                      = 18
      There is no green pen.
      P(a green pen) = 0
  (b) P(not a green pen) = 1 − P(a green pen)
                         = 1 − 0
                         = 1
  (c) P(a black pen) = $\dfrac{3}{18}$
                      = $\dfrac{1}{6}$
  (d) P(not a black pen) = 1 − P(a black pen)
                        = 1 − $\dfrac{1}{6}$
                      = $\dfrac{5}{6}$

11. A card is drawn at random from a deck of 30 cards, numbered 1 to 30. Find the probability that the number on the card is
  (a) a multiple of 4,
  (b) greater than 20,
  (c) a prime number.

Solution

(a) Outcomes that are multiples of 4 are 4, 8, 12, 16, 20, 24, and 28.

P(a number is a multiple of 4) = $\frac{7}{30}$

(b) Outcomes that are greater than 20 are 21, 22, 23, 24, 25, 26, 27, 28, 29, and 30.

P(a number is greater than 20) = $\frac{10}{30}$

$= \frac{1}{3}$

(c) Outcomes that are prime numbers are 2, 3, 5, 7, 11, 13, 17, 19, 23, and 29.

P(a number is a prime number) = $\frac{10}{30}$

$= \frac{1}{3}$

12. A three-digit number is represented as 7*6, where * represents a digit from 0 to 9. Find the probability that the three-digit number is
(a) an even number,
(b) a multiple of 3,
(c) is not a multiple of 3,
(d) is divisible by 4.

Solution

(a) For * = 0, 1, 2, ..., 9,
7*6 is an even number.

P(an even number) = $\frac{10}{10}$

$= 1$

(b) The numbers 726, 756, and 786 are multiples of 3 (i.e., * = 2, 5, or 8).

P(a number is a multiple of 3) = $\frac{3}{10}$

(c) P(a number is not a multiple of 3)
$= 1 - $ P(a number is a multiple of 3)

$= 1 - \frac{3}{10}$

$= \frac{7}{10}$

(d) The numbers 716, 736, 756, 776, and 796 are divisible by 4 (i.e., * = 1, 3, 5, 7, or 9).

P(a number is divisible by 4) = $\frac{5}{10}$

$= \frac{1}{2}$

13. A number is selected at random from the first 10 prime numbers.
(a) List the sample space S.
(b) Find the probability that the number is
(i) greater than 11,
(ii) less than 11,
(iii) 11.
(c) What is the sum of the three probabilities found in **(b)**?

Solution

(a) Sample space S
$= \{2, 3, 5, 7, 11, 13, 17, 19, 23, 29\}$

(b) **(i)** P(a number is greater than 11) $= \frac{5}{10}$

$= \frac{1}{2}$

(ii) P(a number is less than 11) $= \frac{4}{10}$

$= \frac{2}{5}$

(iii) P(a number is equal to 11) $= \frac{1}{10}$

(c) Sum of the three probabilities in **(b)**
$= \frac{1}{2} + \frac{2}{5} + \frac{1}{10}$

$= 1$

14. Two fair coins are tossed and their outcomes are noted.
(a) List the sample space S.
(b) Find the probability of getting
(i) two heads,
(ii) one head and one tail.

Solution

(a) Sample space $S = \{HH, HT, TH, TT\}$, where HT means the first coin is a head and the second coin is a tail.

(b) **(i)** P(two heads) $= \frac{1}{4}$

(ii) Favorable outcomes for one head and one tail are HT and TH.

P(one head and one tail) $= \frac{2}{4}$

$= \frac{1}{2}$

15. Peter has one $2 bill, one $5 bill, one $10 bill, and one $50 bill in his wallet. Two of these bills are taken out at random and the total amount is recorded.
   (a) List the sample space of the total amount.
   (b) Find the probability that the total amount is
      (i) less than $5,
      (ii) more than $12,
      (iii) over $70.

Solution
   (a) The possible total amounts are as follows:
      $2 + $5 = $7, $2 + $10 = $12,
      $2 + $50 = $52, $5 + $10 = $15,
      $5 + $50 = $55, $10 + $50 = $60.
      Sample space S = {$7, $12, $15, $52, $55, $60}
   (b) **(i)** There is no amount less than $5.
        P(total amount is less than $5) = 0
      (ii) Total amounts that are more than $12 are $15, $52, $55, and $60.

$$\text{P(total amount is more than \$12)} = \frac{4}{6}$$
$$= \frac{2}{3}$$

      (iii) There is no amount over $70.
        P(total amount is over $70) = 0

16. There are three roads, A, B, and C, connecting City X and City Y, and four roads, P, Q, R, and S, connecting City Y and City Z.

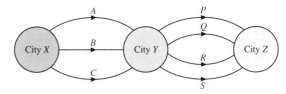

Mr. Wood selects these roads at random to drive from City X to City Z.
   (a) List the sample space of his routes.
   (b) Find the probability that Mr. Wood will drive along Road A and Road R.
   (c) Let E be the event that Mr. Wood will drive along Road Q.
      (i) List all the outcomes of this event.
      (ii) Find P(E),
      (iii) Find P(E').

Solution
   (a) Sample space S
      = {AP, AQ, AR, AS, BP, BQ, BR, BS, CP, CQ, CR, CS}
   (b) P(Mr. Wood drives along Roads A and R) = $\frac{1}{12}$

(c) **(i)** E = {AQ, BQ, CQ}

      (ii) P(E) = $\frac{3}{12}$
$$= \frac{1}{4}$$

      (iii) P(E') = 1 − P(E)
$$= 1 - \frac{1}{4}$$
$$= \frac{3}{4}$$

17. During a fund raising event in a school, 1,000 raffle tickets priced at $20 each were sold. The tickets are numbered from 000 to 999. There are one first prize of $3,000, two second prizes of $1,000 each and three third prizes of $500 each.
   (a) If a ticket is drawn at random, find the probability that
      (i) its three digits are the same,
      (ii) the last digit is a '9',
      (iii) the last digit is not a '9',
      (iv) the last two digits are the same.
   (b) Find the total amount of money raised in the event.

Solution
   (a) **(i)** Outcomes with three digits that are the same are as follows:
        000, 111, 222, 333, 444,
        555, 666, 777, 888, 999.

$$\text{P(three digits are the same)} = \frac{10}{1,000}$$
$$= \frac{1}{100}$$

      (ii) Outcomes with '9' as the last digit are as follows:

        009, 019, 029, ..., 099,
        109, 119, 129, ..., 199,
        209, 219, 229, ..., 299,
        ⋮   ⋮
        909, 919, 929, ..., 999.

$$\text{P(last digit is a '9')} = \frac{10}{1,000}$$
$$= \frac{1}{10}$$

      (iii) P(last digit is not a '9')
        = 1 − P(last digit is a '9')
$$= 1 - \frac{1}{10}$$
$$= \frac{9}{10}$$

(iv) Outcomes with last two digits that are the same are as follows:

$$000, \quad 100, \quad 200, \quad ..., \quad 900,$$
$$011, \quad 111, \quad 211, \quad ..., \quad 911,$$
$$\vdots$$
$$099, \quad 199, \quad 299 \quad ..., \quad 999.$$

$$\text{P(last two digits are the same)} = \frac{100}{1,000}$$
$$= \frac{1}{10}$$

(b) The total amount of money raised
$$= \$20 \times 1,000 - \$3,000 - \$1,000 \times 2 - \$500 \times 3$$
$$= \$13,500$$

Chapter 17   Probability Of Combined Events

Class Activity 1

Objective: To investigate the relationships between P(A), P(B), P(A and B), and P(A or B) for two mutually exclusive events, A and B.

Questions

1. A fair six-sided die is rolled.
    Let A be the event that the number is even,
        B be the event that the number is a multiple of 5,
    and C be the event that the number is a multiple of 3.

    (a)   List the outcomes of the events A, B, and C.

    > A = {number is even}
    >   = {2, 4, 6}
    > B = {number is a multiple of 5}
    >   = {5}
    > C = {number is a multiple of 3}
    >   = {3, 6}

    (b)   **(i)**   Are events A and B mutually exclusive?

    > Since A and B have no outcomes in common,
    > ∴ A and B are mutually exclusive.

    (ii)   Are events A and C mutually exclusive?

    > Since A and C have one common outcome, 6,
    > ∴ A and C are NOT mutually exclusive.

    (c)   Find the following probabilities:
    P(A), P(B), P(C), P(A or B), P(A or C), P(A and B), P(A and C).

    > Sample space S = {1, 2, 3, 4, 5, 6}
    > ∴ $n(S) = 6$
    >
    > $P(A) = \dfrac{3}{6} = \dfrac{1}{2}$
    >
    > $P(B) = \dfrac{1}{6}$
    >
    > $P(C) = \dfrac{2}{6} = \dfrac{1}{3}$
    >
    > A or B = {number is even or a multiple of 5}
    >   = {2, 4, 5, 6}
    > ∴ $P(A \text{ or } B) = \dfrac{4}{6} = \dfrac{2}{3}$
    >
    > A or C = {number is even or a multiple of 3}
    >   = {2, 3, 4, 6}
    > ∴ $P(A \text{ or } C) = \dfrac{4}{6} = \dfrac{2}{3}$
    >
    > Since A and B are mutually exclusive,
    > ∴ P(A and B) = 0.
    > Since A and C have one common outcome, 6,
    >
    > ∴ $P(A \text{ and } C) = \dfrac{1}{6}$

(d) Describe the relationship between

    (i) P(*A*), P(*B*), and P(*A* or *B*);

        P(*A* or *B*) = P(*A*) + P(*B*)

    (ii) P(*A*), P(*C*), and P(*A* or *C*).

        P(*A* or *C*) ≠ P(*A*) + P(*C*)

2. Two unbiased coins are tossed.
Let *A* be the event that there are two heads,
    B be the event that there is one head and one tail,
and *C* be the event that there is at least one head.

(a) List the outcomes of the events *A*, *B*, and *C*.

    A = {there are two heads}
    The outcome of *A* is: *HH*.

    B = {there is one head and one tail}
    The outcomes of *B* are: *HT*, *TH*.

    C = {there is at least one head}
    The outcomes of *C* are: *HT*, *TH*, *HH*.

(b) **(i)** Are events *A* and *B* mutually exclusive?

        Since *A* and *B* have no outcomes in common,
        ∴ *A* and *B* are mutually exclusive.

    (ii) Are events *A* and *C* mutually exclusive?

        Since *A* and *C* have one common outcome, *HH*,
        ∴ *A* and *C* are NOT mutually exclusive.

(c) Find the following probabilities:
P(*A*), P(*B*), P(*C*), P(*A* or *B*), P(*A* or *C*), P(*A* and *B*), P(*A* and *C*).

    Sample *S* = {*HT*, *TH*, *HH*, *TT*}

    ∴ *n*(*S*) = 4

    P(*A*) = $\frac{1}{4}$

    P(*B*) = $\frac{2}{4}$ = $\frac{1}{2}$

    P(*C*) = $\frac{3}{4}$

    A or *B* = {*HH*, *HT*, *TH*}

    ∴ P(*A* or *B*) = $\frac{3}{4}$

    A or *C* = {*HT*, *TH*, *HH*}

    ∴ P(*A* or *C*) = $\frac{3}{4}$

    Since *A* and *B* are mutually exclusive,
    ∴ P(*A* and *B*) = 0

    A and *C* = {*HH*}

    ∴ P(*A* and *C*) = $\frac{1}{4}$

(d) Describe the relationship between

    (i) P(A), P(B), and P(A or B);

       P(A or B) = P(A) + P(B)

    (ii) P(A), P(C), and P(A or C).

       P(A or C) ≠ P(A) + P(C)

3. If A and B are mutually exclusive events, what can you say about

    (a) P(A and B),

       If A and B are mutually exclusive events, P(A and B) = 0.

    (b) the relationship between P(A), P(B), and P(A or B)?

       P(A or B) = P(A) + P(B)

Class Activity 2

Objective: To investigate the relationship between P(A), P(B), and P(A and B) for two independent events, A and B.

Questions

1. An unbiased coin is tossed and an unbiased die is rolled. Let A be the event of getting a head and B be the event of getting a number greater than 4.

The sample space is shown below.

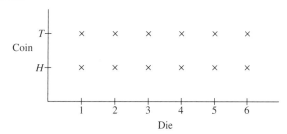

(a) Are the events, A and B, independent?

    Since the outcome in tossing a coin does not affect the probability of any event in rolling a die, the events A and B are independent.

(b) Using the possibility diagram shown, find the following probabilities:
P(A), P(B), P(A and B).

$$A = \{1H, 2H, 3H, 4H, 5H, 6H\}$$
$$P(A) = \frac{6}{12}$$
$$= \frac{1}{2}$$

$$B = \{5H, 6H, 5T, 6T\}$$
$$P(B) = \frac{4}{12}$$
$$= \frac{1}{3}$$

$$A \text{ and } B = \{5H, 6H\}$$
$$P(A \text{ and } B) = \frac{2}{12}$$
$$= \frac{1}{6}$$

(c) What is the relationship between P(A), P(B), and P(A and B)?

    P(A and B) = P(A) × P(B)

2. A bag contains two red balls and one green ball. Two balls are drawn at random from the bag, one at a time with replacement (that is, the first ball drawn is put back into the bag before the second ball is drawn).
Let A be the event that the first ball drawn is red
and B be the event that the second ball drawn is green.

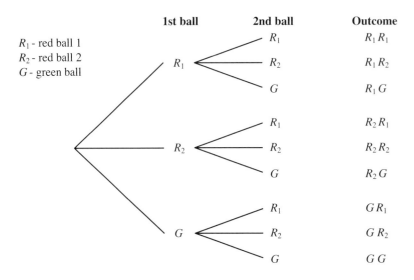

R_1 - red ball 1
R_2 - red ball 2
G - green ball

(a) Are the events, A and B, independent?

Since the balls are drawn with replacement, the event A does not affect the probability of event B.
A and B are independent events.

(b) Using the tree diagram above, find the following probabilities:
P(A), P(B), P(A and B).

$$A = \{R_1R_1,\ R_1R_2,\ R_1G,\ R_2R_1,\ R_2R_2,\ R_2G\}$$

$$P(A) = \frac{6}{9}$$

$$= \frac{2}{3}$$

$$B = \{R_1G,\ R_2G,\ GG\}$$

$$P(B) = \frac{3}{9}$$

$$= \frac{1}{3}$$

$$A \text{ and } B = \{R_1G,\ R_2G\}$$

$$P(A \text{ and } B) = \frac{2}{9}$$

(c) What is the relationship between P(A), P(B), and P(A and B)?

$$P(A \text{ and } B) = P(A) \times P(B)$$

Discuss

Page 211

There is no effect on the outcome whether the three coins are tossed at the same time or one after another. Explain why.

Each coin toss is independent from the others.

Page 216

Is each of the following mutually exclusive?

- Getting a 5 and getting an odd number with one roll of a die
  No because 5 is an odd number.

- Getting a club and getting a king when one card is drawn at random from a deck of 52 playing cards
  No because there is a club king in the deck of playing cards.

Page 221

If A and B are mutually exclusive events, are A and B independent events too?

No. If A and B are mutually exclusive, then if A occurs, then B cannot also occur; and vice versa. This stands in contrast to saying the outcome of A does not affect the outcome of B, which is independence of events.

Extend Your Learning Curve

Buffon's Needle Problem

Buffon's needle problem in probability was first raised by a French mathematician Buffon in 1777. A needle of length y cm is dropped randomly on a sheet of paper with parallel lines equally spaced at d cm apart. The problem is to determine the probability that the needle will cross one of the parallel lines on the paper. It is interesting to note that the result is related to the value of π.

Find out more about Buffon's needle problem and do the experiment yourself by setting $d = y$ (for example, take $y = 3$). Then determine if the value of the probability is close to $\dfrac{2}{\pi}$.

Suggestion: For the experiment, you can use a toothpick as an alternative to the needle.

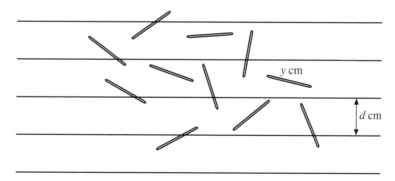

Suggested Answer:

Students may refer to information about Buffon's needle from the following websites.

1. http://en.wikipedia.org/wiki/Buffon's_needle
2. http://www.cut-the-knot.org/fta/Buffon/buffon9.shtml

When $d \geqslant y$, P(the needle will cross one of the parallel lines) $= \dfrac{2y}{d\pi}$.

When $d = y$, it becomes

P(the needle will cross one of the parallel lines) = $\dfrac{2}{\pi}$.

When $d > y$, P(the needle will cross one of the parallel lines) = $\dfrac{2y}{d\pi} - \dfrac{2}{d\pi}\left[\sqrt{y^2 - d^2} - d \sec^{-1}\left(\dfrac{y}{d}\right)\right]$.

Although the proofs of the above results are beyond the understanding of students at this level and students do not yet have the background for the equation for $d > y$, they are encouraged to do the experiment themselves.

For $d = y$, if the needle crosses one of the parallel lines f out of N times, then $\dfrac{f}{N} \approx \dfrac{2}{\pi}$.

Hence, $$\pi \approx \dfrac{2N}{f} .$$

We can use the above formula to estimate the value of π.

Try It!

Section 17.1

1. A letter is selected at random from each of the words, *SURE* and *WIN*.
   (a) Draw a possibility diagram to represent the sample space.
   (b) Find the probability of getting
      (i) two vowels,
      (ii) the letter *W*.

Solution

(a)

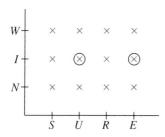

(b) (i) The outcomes of getting two vowels are *UI* and *EI*.

$$\therefore \text{P(getting two vowels)} = \frac{2}{12}$$
$$= \frac{1}{6}$$

   (ii) The outcomes of getting the letter *W* are *SW*, *UW*, *RW*, and *EW*.

$$\therefore \text{P(getting the letter W)} = \frac{4}{12}$$
$$= \frac{1}{3}$$

2. Two fair six-sided dice are rolled. Find the probability that
   (a) the sum of the two numbers shown is 6,
   (b) both dice show the same number.

Solution

(a) The outcomes of getting a sum of 6 are:

$$(1, 5), (2, 4), (3, 3), (4, 2), (5, 1).$$

$$\therefore \text{P(sum of two numbers is 6)} = \frac{5}{36}$$

(b) The outcomes of having both dice showing the same number are:

$$(1, 1), (2, 2), (3, 3), (4, 4), (5, 5), (6, 6).$$

$$\therefore \text{P(both dice show the same number)} = \frac{6}{36}$$
$$= \frac{1}{6}$$

3. A family has two children.
   (a) Draw a tree diagram to show the possible genders of the children.
   (b) Assume that the probability of having a male child and the probability of having a female child are equal. Find the probability that
      (i) both children are boys,
      (ii) there is one boy and one girl.

Solution

(a) The required tree diagram is shown below.

1st Child	2nd Child	Outcome	
B	B	BB	B - boy
	G	BG	G - girl
G	B	GB	
	G	GG	

(b) (i) P(both children are boys) = P(*BB*)

$$= \frac{1}{4}$$

   (ii) P(one boy and one girl)
   = P(outcome is *BG* or *GB*)

$$= \frac{2}{4}$$
$$= \frac{1}{2}$$

4. Box *A* contains a red ball, a green ball, and a blue ball. Box *B* contains a red ball and a blue ball. A ball is drawn from each box at random.
   (a) Draw a tree diagram to show all the possible outcomes.
   (b) Find the probability that the two balls drawn are
      (i) both red,
      (ii) both green,
      (iii) of the same color,
      (iv) of different colors.

Solution

(a) The required tree diagram is shown below.

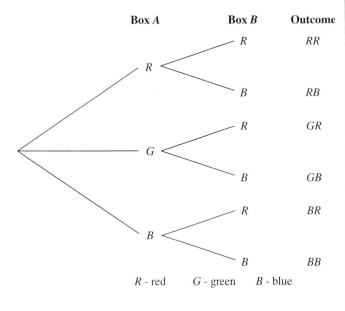

Box *A*   Box *B*   Outcome

		Outcome
R	R	RR
R	B	RB
G	R	GR
G	B	GB
B	R	BR
B	B	BB

R - red   *G* - green   *B* - blue

(b) (i) P(two balls drawn are both red) = P(*RR*)

$$= \frac{1}{6}$$

(ii) P(two balls drawn are both green) = 0

(iii) P(two balls drawn are both of the same color)
= P(*RR* or *BB*)

$$= \frac{2}{6}$$

$$= \frac{1}{3}$$

(iv) P(two balls drawn are both of different colors)
= 1 − P(two balls drawn are both of the same color)

$$= 1 - \frac{1}{3}$$

$$= \frac{2}{3}$$

Section 17.2

5. The probabilities of Serena, Sarah, and Stephy winning the tennis championship title is $\frac{1}{3}$, $\frac{5}{12}$, and $\frac{13}{36}$ respectively. Find the probability that
(a) Serena or Sarah will win the title,
(b) Sarah or Stephy will win the title,
(c) neither Sarah nor Stephy will win the title.

Solution

(a) Let *A* be the event that Serena will win the title,
    B be the event that Sarah will win the title,
    and *C* be the event that Stephy will win the title.

Since there is only one winner in the championship, the events, *A*, *B*, and *C*, are mutually exclusive.
P(Serena or Sarah will win the title) = P(*A* or *B*)

$$= P(A) + P(B)$$

$$= \frac{1}{3} + \frac{5}{12}$$

$$= \frac{3}{4}$$

(b) P(Sarah or Stephy will win the title) = P(*B* or *C*)
$$= P(B) + P(C)$$

$$= \frac{5}{12} + \frac{13}{36}$$

$$= \frac{7}{9}$$

(c) P(neither Sarah nor Stephy will win the title)
= 1 − P(Sarah or Stephy will win the title)

$$= 1 - \frac{7}{9}$$

$$= \frac{2}{9}$$

6. Three unbiased coins are tossed. Draw a tree diagram to show all the possible outcomes and find the probability of getting
(a) three heads or two heads,
(b) three heads or the first coin being a head.

Solution

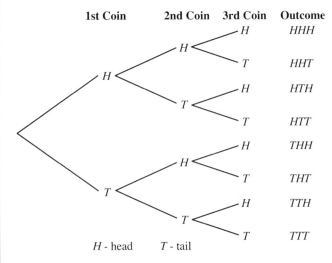

1st Coin   2nd Coin   3rd Coin   Outcome

			Outcome
H	H	H	HHH
H	H	T	HHT
H	T	H	HTH
H	T	T	HTT
T	H	H	THH
T	H	T	THT
T	T	H	TTH
T	T	T	TTT

H - head   *T* - tail

(a) Let *A* be the event of getting three heads and *B* be the event of getting two heads.
A = {*HHH*}
B = {*HHT*, *HTH*, *THH*}
Since *A* and *B* are mutually exclusive events,
∴ P(three heads or two heads) = P(*A* or *B*)
$$= P(A) + P(B)$$

$$= \frac{1}{8} + \frac{3}{8}$$

$$= \frac{1}{2}$$

(b) The outcomes with three heads or the first coin being a head are: *HHH, HHT, HTH, HTT*.

∴ the required probability $= \dfrac{4}{8}$

$= \dfrac{1}{2}$

Section 17.3

7. A letter is selected at random from each of the words, *BREAD* and *BUTTER*. Find the probability that both letters selected are vowels.

Solution

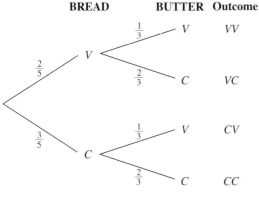

BREAD　　**BUTTER**　Outcome

V - vowel　　*C* - consonant

P(both letters selected are vowels) = P(*VV*)

$= \dfrac{2}{5} \times \dfrac{1}{3}$

$= \dfrac{2}{15}$

8. Sarah and Ryan work independently on a problem. The probabilities that the problem can be solved by Sarah and Ryan are $\dfrac{2}{3}$ and $\dfrac{4}{7}$ respectively. Find the probability that the problem can be solved by either Sarah or Ryan or both of them.

Solution

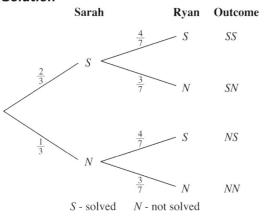

Sarah　　　Ryan　Outcome

S - solved　　*N* - not solved

P(the problem can be solved by either Sarah or Ryan or both of them)

$= \text{P}(SS) + \text{P}(SN) + \text{P}(NS)$

$= \dfrac{2}{3} \times \dfrac{4}{7} + \dfrac{2}{3} \times \dfrac{3}{7} + \dfrac{1}{3} \times \dfrac{4}{7}$

$= \dfrac{8}{21} + \dfrac{6}{21} + \dfrac{4}{21}$

$= \dfrac{6}{7}$

9. The probability that a certain model of MP3 player fails within one year of purchase is 0.15. Mr. Hunter buys three such MP3 players. Find the probability that, within one year,

(a) all three MP3 players will fail,

(b) at least one MP3 player will not fail.

Solution

1st Player	2nd Player	3rd Player	Outcome

F - fail　　*N* - will not fail

(a) P(all three players will fail)

= P(*FFF*)

= 0.15 × 0.15 × 0.15

= 0.003375

(b) P(at least one player will not fail)

= 1 − P(all three players will fail)

= 1 − 0.003375

= 0.996625

Section 17.4

10. Box *X* contains 4 red pens and 2 black pens. Box *Y* contains 3 red pens and 7 black pens. Rex chooses one of the boxes at random and then selects a pen at random. Find the probability that the pen selected is a red one.

Solution

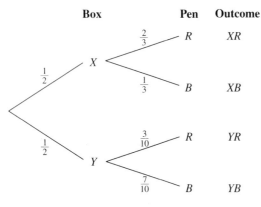

Box   Pen   Outcome

R — red B — black

P(getting a red pen) = P(XR) + P(YR)

$$= \frac{1}{2} \times \frac{2}{3} + \frac{1}{2} \times \frac{3}{10}$$

$$= \frac{1}{3} + \frac{3}{20}$$

$$= \frac{29}{60}$$

11. The lengths of 50 fish in a pond are recorded in the table below.

Length (x cm)	$0 < x \leqslant 5$	$5 < x \leqslant 10$	$10 < x \leqslant 15$	$15 < x \leqslant 20$	$20 < x \leqslant 25$
Number of fish	10	15	13	8	4

Two fish were chosen at random. Find the probability that
(a) both fish chosen measured more than 5 cm but less than or equal to 15 cm,
(b) the length of one fish was 5 cm or less and of the other fish was more than 15 cm.

Solution

Number of fish with length longer than 5 cm but less than or equal to 15 cm = 15 + 13

                          = 28

(a) P(both fish with length : 5 cm < length $\leqslant$ 15 cm)

$$= \frac{28}{50} \times \frac{27}{49}$$

$$= \frac{54}{175}$$

(b) Number of fish with length 5 cm or less = 10
Number of fish with length longer than 15 cm
$$= 8 + 4$$
$$= 12$$
P(the length of one fish was 5 cm or less and of the other fish was longer than 15 cm)

$$= \frac{10}{50} \times \frac{12}{49} + \frac{12}{50} \times \frac{10}{49}$$

$$= \frac{24}{245}$$

Exercise 17.1

Basic Practice

1. Two unbiased coins are tossed.
   (a) Represent the sample space using a possibility diagram.
   (b) Find the probability of getting
       (i) two heads,
       (ii) at least one head.

Solution

(a) The required sample space is represented by the possibility diagram below.

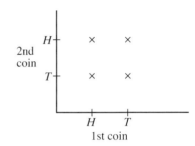

(b) (i) P(two heads) = P(HH)
    $$= \frac{1}{4}$$

   (ii) P(at least one head)
        = P(getting HH, HT, or TH)
        $$= \frac{3}{4}$$

2. An unbiased coin is tossed and a fair die is rolled.
   (a) Represent the sample space using a possibility diagram.
   (b) Find the probability of getting
       (i) a head on the coin and an even number on the die,
       (ii) a number less than 5 on the die.

Solution

(a) The required sample space is represented by the possibility diagram below.

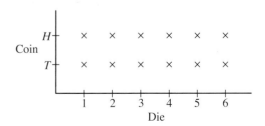

(b) (i) P(a head on the coin and an even number on the die)
    = P(getting H2, H4, or H6)
    $$= \frac{3}{12}$$
    $$= \frac{1}{4}$$

   (ii) P(a number less than 5 on the die)
        = P(getting H1 to H4 or T1 to T4)
        $$= \frac{8}{12}$$
        $$= \frac{2}{3}$$

3. A letter is selected at random from each of the words, *NICE* and *ICE*.
   (a) Represent the sample space using a possibility diagram.
   (b) Find the probability that the two letters are
       (i) the same,
       (ii) vowels.

Solution

(a) The required sample space is represented by the possibility diagram below.

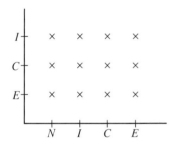

(b) (i) P(two letters are the same)
    = P(getting II, CC, or EE)
    $$= \frac{3}{12}$$
    $$= \frac{1}{4}$$

   (ii) P(two letters are vowels)
        = P(getting IE, II, EE, or EI)
        $$= \frac{4}{12}$$
        $$= \frac{1}{3}$$

4. On a console of a model helicopter, both the motion (up or down) and the direction (North, South, East, or West) are selected at random.
   (a) Represent the sample space using a tree diagram.
   (b) Find the probability of selecting the upward motion and the North direction.

Solution

(a) The diagram below is the required tree diagram.

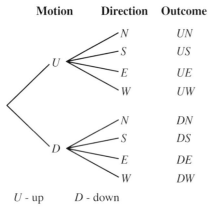

Motion	Direction	Outcome

U - up D - down

N - North S - South E - East W - West

(b) P(selecting upward motion and North direction)
   = P(UN)
   = $\dfrac{1}{8}$

5. A representative is chosen at random from a boy and a girl. A flag is chosen at random from a red one, a green one, and a yellow one. The chosen representative will carry the hoisted flag in a school parade.
   (a) Represent the sample space of choosing the representative and the flag using a tree diagram.
   (b) Find the probability that the chosen representative is a boy and the flag is not a red one.

Solution

(a) The diagram below is the required tree diagram.

Representative	Flag	Outcome
M	R	MR
	G	MG
	Y	MY
F	R	FR
	G	FG
	Y	FY

M - boy F - girl

R - red flag G - green flag Y - yellow flag

(b) P(choosing a boy and getting a non-red flag)
   = P(MG or MY)
   = $\dfrac{2}{6}$
   = $\dfrac{1}{3}$

6. A wallet contains a \$5-bill, a \$10-bill, and a \$50-bill. One bill is taken out from the wallet at random and then replaced. A second bill is then taken out at random.
   (a) Represent the sample space using a tree diagram.
   (b) Find the probability that the sum of the bills taken out is
      (i) \$20,
      (ii) more than \$15.

Solution

(a) The diagram below is the required tree diagram.

1st bill	2nd bill	Outcome
5	5	(5, 5)
	10	(5, 10)
	50	(5, 50)
10	5	(10, 5)
	10	(10, 10)
	50	(10, 50)
50	5	(50, 5)
	10	(50, 10)
	50	(50, 50)

(b) (i) P(sum of bills is \$20)
      = P(getting (10, 10))
      = $\dfrac{1}{9}$

   (ii) The outcomes with the sum of bills more than \$15 are:

   (5, 50), (10, 10), (10, 50),
   (50, 5), (50, 10), (50, 50).

   ∴ P(sum of bills more than \$15)
      = $\dfrac{6}{9}$
      = $\dfrac{2}{3}$

Further Practice

7. A letter is selected at random from each of the words, *GOOD* and *APPLE*.
   (a) Represent the sample space using a possibility diagram.
   (b) Find the probability that the two letters selected are
       (i) both vowels,
       (ii) both consonants,
       (iii) a vowel and a consonant.

Solution

(a) The diagram below is the required possibility diagram.

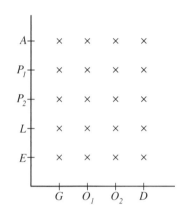

(b) (i) The outcomes with two vowels are:

$$O_1A, O_1E, O_2A, O_2E.$$

$$\therefore \text{ P(two vowels)} = \frac{4}{20}$$

$$= \frac{1}{5}$$

(ii) The outcomes with two consonants are:

$$GP_1, GP_2, GL, DP_1, DP_2, DL.$$

$$\therefore \text{ P(two consonants)} = \frac{6}{20}$$

$$= \frac{3}{10}$$

(iii) P(a vowel and a consonant)

$$= 1 - \text{P(two vowels)} - \text{P(two consonants)}$$

$$= 1 - \frac{1}{5} - \frac{3}{10}$$

$$= \frac{1}{2}$$

8. Two fair dice, each in the form of a regular tetrahedron as shown, are rolled. Each die has the numbers 1, 2, 3, and 4 marked on its faces. When the two dice are rolled, the number on the landing face of each die is observed.

(a) Represent the sample space using a possibility diagram.
(b) Find the probability that the numbers observed
    (i) are equal,
    (ii) add up to 6,
    (iii) are odd numbers.

Solution

(a) The sample space is shown below.

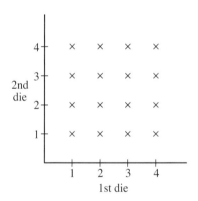

(b) (i) The outcomes with the numbers observed being equal are:

$$(1, 1), (2, 2), (3, 3), (4, 4).$$

P(numbers observed being equal) $= \dfrac{4}{16}$

$$= \frac{1}{4}$$

(ii) The outcomes with the sum of numbers being 6 are:

$$(2, 4), (3, 3), (4, 2).$$

P(sum of numbers being 6) $= \dfrac{3}{16}$

(iii) The outcomes with two odd numbers are:

$$(1, 1), (1, 3), (3, 1), (3, 3).$$

P(two odd numbers) $= \dfrac{4}{16}$

$$= \frac{1}{4}$$

9. There are going to be three newborn babies in a certain hospital. Assume that the probability of giving birth to a boy (B) is equal to the probability of giving birth to a girl (G).

(a) Draw a tree diagram to show the possible genders of these three newborn babies.

(b) Find the probability that there will be
   (i) three girls,
   (ii) two girls,
   (iii) at least one girl.

Solution

(a) The required tree diagram is shown below.

1st baby	2nd baby	3rd baby	Outcome
		B	BBB
	B	G	BBG
B		B	BGB
	G	G	BGG
		B	GBB
	B	G	GBG
G		B	GGB
	G	G	GGG

B - boy G - girl

(b) (i) P(three girls will be born) = P(GGG)
$$= \frac{1}{8}$$

(ii) P(two girls will be born)
= P(BGG, GBG, or GGB)
$$= \frac{3}{8}$$

(iii) P(at least one girl will be born)
= 1 − P(all boys)
$$= 1 - \frac{1}{8}$$
$$= \frac{7}{8}$$

10. Box X contains a gold coin and a silver coin. Box Y contain a copper coin, a gold coin, and a silver coin. Paul picks a coin at random from each box.

(a) Show all the possible outcomes using a probability tree diagram.

(b) Find the probability that he will pick
   (i) two gold coins,
   (ii) one gold coin and one silver coin,
   (iii) at least one silver coin.

Solution

(a) The required tree diagram is shown below.

Box X	Box Y	Outcome
	C	GC
G	G	GG
	S	GS
	C	SC
S	G	SG
	S	SS

(b) (i) P(two gold coins) = P(GG)
$$= \frac{1}{6}$$

(ii) P(one gold coin and one silver coin)
= P(GS or SG)
$$= \frac{2}{6}$$
$$= \frac{1}{3}$$

(iii) P(at least one silver coin)
= P(GS, SC, SG, or SS)
$$= \frac{4}{6}$$
$$= \frac{2}{3}$$

Math@Work

11. Joanne plays a game on two spinners which are divided into four equal quadrants as shown below. The pointer of each spinner is equally likely to come to rest in any of the four equal quadrants. Each quadrant has been indicated by a number.

Spinner 1   Spinner 2

Joanne can only spin each pointer once.

(a) Use a possibility diagram to show all the possible outcomes.

(b) Find the probability that
   (i) the pointers will stop at the same number for both spinners,
   (ii) the first spinner shows a larger number,
   (iii) the sum of the two numbers is greater than 6.

Solution

(a) The required possibility diagram is shown below.

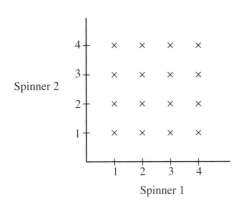

Spinner 2 (vertical axis: 1, 2, 3, 4)
Spinner 1 (horizontal axis: 1, 2, 3, 4)

(b) **(i)** The outcomes with the pointers stopping at the same number for both spinners are:

$$(1, 1), (2, 2), (3, 3), (4, 4).$$

∴ the required probability

$$= \frac{4}{16}$$

$$= \frac{1}{4}$$

(ii) The outcomes with the first spinner showing a larger number are:

$$(2, 1), (3, 1), (3, 2), (4, 1), (4, 2), (4, 3).$$

∴ the required probability

$$= \frac{6}{16}$$

$$= \frac{3}{8}$$

(iii) The outcomes with the sum of the two numbers being greater than 6 are:

$$(3, 4), (4, 3), (4, 4).$$

∴ the required probability $= \dfrac{3}{16}$

12. Mrs. Lee is equally likely to read newspapers A, B, or C in the morning, and watch a TV program either on the Discovery channel or the Movie channel in the evening on a certain day.
   (a) Draw a tree diagram to display the possible choices of the newspaper and the TV channel.
   (b) Find the probability that she will read newspaper B and watch a program on the Movie channel on that certain day.

Solution

(a) The required tree diagram is shown below.

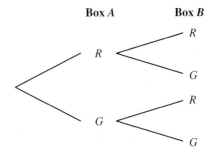

Newspaper — TV Channel — Outcome

A → D : AD
A → M : AM
B → D : BD
B → M : BM
C → D : CD
C → M : CM

D - Discovery channel
M - Movie channel

(b) P(selecting newspaper B and Movie channel)
= P(BM)
$$= \frac{1}{6}$$

Brainworks

13. Box A contains 3 red balls and 1 green ball. Box B contains 1 red ball and 2 green balls. A ball is taken out at random from each box and its color is noted.
   (a) Draw a possibility diagram to show the sample space.
   (b) Find the probability of getting one red ball and one green ball.
   (c) Discuss whether it is appropriate to draw a tree diagram as shown below, denoting a red ball by R and a green ball by G.

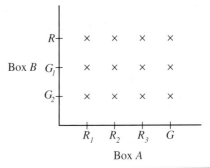

Box A — Box B

R → R
R → G
G → R
G → G

Solution

(a) The sample space can be represented by the following possibility diagram.

Box B: R, G_1, G_2
Box A: R_1, R_2, R_3, G

(b) The outcomes of getting one red ball and one green ball are:

$$R_1G_1, R_1G_2, R_2G_1, R_2G_2, R_3G_1, R_3G_2, GR.$$

∴ P(getting one red ball and one green ball)

$$= \frac{7}{12}$$

(c) We can present a tree diagram as shown in the book. However, the outcomes shown by the tree diagram are not equally likely. We have to find the probability represented by each branch in the tree diagram and multiply the probabilities along the required branches to solve the problem.

Exercise 17.2
Basic Practice

1. In each of the following, determine whether events A and B are mutually exclusive.
   (a) One card is chosen at random from a deck of 52 playing cards.
   $A = \{$getting a club$\}$;
   $B = \{$getting a jack$\}$
   (b) One month of the year is chosen at random.
   $A = \{$choosing July$\}$;
   $B = \{$choosing a fall month$\}$
   (c) $A = \{N, S, E, W\}$;
   $B = \{NE, NW, SE, SW\}$
   (d) $A = \{N, S, E, W\}$; $B = \{N, S, NE\}$
   (e) Two dice are rolled.
   $A = \{$a die shows a 3$\}$;
   $B = \{$sum of the resulting numbers is 10$\}$
   (f) Two dice are rolled.
   $A = \{$a die shows a 5$\}$;
   $B = \{$sum of the resulting numbers is 6$\}$

Solution
(a) Since there is one club jack,
   ∴ A and B are NOT mutually exclusive.

(b) $A = \{$choosing July$\}$
   $B = \{$choosing a fall month$\}$
   $= \{$choosing September, October, or November$\}$
   Since A and B have no outcomes in common,
   ∴ A and B are mutually exclusive.

(c) Since A and B have no outcomes in common,
   ∴ A and B are mutually exclusive.

(d) Since A and B have common outcomes, N and S,
   ∴ A and B are NOT mutually exclusive.

(e) $A = \{$a die shows a 3$\}$
   $= \{(1, 3), (2, 3), (3, 3), (4, 3), (5, 3), (6, 3), (3, 1),$
   $(3, 2), (3, 4), (3, 5), (3, 6)\}$
   $B = \{$sum is 10$\}$
   $= \{(4, 6), (5, 5), (6, 4)\}$
   Since A and B have no outcomes in common,
   ∴ A and B and are mutually exclusive.

(f) $A = \{$a die shows a 5$\}$
   $= \{(1, 5), (2, 5), (3, 5), (4, 5), (5, 5), (6, 5),$
   $(5, 1), (5, 2), (5, 3), (5, 4), (5, 6)\}$
   $B = \{$sum is 6$\}$
   $= \{(1, 5), (2, 4), (3, 3), (4, 2), (5, 1)\}$
   Since A and B have common outcomes, $(1, 5)$ and $(5, 1)$,
   ∴ A and B are NOT mutually exclusive.

2. A bag contains 2 red balls, 3 white balls, and 15 yellow balls. A ball is drawn at random. Find the probability that the ball drawn is
   (a) red,
   (b) white,
   (c) red or white.

Solution
(a) Total number of balls = 2 + 3 + 15
   $= 20$
   P(drawing a red ball) $= \frac{2}{20}$
   $= \frac{1}{10}$

(b) P(drawing a white ball) $= \frac{3}{20}$

(c) P(drawing a red or white ball)
   = P(drawing a red ball) + P(drawing a white ball)
   $= \frac{1}{10} + \frac{3}{20}$
   $= \frac{1}{4}$

3. Twelve cards are numbered from 1 to 12. A card is drawn at random. Find the probability that the number on the card is
   (a) less than 4,
   (b) greater than 7,
   (c) less than 4 or greater than 7.

Solution
(a) P(number less than 4) = P(1, 2, or 3)
   $= \frac{3}{12}$
   $= \frac{1}{4}$

(b) P(number greater than 7) = P(8, 9, 10, 11, or 12)
   $= \frac{5}{12}$

(c) P(number less than 4 or greater than 7)
   = P(number less than 4) + P(number greater than 7)
   $= \frac{1}{4} + \frac{5}{12}$
   $= \frac{2}{3}$

4. Thomas caught eight fish whose lengths were 18 cm, 21 cm, 22 cm, 26 cm, 27 cm, 31 cm, 35 cm, and 40 cm respectively. One of the fish is selected at random for cooking. Let A be the event that the selected fish is longer than 30 cm and B be the event that the selected fish is between 25 cm and 30 cm. Find

(a) $P(A)$,

(b) $P(B)$,

(c) $P(A \text{ or } B)$.

Solution

(a) $P(A) = P(\text{length longer than 30 cm})$
$= P(31 \text{ cm}, 35 \text{ cm, or } 40 \text{ cm})$
$= \dfrac{3}{8}$

(b) $P(B) = P(\text{length between 25 cm and 30 cm})$
$= P(26 \text{ cm or } 27 \text{ cm})$
$= \dfrac{2}{8}$
$= \dfrac{1}{4}$

(c) $P(A \text{ or } B) = P(A) + P(B)$
$= \dfrac{3}{8} + \dfrac{1}{4}$
$= \dfrac{5}{8}$

5. A day of the week is chosen at random. Find the probability of choosing a Thursday or a weekend day.

Solution

$P(\text{choosing a Thursday or a weekend day})$
$= P(\text{choosing a Thursday}) + P(\text{choosing a weekend day})$
$= \dfrac{1}{7} + \dfrac{2}{7}$
$= \dfrac{3}{7}$

6. There are 5 parents, 3 students, and 4 teachers in a room. If a person is selected at random, what is the probability that the person is a parent or a student?

Solution

$P(\text{selecting a parent or a student})$
$= P(\text{selecting a parent}) + P(\text{selecting a student})$
$= \dfrac{5}{12} + \dfrac{3}{12}$
$= \dfrac{2}{3}$

7. A single letter is chosen at random from the word *SCHOOL*. What is the probability that an S or an O is chosen?

Solution

$P(\text{choosing an } S \text{ or an } O)$
$= P(\text{choosing an } S) + P(\text{choosing an } O)$
$= \dfrac{1}{6} + \dfrac{2}{6}$
$= \dfrac{1}{2}$

8. A card is drawn at random from a deck of 52 playing cards. Find the probability that the card drawn is

(a) a king or a queen, **(b)** a queen or a spade.

Solution

(a) $P(\text{drawing a king or a queen})$
$= P(\text{drawing a king}) + P(\text{drawing a queen})$
$= \dfrac{4}{52} + \dfrac{4}{52}$
$= \dfrac{2}{13}$

(b) Since there are 12 non-queen spades,
number of favorable cards $= 4 + 12$
$= 16$
$\therefore P(\text{drawing a queen or a spade}) = \dfrac{16}{52}$
$= \dfrac{4}{13}$

Further Practice

9. One letter is chosen at random from the word *WASHINGTON*. Find the probability of choosing

(a) the letter N or a vowel,

(b) the letter W or a consonant,

(c) none of these three letters W, I, and N.

Solution

(a) $P(\text{choosing the letter } N \text{ or a vowel})$
$= P(\text{choosing the letter } N) + P(\text{choosing a vowel})$
$= \dfrac{2}{10} + \dfrac{3}{10}$
$= \dfrac{1}{2}$

(b) Besides the letter W, there are 6 consonants in the word.
Number of favorable letters $= 1 + 6 = 7$
$\therefore P(\text{choosing the letter } W \text{ or a consonant}) = \dfrac{7}{10}$

(c) $P(\text{none of the letters } W, I, \text{ and } N \text{ are chosen})$
$= P(\text{choosing the letters } A, S, H, G, T, \text{ or } O)$
$= \dfrac{6}{10}$
$= \dfrac{3}{5}$

10. Michael has one penny, one nickel, one quarter, and one half-dollar in his right pocket. He has one nickel, one quarter, and one half-dollar in his left pocket. A coin is taken out at random from each pocket. Find the probability that the total value of the two coins taken out is

(a) 55 cents,
(b) more than 55 cents,
(c) 55 cents or more.

Solution

(a)

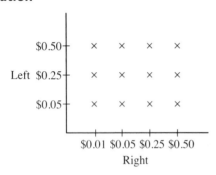

A = {sum is 55 cents}
= {($0.05, $0.50), ($0.50, $0.05)}

∴ P(sum is 55 cents) = $\dfrac{2}{12}$

= $\dfrac{1}{6}$

(b) B = {sum is more than 55 cents}
= {($0.25, $0.50), ($0.50 $0.25), ($0.50, $0.50)}

∴ P(sum is more than 55 cents) = $\dfrac{3}{12}$

= $\dfrac{1}{4}$

(c) P(sum is 55 cents or more) = P(A or B)
= P(A) + P(B)

= $\dfrac{1}{6} + \dfrac{1}{4}$

= $\dfrac{5}{12}$

11. (a) List all the factors of 60.
(b) One of the factors is selected at random. Find the probability that it is
  (i) less than 6,
  (ii) greater than 10,
  (iii) less than 6 or greater than 10.

Solution

(a) 60 = 1 × 60 = 2 × 30 = 3 × 20
= 4 × 15 = 5 × 12 = 6 × 10

∴ the factors of 60 are: 1, 2, 3, 4, 5, 6, 10, 12, 15, 20, 30, 60.

(b) (i) A = {the factor is less than 6}
= {1, 2, 3, 4, 5}
∴ P(factor is less than 6) = P(A)

= $\dfrac{5}{12}$

(ii) B = {the factor is greater than 10}
= {12, 15, 20, 30, 60}

∴ P(factor is greater than 10) = $\dfrac{5}{12}$

(iii) P(factor is less than 6 or greater than 10)
= P(A or B)
= P(A) + P(B)

= $\dfrac{5}{12} + \dfrac{5}{12}$

= $\dfrac{5}{6}$

12.

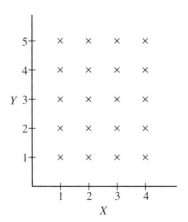

Spinner X Spinner Y

The above diagram shows two spinners, X and Y. The pointer of each spinner is equally likely to come to rest in any of the section of the spinner that has been indicated by a number.

(a) Show the sample space using a possibility diagram.
(b) Let A be the event that the sum of the numbers indicated is 7 and B be the event that at least one of the numbers indicated is 1.
  (i) List the outcomes of each event.
  (ii) Are events A and B mutually exclusive?
  (iii) Find P(A), P(B), and P(A or B).

Solution

(a) The required sample space is represented by the possibility diagram below.

(b) (i) The outcomes of event A are: (2, 5), (3, 4), (4, 3).

The outcomes of event B are: (1, 1), (1, 2), 1, 3), (1, 4), (1, 5), (2, 1), (3, 1), (4, 1).

(ii) Since A and B have no outcomes in common,
∴ A and B are mutually exclusive events.

(iii) $P(A) = \dfrac{3}{20}$

$P(B) = \dfrac{8}{20}$

$= \dfrac{2}{5}$

$P(A \text{ or } B) = P(A) + P(B)$

$= \dfrac{3}{20} + \dfrac{2}{5}$

$= \dfrac{11}{20}$

---

13. Two fair dice are rolled. Show the sample space using a possibility diagram and hence find the probability that
(a) the sum of the two numbers shown is 9 or the numbers shown on the two dice are the same,
(b) the sum of the two numbers shown is 6 or the numbers shown on the two dice are even.

Solution

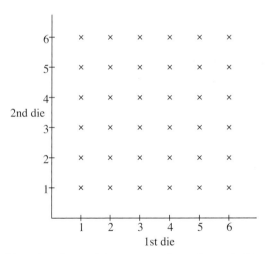

2nd die

1st die

(a) $A = \{\text{sum of the two numbers shown is 9}\}$
$= \{(3, 6), (4, 5), (5, 4), (6, 3)\}$
$B = \{\text{two dice show the same number}\}$
$= \{(1, 1), (2, 2), (3, 3), (4, 4), (5, 5), (6, 6)\}$
A and B are mutually exclusive events.

$P(\text{sum of two numbers shown is 9 or two dice show the same number})$
$= P(A \text{ or } B)$
$= P(A) + P(B)$
$= \dfrac{4}{16} + \dfrac{6}{36}$
$= \dfrac{5}{18}$

(b) $C = \{\text{sum of the two numbers shown is 6}\}$
$= \{(1, 5), (2, 4), (3, 3), (4, 2), (5, 1)\}$
$D = \{\text{both dice show even numbers}\}$
$= \{(2, 2), (2, 4), (2, 6), (4, 2), (4, 4), (4, 6),$
$(6, 2), (6, 4), (6, 6)\}$

Since C and D have the common outcomes, (2, 4) and (4, 2),
∴ C and D are not mutually exclusive events.

$n(C \text{ or } D) = 12$
∴ $P(\text{sum of the two numbers shown is 6 or both dice show even numbers})$
$= P(C \text{ or } D)$
$= \dfrac{12}{36}$
$= \dfrac{1}{3}$

Math@Work

14. The probabilities that Yvonne and Joyce will win the championship title in a golf tournament are 0.32 and 0.25 respectively. Find the probability that
(a) either Yvonne or Joyce will win,
(b) neither Yvonne nor Joyce will win.

Solution

(a) P(Yvonne or Joyce will win)
$= $ P(Yvonne will win) $+$ P(Joyce will win)
$= 0.32 + 0.25$
$= 0.57$

(b) P(neither Yvonne nor Joyce will win)
$= 1 - 0.32 - 0.25$
$= 0.43$

---

15. There are five service counters in a bank. The following table shows the probabilities of different numbers of service counters which will be opened to serve its customers at any one time.

Number of open counters	0	1	2	3	4	5
Probability	0	0.12	0.17	0.34	0.20	x

(a) Find the probability that two or three counters are open.
(b) Find the value of x.
(c) Find the probability that at least four counters are open.

Solution

(a) P(two or three open counters) $= 0.17 + 0.34$
$= 0.51$

(b) P(sample space) = 1

∴ 0 + 0.12 + 0.17 + 0.34 + 0.20 + x = 1

0.83 + x = 1

x = 0.17

(c) P(at least four open counters)

= P(four or five open counters)

= 0.20 + 0.17

= 0.37

Brainworks

16. A class has 40 students where 20 of them take geography and 25 take history. A student of the class is selected at random. Let G be the event that the student takes geography and H be the event that the student takes history.

(a) Are the events, G and H, mutually exclusive? Explain briefly.

(b) What other information is required in order to calculate P(G or H)?

Solution

(a) Since 20 + 25 = 45 > 40, there are some students taking both geography and history.

i.e., G and H have common outcomes.

∴ G and H are not mutually exclusive events.

(b) In order to calculate P(G or H), we need to know one of the following:

1. the number of students taking both geography and history;

2. the number of students taking geography but not history;

3. the number of students taking history but not geography.

Exercise 17.3

Basic Practice

1. A box contains 3 yellow chips and 5 blue chips. Two chips are drawn at random one at a time from the box with replacement.

(a) Copy and complete the tree diagram.

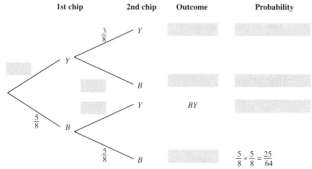

Y - yellow chip

B - blue chip

(b) Find the probability that

(i) both chips are yellow,

(ii) one chip is yellow and one chip is blue.

Solution

(a)

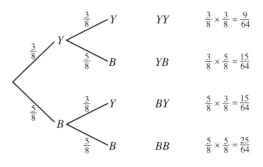

(b) (i) P(both chips are yellow) = P(YY)

$$= \frac{9}{64}$$

(ii) P(one yellow chip and one blue chip)

= P(YB) + P(BY)

$$= \frac{15}{64} + \frac{15}{64}$$

$$= \frac{15}{32}$$

2. An unbiased die is rolled twice.

(a) Copy and complete the tree diagram which shows all the possible events of 'six' and 'not six' occurring.

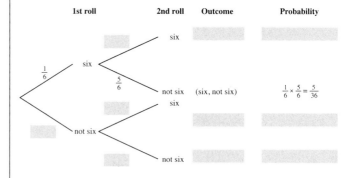

(b) Find the probability of rolling

(i) double sixes,

(ii) no six,

(iii) at least one six.

Solution

(a)

1st roll	2nd roll	Outcome	Probability
	six $\frac{1}{6}$ → six	(six, six)	$\frac{1}{6} \times \frac{1}{6} = \frac{1}{36}$
$\frac{1}{6}$ six	$\frac{5}{6}$ → not six	(six, not six)	$\frac{1}{6} \times \frac{5}{6} = \frac{5}{36}$
$\frac{5}{6}$ not six	$\frac{1}{6}$ → six	(not six, six)	$\frac{5}{6} \times \frac{1}{6} = \frac{5}{36}$
	$\frac{5}{6}$ → not six	(not six, not six)	$\frac{5}{6} \times \frac{5}{6} = \frac{25}{36}$

(b) **(i)** P(double sixes) = P((six, six))

$$= \frac{1}{36}$$

(ii) P(no six) = P((not six, not six))

$$= \frac{25}{36}$$

(iii) P(at least one six) = 1 − P(no six)

$$= 1 - \frac{25}{36}$$

$$= \frac{11}{36}$$

3. A box contains 5 red balls, 3 green balls, and 7 yellow balls. Two balls are picked at random from the box, one at a time with replacement.

(a) Copy and complete the tree diagram.

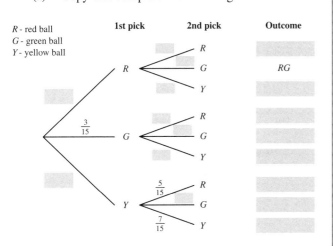

R - red ball
G - green ball
Y - yellow ball

(b) Find the probability that
(i) both balls are green,
(ii) one ball is red and one ball is yellow,
(iii) two balls are of different colors.

Solution

(a)

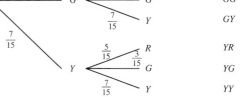

(b) **(i)** P(both balls are green) = P(GG)

$$= \frac{3}{15} \times \frac{3}{15}$$

$$= \frac{1}{25}$$

(ii) P(one red ball and one yellow ball)
= P(RY) + P(YR)

$$= \frac{5}{15} \times \frac{7}{15} + \frac{7}{15} \times \frac{5}{15}$$

$$= \frac{14}{45}$$

(iii) P(two balls are of different colors)
= 1 − P(two balls are of same color)
= 1 − P(RR) − P(GG) − P(YY)

$$= 1 - \frac{5}{15} \times \frac{5}{15} - \frac{3}{15} \times \frac{3}{15} - \frac{7}{15} \times \frac{7}{15}$$

$$= \frac{142}{225}$$

4. Seven cards are numbered from 1 to 7. A card is drawn at random and an unbiased coin is tossed. What is the probability of getting an odd number on the card and a tail on the coin?

Solution
P(getting an odd number on the card and a tail on the coin)

$$= \frac{4}{7} \times \frac{1}{2}$$

$$= \frac{2}{7}$$

5. Two cards are drawn at random from a deck of 52 playing cards one at a time with replacement. Find the probability of getting
(a) two hearts,
(b) one king and one queen.

Solution

(a) P(two hearts) $= \dfrac{1}{4} \times \dfrac{1}{4}$

$= \dfrac{1}{16}$

(b) P(one king and one queen) $= 2 \times \dfrac{4}{52} \times \dfrac{4}{52}$

$= \dfrac{2}{169}$

6. In a 100-meter race, the probabilities that Michael and Shawn will break the national record are 0.1 and 0.15 respectively. Find the probability that the record
  (a) will be broken by both Michael and Shawn,
  (b) will not be broken by either of them or both.

Solution

(a) P(record will be broken by both) $= 0.1 \times 0.15$
$= 0.015$

(b) P(record will not be broken)
$= (1 - 0.1) \times (1 - 0.15)$
$= 0.9 \times 0.85$
$= 0.765$

7. The probabilities that airplane A and airplane B will arrive at Detroit International Airport on time are $\dfrac{3}{4}$ and $\dfrac{5}{6}$ respectively. Find the probability that
  (a) airplane A will arrive on time while airplane B will not,
  (b) both airplanes, A and B, will not arrive on time.

Solution

(a) P(A will arrive on time and B will not)

$= \dfrac{3}{4} \times \left(1 - \dfrac{5}{6}\right)$

$= \dfrac{3}{4} \times \dfrac{1}{6}$

$= \dfrac{1}{8}$

(b) P(both airplanes will not arrive on time)

$= \left(1 - \dfrac{3}{4}\right) \times \left(1 - \dfrac{5}{6}\right)$

$= \dfrac{1}{4} \times \dfrac{1}{6}$

$= \dfrac{1}{24}$

8. The probabilities that Lisa and May will pass a driving test are $\dfrac{2}{3}$ and $\dfrac{3}{8}$ respectively. Find the probability that
  (a) both Lisa and May will pass the test,
  (b) only one of them will pass the test.

Solution

(a) P(both will pass) $= \dfrac{2}{3} \times \dfrac{3}{8}$

$= \dfrac{1}{4}$

(b) P(only one of them will pass)
$=$ P(Lisa will pass and May will fail)
    $+$ P(Lisa will fail and May will pass)

$= \dfrac{2}{3} \times \left(1 - \dfrac{3}{8}\right) + \left(1 - \dfrac{2}{3}\right) \times \dfrac{3}{8}$

$= \dfrac{2}{3} \times \dfrac{5}{8} + \dfrac{1}{3} \times \dfrac{3}{8}$

$= \dfrac{13}{24}$

9. A school survey found that nine out of 10 students like pizza. If three students are chosen at random with replacement, what is the probability that all three students like pizza?

Solution

P(choosing a student who likes pizza)

$= \dfrac{9}{10}$

P(all three students chosen like pizza)

$= \dfrac{9}{10} \times \dfrac{9}{10} \times \dfrac{9}{10}$

$= \dfrac{729}{1,000}$

Further Practice

10. One letter is selected at random from the word *PRINCETON* and one letter is selected from the word *UNIVERSITY*. Find the probability that
  (a) both letters selected are I,
  (b) neither of the letters selected is an I.

Solution

(a) P(both letters are I) $= \dfrac{1}{9} \times \dfrac{2}{10}$

$= \dfrac{1}{45}$

(b) P(both letters are not I) $= \dfrac{8}{9} \times \dfrac{8}{10}$

$= \dfrac{32}{45}$

11. A rack contains 3 education CDs, 4 game CDs, and 5 music CDs. Two CDs are drawn at random one at a time from the rack with replacement. Find the probability that
  (a) both CDs are game CDs,
  (b) both CDs are of the same type,
  (c) one is a music CD and the other is an education CD.

Solution

(a) P(both CDs are game CDs)

$$= \frac{4}{12} \times \frac{4}{12}$$

$$= \frac{1}{9}$$

(b) P(both CDs are of the same type)
= P(both CDs are game CDs)
  + P(both CDs are education CDs)
  + P(both CDs are music CDs)

$$= \frac{1}{9} + \frac{3}{12} \times \frac{3}{12} + \frac{5}{12} \times \frac{5}{12}$$

$$= \frac{25}{72}$$

(c) P(one music CD and one education CD)

$$= \frac{5}{12} \times \frac{3}{12} + \frac{3}{12} \times \frac{5}{12}$$

$$= \frac{5}{24}$$

12. An unbiased die is rolled three times. Find the probability of getting
  (a) three 6's,
  (b) three 5's,
  (c) three 6's or three 5's.

Solution

(a) P(three 6's) $= \frac{1}{6} \times \frac{1}{6} \times \frac{1}{6}$

$$= \frac{1}{216}$$

(b) P(three 5's) $= \frac{1}{6} \times \frac{1}{6} \times \frac{1}{6}$

$$= \frac{1}{216}$$

(c) P(three 6's or three 5's)
= P(three 6's) + P(three 5's)

$$= \frac{1}{216} + \frac{1}{216}$$

$$= \frac{1}{108}$$

13. The probabilities that Alex, Bob, and Cliff will pass an art examination are $\frac{4}{5}$, $\frac{5}{7}$, and $\frac{2}{3}$ respectively. Find the probability that
  (a) all three of them will pass the art examination,
  (b) at least one of them will pass the art examination,
  (c) only Alex will pass the art examination.

Solution

(a) P(all of them will pass)

$$= \frac{4}{5} \times \frac{5}{7} \times \frac{2}{3}$$

$$= \frac{8}{21}$$

(b) P(all of them will fail)

$$= \left(1 - \frac{4}{5}\right) \times \left(1 - \frac{5}{7}\right) \times \left(1 - \frac{2}{3}\right)$$

$$= \frac{1}{5} \times \frac{2}{7} \times \frac{1}{3}$$

$$= \frac{2}{105}$$

∴ P(at least one will pass)
= 1 − P(all of them will fail)

$$= 1 - \frac{2}{105}$$

$$= \frac{103}{105}$$

(c) P(only Alex will pass)

$$= \frac{4}{5} \times \left(1 - \frac{5}{7}\right) \times \left(1 - \frac{2}{3}\right)$$

$$= \frac{4}{5} \times \frac{2}{7} \times \frac{1}{3}$$

$$= \frac{6}{105}$$

Math@Work

14. In the United States, 43% of people fasten their seat belts while driving. If two people are chosen at random, what is the probability that both of them fasten their seat belts while driving?

Solution

P(both of them fasten their seat belts while driving)
$= 0.43 \times 0.43$
$= 0.1849$

15. A nationwide survey showed that 65% of all children in the United States dislike eating vegetables. If four children are chosen at random, find the probability that all of them dislike eating vegetables. Round your answer to the nearest percent.

Solution

P(all of them dislike eating vegetables)
$= 0.65 \times 0.65 \times 0.65 \times 0.65$
$= 0.1785$ (correct to 4 d.p.)
$= 17.85\%$
$= 18\%$ (correct to nearest percent)

16. A boat has two independent identical propellors. The boat will only move if at least one propellor is working. The probability that a propellor will fail during a trip is 0.05. Find the probability that
(a) both propellors will fail during the trip,
(b) the boat will complete the trip.

Solution

(a) P(all propellors will fail) $= 0.05 \times 0.05$
$= 0.0025$

(b) P(boat will complete the trip) $= 1 - 0.0025$
$= 0.9975$

17. Based on a genetic theory, the probability that a first generation seed of a bean plant will yield red beans is $\frac{1}{4}$.

Three of those seeds are germinated. Find the probability that
(a) all three seeds will yield red beans,
(b) none of the seeds will yield red beans.

Solution

(a) P(all will yield red beans) $= \frac{1}{4} \times \frac{1}{4} \times \frac{1}{4}$

$= \frac{1}{64}$

(b) P(none will yield red beans) $= \left(1 - \frac{1}{4}\right)^3$

$= \left(\frac{3}{4}\right)^3$

$= \frac{27}{64}$

Brainworks

18. The probability that a missile will hit a target is 0.9. The commander wants to ensure that the probability of hitting the target is more than 97%.
(a) Find the least number of missiles that should be fired at the target.
(b) Can we ensure a 100% hit? Why?

Solution

(a) Let n missiles be required for firing.
P(all will miss) $= (1 - 0.9)^n$
$= 0.1^n$
P(at least 1 will hit) $= 1 - 0.1^n$
We require
$$1 - 0.1^n > 0.97 \dots\dots\dots\dots\dots (1)$$

n	1	2	3
$1 - 0.1^n$	0.9	0.99	0.999

$\therefore$ $n = 2$ is the smallest integer that satisfies (1).

$\therefore$ at least 2 missiles should be fired.

(b) Since $1 - 0.1^n > 0$ for all positive integers n, we CANNOT ensure a 100% hit.

Exercise 17.4
Basic Practice

1. A bag contains 4 gold coins and 5 silver coins. Two coins are taken out at random from the bag, one at a time, without replacement.
(a) Copy and complete the tree diagram.

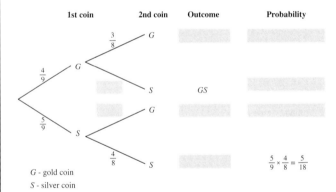

G - gold coin
S - silver coin

(b) Find the probability that
(i) both coins are gold,
(ii) the first coin is silver and the second coin is gold.

Solution

(a)

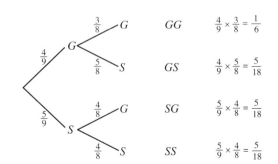

(b) **(i)** P(both coins are gold coins) = P(*GG*)

$$= \frac{1}{6}$$

(ii) P(1st coin is silver and 2nd coin is gold)
= P(*SG*)

$$= \frac{5}{18}$$

2. A box of 12 eggs contains 3 rotten ones. Two eggs are picked at random from the box.

(a) Copy and complete the tree diagram.

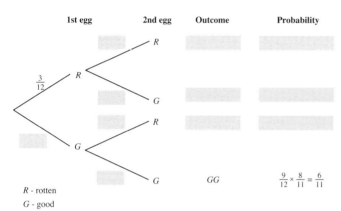

1st egg   2nd egg   Outcome   Probability

$\frac{3}{12}$ *R*

R

G

G

GG $\frac{9}{12} \times \frac{8}{11} = \frac{6}{11}$

R - rotten
G - good

(b) Find the probability that
(i) both eggs are rotten,
(ii) one egg is good and one egg is rotten.

Solution

(a)

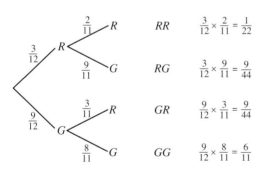

1st egg   2nd egg   Outcome   Probability

$\frac{3}{12}$ *R*

$\frac{2}{11}$ *R*   *RR* $\frac{3}{12} \times \frac{2}{11} = \frac{1}{22}$

$\frac{9}{11}$ *G*   *RG* $\frac{3}{12} \times \frac{9}{11} = \frac{9}{44}$

$\frac{9}{12}$ *G*

$\frac{3}{11}$ *R*   *GR* $\frac{9}{12} \times \frac{3}{11} = \frac{9}{44}$

$\frac{8}{11}$ *G*   *GG* $\frac{9}{12} \times \frac{8}{11} = \frac{6}{11}$

(b) **(i)** P(both eggs are rotten) = P(*RR*)

$$= \frac{1}{22}$$

(ii) P(one egg is good and one egg is rotten)
= P(*RG*) + P(*GR*)

$$= \frac{9}{44} + \frac{9}{44}$$

$$= \frac{9}{22}$$

3. In a shipment of 25 tablet PCs, two of them are defective. If two tablet PCs are randomly selected and tested, what is the probability that both are defective if the first one is not replaced after it has been tested?

Solution

P(both PCs are defective) $= \frac{2}{25} \times \frac{1}{24}$

$$= \frac{1}{300}$$

4. In a class consisting of 18 girls and 12 boys, Miss Mandy needs two students to assist her in a science demonstration. She randomly selects one student to come to the front of the classroom and then randomly selects another student from those still seated. Find the probability that both students selected are girls.

Solution

Number of students in the class = 18 + 12
$$= 30$$

P(both students are girls) $= \frac{18}{30} \times \frac{17}{29}$

$$= \frac{51}{145}$$

5. Two letters are selected at random from the word *CHICAGO*. Find the probability that
(a) both letters are *C*,
(b) only one letter is *C*.

Solution

(a) P(both letters are *C*) $= \frac{2}{7} \times \frac{1}{6}$

$$= \frac{1}{21}$$

(b) P(only one letter is *C*) $= \frac{2}{7} \times \frac{5}{6} + \frac{5}{7} \times \frac{2}{6}$

$$= \frac{10}{21}$$

6. Two cards are drawn at random from a deck of 52 playing cards, one at a time, without replacement. Find the probability that
(a) both cards drawn are red,
(b) the first card drawn is an ace and the second one is a king.

Solution

(a) P(both cards are red) $= \frac{26}{52} \times \frac{25}{31}$

$$= \frac{25}{102}$$

(b) P(first card is an ace and second card is a king)

$$= \frac{4}{52} \times \frac{4}{51}$$

$$= \frac{4}{663}$$

7. The Austin family has 3 boys and 1 girl. The Blake family has 2 boys and 3 girls. One of these two families is selected at random, and then a child is selected at random from the selected family to do a survey. Find the probability that the survey will be done by a boy.

Solution

P(survey done by a boy)
= P(selecting the Austin family and selecting a boy)
  + P(selecting the Blake family and selecting a boy)

$$= \frac{1}{2} \times \frac{3}{4} + \frac{1}{2} \times \frac{2}{5}$$

$$= \frac{23}{40}$$

Further Practice

8. Mrs. Costa has 6 grade A and 4 grade B tulip bulbs. The probability that a grade A tulip bulb will flower is $\frac{6}{7}$.

The probability that a grade B tulip bulb will flower is $\frac{3}{5}$. If she selects one of the 10 tulip bulbs at random and plant it, find the probability that the tulip bulb will flower.

Solution

P(tulip bulb will flower)
= P(selecting a bulb of grade A and the bulb will flower)
  + P(selecting a bulb of grade B and the bulb will flower)

$$= \frac{6}{10} \times \frac{6}{7} + \frac{4}{10} \times \frac{3}{5}$$

$$= \frac{132}{175}$$

9. A box contains seven cards numbered 1 to 7. Two cards are drawn at random. Find the probability that the numbers on the two cards drawn give
(a) an odd product,
(b) an odd sum.

Solution

(a) P(odd product) = P(both numbers are odd)

$$= \frac{4}{7} \times \frac{3}{6}$$

$$= \frac{2}{7}$$

(b) P(odd sum)
= P(one number is odd and the other number is even)

$$= \frac{4}{7} \times \frac{3}{6} + \frac{3}{7} \times \frac{4}{6}$$

$$= \frac{4}{7}$$

10. A bag contains 1 red ball, 3 yellow balls, and 4 blue balls. Two balls are drawn at random from the bag, one at a time, without replacement. Find the probability that
(a) one ball is yellow and one ball is blue,
(b) both balls are of the same color,
(c) both balls are of different colors,
(d) the second ball is red.

Solution

(a) P(one yellow ball and one blue ball)

$$= \frac{3}{8} \times \frac{4}{7} + \frac{4}{8} \times \frac{3}{7}$$

$$= \frac{3}{7}$$

(b) P(both balls are of the same color)
= P(both balls are yellow) + P(both balls are blue)

$$= \frac{3}{8} \times \frac{2}{7} + \frac{4}{8} \times \frac{3}{7}$$

$$= \frac{9}{28}$$

(c) P(both balls are of different colors)
= 1 − P(both balls are of the same color)

$$= 1 - \frac{9}{28}$$

$$= \frac{19}{28}$$

(d) B: blue ball
R: red ball
Y: yellow ball

P(2nd ball is red) = P(YR) + P(BR)

$$= \frac{3}{8} \times \frac{1}{7} + \frac{4}{8} \times \frac{1}{7}$$

$$= \frac{1}{8}$$

11. The table below shows the number of members in a dancing club whose ages are categorized into different age ranges.

Age range (x years)	Number of members
$20 < x \leqslant 25$	9
$25 < x \leqslant 30$	21
$30 < x \leqslant 35$	25
$35 < x \leqslant 40$	17
$40 < x \leqslant 45$	8

Two members are selected at random. Find the probability that
(a) both members are 30 years old or less,
(b) one member is more than 40 years old and the other member is not more than 40 years old.

Solution

(a) Number of members who are 30 years old or less

$= 9 + 21$

$= 30$

P(both are 30 years old or less) $= \dfrac{30}{80} \times \dfrac{29}{79}$

$= \dfrac{87}{632}$

(b) P(one is more than 40 years old and the other is not more than 40 years old)

$= \dfrac{8}{80} \times \dfrac{72}{79} + \dfrac{72}{80} \times \dfrac{8}{79}$

$= \dfrac{72}{395}$

Math@Work

12. An office has 12 male and 18 female staff members. Two staff members are selected at random to attend a training course. Find the probability that

(a) both staff members are female,

(b) one staff member is male and the other is female.

Solution

(a) P(both staff members are female) $= \dfrac{18}{30} \times \dfrac{17}{29}$

$= \dfrac{51}{145}$

(b) P(one staff member is male and the other is female)

$= \dfrac{12}{30} \times \dfrac{18}{29} + \dfrac{18}{30} \times \dfrac{12}{29}$

$= \dfrac{72}{145}$

13. In a country, 25% of the adults are smokers. The probability that a smoker will have lung cancer is 0.050. The probability that a non-smoker will have lung cancer is 0.002. If an adult from the country is selected at random, what is the probability that the person will have lung cancer?

Solution

P(lung cancer)

= P(smoker who has lung cancer)

  + P(non-smoker who has lung cancer)

$= 25\% \times 0.050 + (100\% - 25\%) \times 0.002$

$= 0.25 \times 0.050 + 0.75 \times 0.002$

$= 0.014$

14. A boy forgot his password for his Internet account. He has a total of 8 passwords for various accounts. If he tries these passwords at random, one at a time, without repetition, what is the probability that he will log in to his Internet account *within* two attempts?

Solution

P(within two attempts)

= P(one attempt only) + P(two attempts only)

$= \dfrac{1}{8} + \dfrac{7}{8} \times \dfrac{1}{7}$

$= \dfrac{1}{4}$

Brainworks

15. There are 6 black cards and 1 red card in a box. Simon and Mary take turns to draw a card at random from the box, with Simon being the first to draw. The first person who draws the red card will win the game.

(a) If the cards are drawn without replacement, find the probability that Mary will win.

(b) If the cards are drawn with replacement, is it possible to work out the probability that Mary will win? If so, explain it briefly, with a diagram if necessary.

Solution

(a) Let B stands for a black card and R a red card.

P(Mary will win)

$= P(BR) + P(BBBR) + P(BBBBBR)$

$= \dfrac{6}{7} \times \dfrac{1}{6} + \dfrac{6}{7} \times \dfrac{5}{6} \times \dfrac{4}{5} \times \dfrac{1}{4}$

$\quad + \dfrac{6}{7} \times \dfrac{5}{6} \times \dfrac{4}{5} \times \dfrac{3}{4} \times \dfrac{2}{3} \times \dfrac{1}{2}$

$= \dfrac{3}{7}$

Note: "*BBBR*" stands for the colors of the first 4 cards drawn by Simon and Mary, which are 3 blacks followed by 1 red.

(b) If the cards are drawn with replacement,

P(Mary will win)

$= P(BR) + P(BBBR) + P(BBBBBR)$

$\quad + P(BBBBBBBR) + \ldots$

$= \dfrac{6}{7} \times \dfrac{1}{7} + \dfrac{6}{7} \times \dfrac{6}{7} \times \dfrac{6}{7} \times \dfrac{1}{7}$

$\quad + \dfrac{6}{7} \times \dfrac{6}{7} \times \dfrac{6}{7} \times \dfrac{6}{7} \times \dfrac{6}{7} \times \dfrac{1}{7} + \ldots$

$= \dfrac{6}{7} \times \dfrac{1}{7} + \left(\dfrac{6}{7}\right)^3 \times \dfrac{1}{7} + \left(\dfrac{6}{7}\right)^5 \times \dfrac{1}{7} + \ldots$

We can find an approximate value of the above probability by evaluating 10 terms of the expression using a calculator or a spreadsheet program.

The required probability is

$\dfrac{6}{13}$ or 0.4615   (correct to 4 d.p.).

Review Exercise 17

1. In a pet store, there are 6 puppies, 9 kittens, 4 gerbils, and 7 parakeets. If a pet is chosen at random, what is the probability of choosing a puppy or a parakeet?

   Solution

   Number of pets in the pet store = 6 + 9 + 4 + 7
   $$= 26$$
   P(choosing a puppy or a parakeet)
   = P(choosing a puppy) + P(choosing a parakeet)
   $$= \frac{6}{26} + \frac{7}{26}$$
   $$= \frac{1}{2}$$

2. In a basketball tournament, three of the participating teams, Knicks, Blazers, and Magic, have the probabilities $\frac{1}{5}$, $\frac{2}{15}$, and $\frac{3}{20}$ respectively of winning the tournament.

   Find the probability that
   (a) Magic will not win the tournament,
   (b) Knicks or Blazers will win the tournament,
   (c) neither Knicks nor Blazers will win the tournament,
   (d) none of these three teams will win the tournament.

   Solution

   (a) P(Magic will not win)
   = 1 − P(Magic will win)
   $$= 1 - \frac{3}{20}$$
   $$= \frac{17}{20}$$

   (b) P(Knicks or Blazers will win)
   = P(Knicks will win) + P(Blazers will win)
   $$= \frac{1}{5} + \frac{2}{15}$$
   $$= \frac{1}{3}$$

   (c) P(neither Knicks nor Blazers will win)
   = 1 − P(Knicks or Blazers will win)
   $$= 1 - \frac{1}{3}$$
   $$= \frac{2}{3}$$

   (d) P(none of these three teams will win)
   = 1 − P(Knicks, Blazers, or Magic will win)
   = 1 − P(Knicks will win) − P(Blazers will win) − P(Magic will win)
   $$= 1 - \frac{1}{5} - \frac{2}{15} - \frac{3}{20}$$
   $$= \frac{31}{60}$$

3. Samuel has a deck of 52 playing cards and a bag containing one red marble, one black marble, and one white marble. He draws, at random, a marble from the bag and a card from the deck of playing cards. Find the probability that the two items drawn are
   (a) both red,
   (b) both black,
   (c) both red or both black,
   (d) of different colors.

   Solution

   (a) P(red marble and red card)
   = P(red marble) × P(red card)
   $$= \frac{1}{3} \times \frac{26}{52}$$
   $$= \frac{1}{6}$$

   (b) P(black marble and black card)
   = P(black marble) × P(black card)
   $$= \frac{1}{3} \times \frac{26}{52}$$
   $$= \frac{1}{6}$$

   (c) P(both red or both black)
   = P(red marble and red card) + P(black marble and black card)
   $$= \frac{1}{6} + \frac{1}{6}$$
   $$= \frac{1}{3}$$

   (d) P(both items are of different colors)
   = 1 − P(both red or both black)
   $$= 1 - \frac{1}{3}$$
   $$= \frac{2}{3}$$

4. A survey found that 47% of teenagers hold a part-time job and 78% plan to attend college. If a teenager is chosen at random, what is the probability that the teenager holds a part-time job and plans to attend college?

   Solution

   P(choosing a teenager who holds a part-time job and plans to attend college)
   = P(choosing a teenager who holds a part-time job) × P(choosing a teenager who plans to attend college)
   = 0.47 × 0.78
   = 0.3666

5. There are 10 blue hats and 8 black hats in a drawer. Two hats are taken out from the drawer at random. Find the probability that
   (a) both hats are black,
   (b) the two hats are of different colors.

Solution
(a) P(both hats are black) $= \dfrac{8}{18} \times \dfrac{7}{17}$
$$= \dfrac{28}{153}$$

(b) P(both hats are of different colors)
$$= \dfrac{10}{18} \times \dfrac{8}{17} + \dfrac{8}{18} \times \dfrac{10}{17}$$
$$= \dfrac{80}{153}$$

6. In a city, 80% of the drivers fasten their seat belts. If three drivers are checked at random, find the probability that
   (a) none of the three drivers fastens his seat belt,
   (b) all three drivers fasten their seat belts,
   (c) at least one of the three drivers fastens his seat belt.

Solution
(a) P(none fastens his seat belt)
$$= (100\% - 80\%)^3$$
$$= \left(\dfrac{1}{5}\right)^3$$
$$= \dfrac{1}{125}$$

(b) P(all fasten their seat belts) $= \left(\dfrac{4}{5}\right)^3$
$$= \dfrac{64}{125}$$

(c) P(at least one fastens his seat belt)
$$= 1 - \text{P(none fastens his seat belt)}$$
$$= 1 - \dfrac{1}{125}$$
$$= \dfrac{124}{125}$$

7. The dot plot shows the age distribution of a sample of students. If two students are selected at random from the sample, find the probability that
   (a) both their ages are 15,
   (b) the sum of their ages is more than 30.

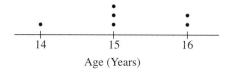

Dot Plot for the Ages of Students

Age (Years)

Solution
(a) Total number of students $= 1 + 3 + 2$
$$= 6$$
P(both their ages are 15) $= \dfrac{3}{6} \times \dfrac{2}{5}$
$$= \dfrac{1}{5}$$

(b) P(sum of their ages > 30)
$= $ P(1st student is 15 and the 2nd student is 16) + P(1st student is 16 and the 2nd student is 15 or 16)
$$= \dfrac{3}{6} \times \dfrac{2}{5} + \dfrac{2}{6} \times \dfrac{4}{5}$$
$$= \dfrac{7}{15}$$

8. John either walks or cycles to school every morning. The probability that he walks to school is $\dfrac{4}{9}$. When he walks, the probability that he is late for school is $\dfrac{5}{8}$. When he cycles, the probability that he is late for school is $\dfrac{3}{10}$. Find the probability that on a particular morning
   (a) he walks and is not late for school,
   (b) he is late for school.

Solution

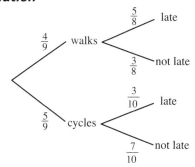

(a) P(John walks and is not late for school)
$$= \dfrac{4}{9} \times \dfrac{3}{8}$$
$$= \dfrac{1}{6}$$

(b) P(John is late for school)
$= $ P(John walks and is late for school) + P(John cycles and is late for school)
$$= \dfrac{4}{9} \times \dfrac{5}{8} + \dfrac{5}{9} \times \dfrac{3}{10}$$
$$= \dfrac{4}{9}$$

9. Mr. Carter has 4 dimes, 10 quarters, and 2 half-dollars in his pocket. He takes two coins at random from his pocket, one after the other without replacement.
  (a) Draw a tree diagram to show all the possible outcomes.
  (b) Find the probability that
      (i) the first coin has a lower value than the second coin,
      (ii) the second coin he takes out from his pocket is a dime,
      (iii) the total value of the two coins is more than 60 cents.

Solution

(a) The required tree diagram is shown below.

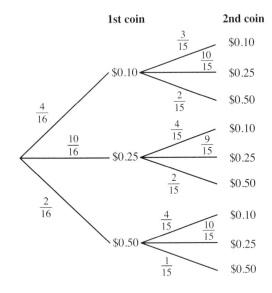

(b) **(i)** P(the 1st coin has a lower value than the 2nd coin)
= P({($0.10, $0.25), ($0.10, $0.50), or ($0.25, $0.50)})
$= \dfrac{4}{16} \times \dfrac{10}{15} + \dfrac{4}{16} \times \dfrac{2}{15} + \dfrac{10}{16} \times \dfrac{2}{15}$
$= \dfrac{17}{60}$

(ii) P(the 2nd coin is a dime)
= P({($0.10, $0.10), ($0.25, $0.10), or ($0.50, $0.10)})
$= \dfrac{4}{16} \times \dfrac{3}{15} + \dfrac{10}{16} \times \dfrac{4}{15} + \dfrac{2}{16} \times \dfrac{4}{15}$
$= \dfrac{1}{4}$

(iii) P(the total value of coins is more than $0.60)
= P({($0.25, $0.50), ($0.50, $0.25), or ($0.50, $0.50)})
$= \dfrac{10}{16} \times \dfrac{2}{15} + \dfrac{2}{16} \times \dfrac{10}{15} + \dfrac{2}{16} \times \dfrac{1}{15}$
$= \dfrac{7}{40}$